# PLAGUE ON US

# PLAGUE
# ON US

## BY GEDDES SMITH

NEW YORK · THE COMMONWEALTH FUND · 1941
LONDON · HUMPHREY MILFORD · OXFORD UNIVERSITY PRESS

PUBLISHED BY
HARVARD UNIVERSITY PRESS
CAMBRIDGE, MASS.

*The decoration on the title page is from a water color by William Blake entitled Pestilence: The Death of the First Born. It is reproduced here by courtesy of the Museum of Fine Arts, Boston.*

PUBLISHED BY THE COMMONWEALTH FUND
41 EAST 57TH STREET, NEW YORK 22, N.Y.

PRINTED IN THE UNITED STATES OF AMERICA
BY E. L. HILDRETH & COMPANY, INC.

*To the memory of*
W. H. S. *and* W. H. F.

# TABLE OF CONTENTS

# FOREWORD

THOUGH *laymen are the stuff of which epidemics are made, they shouldn't meddle with epidemiology, which is an exacting science. Noah Webster, who went so wrong in his* Brief History of Epidemic and Pestilential Diseases, *is a horrible example of what may happen when they do. But he had a thesis to prove; I merely set down as clearly as I can some facts and theories about communicable disease that have interested me and, I hope, will interest other laymen.*

*Everything here is borrowed, and every page would groan with references if I made strict accounting for my borrowings. It seems better not to do so. I have given footnote references for the more important direct quotations, and have indicated at the end of each chapter the principal sources on which I have drawn, especially those which the reader may find interesting if he too wishes to browse in this field. I am heavily indebted to the medical histories, the standard texts, the current journals, and most of all to many individual scientists who have been good enough to talk to me with astonishing patience and courtesy.*

*This book would not have been written except for the generous initiative of the General Director of the Commonwealth Fund. My colleagues on the staff of the Fund have helped me royally at every turn: I want to thank them all, and especially Dr. Clarence L. Scamman, an enthusiastic guide and modest preceptor. Dr. Benjamin White opened doors for me; Dr. Wade Hampton Frost stimulated, heartened, and steadied my work; I wish I could have thanked them both more adequately while they were still living.*

*Friendly critics who read the manuscript in whole or in part have saved me from many errors. I hope, with their help, the book has been made reasonably accurate, but I must take responsibility for it as it stands.*
                                                        G. S.

NOVEMBER, 1940

# I

## PROLOGUE

Finding a mouse dead in a cage in New York, a man in a
white coat knows that a certain black man in Africa could not
have had yellow fever. Pestilence used to be something visited
on sinners by the angry gods; now it is visited also on mice and
rabbits by men in search of knowledge. These men have traced
the agents of disease through the stomach of the flea, the rectum
of the louse, the spittle of the droning mosquito. They brew in
their test-tubes lethal stuff that they cannot see, and contrive to
make it their servant in keeping death at bay. Nothing is too
small for them, nothing (save influenza, perhaps) too large.

The black plague that ravaged Europe is all but gone. The
yellow fever that made men pray for winter is all but gone. The
malignant choking death that struck at children is all but gone.
Purging fevers no longer haunt the water that cities drink.
Cheeks that would once have been pitted with smallpox are
smooth and fresh. Men and women die old.

Are we then so wise that we have beaten our parasites? Sal-
low-faced farmers shivering and burning with malaria, bedside
watchers listening to the anxious breathing of pneumonia, jaded
nurses tending the wrecks of syphilis, millions exasperated by
the nagging misery of the common cold know the answer. We
have not rid the world entirely of any single infection known to
man, and some we have not yet begun to fight. As for the premises for action, we do not yet know why one man sickens and the

I

next goes free, why one pest seeks out the lungs and another the liver, how drugs cure the ills they seem to cure, how disease begins or how it ends.

Influenza kept step with the last war. If it came tomorrow we could not stop it. The lords of Europe are fighting again. Masses of men are bombed out of their homes and cities, hounded into exile, driven hither and thither in a greater dislocation of ordered living than any rational man would have thought possible. Such a world is in peril of pestilence. It is early to boast.

# Ein nutzliche trostliche
vnd kurtze vnderrichtung/wie man
sich in disen schwären leüffen der Pestilentz hal-
ten soll/dem gemeinen mann zů hilff
vnnd gůtem/der nit andern bey-
stand hat/verordnet.

Durch D. Ambrosium Jungen/den ältesten vnd
erfarnesten Artzet/zů Augspurg.

## M. D. XXXV.

*Pestilence: title page of "a brief, practical and comforting treatise" (1535) by Ambrosius Jung, "the oldest and most experienced physician of Augsburg"*

# 2

## PESTILENCE

IT IS very recently that we have learned to watch mice in laboratory cages and fortify the blood-stream to defend ourselves against disease. But the world has known pestilence for a long time, and repeatedly men have shrunk from it in terror for themselves and for the race. A poignant expression of that fear comes from an Irish monk who was keeping a chronicle in his cell at Kilkenny in 1349. "Lest the writing should perish with the writer," his black-letter runs, "and the work fail together with the workman, I leave parchment for continuing the work, if haply any man survive, and any of the race of Adam escape this pestilence and continue the work which I have commenced."[1] For himself, his foreboding was justified; he died soon afterward, and with him died every fourth person in Europe.

But there was another scribe to take up his task, and the Irish in Kilkenny survived to make a name for themselves in other ways. The waves of pestilence rise and fall throughout recorded history, and we can trace here the course of only a few that for one reason or another stand out in the long sequence.

### THE BLACK DEATH

It was the Black Death that carried off the Kilkenny chronicler, and though there are plenty of references to tidal waves of disease before the fourteenth century—the plagues of Egypt and the Israelites, the epidemic described by Thucydides, and the great

3

sickness of Justinian's reign in the sixth century, for example—
this particular epidemic is so fully documented that a word or
two about it makes a good beginning for our story. Creeping out
of Asia, the plague had been at the threshold of Europe in 1346,
had crossed to Constantinople and the Mediterranean ports in
1347, and by 1349 or 1350 had spread over the European world.
(Guy de Chauliac, the Pope's physician, thought the trouble had
begun with a grand conjunction of Saturn, Jupiter, and Mars in
the sign of Aquarius in 1345. A "thick stinking mist" had blown
out of the East over Italy.) Italian merchants besieged in a Crimean port by plague-ridden Tartars (who, it was said, had bom-
barded the town with corpses) had escaped only to carry infection with them along the sea lanes.

( Quarantine at Genoa and Venice came too late. At Avignon
the Pope had to consecrate the Rhone so that bodies might be
thrown into it for Christian burial.` Half London died. Ships
without crews drifted about the Mediterranean and the North
Sea, spreading the plague wherever they were driven ashore.
Petrarch wrote movingly of "the empty houses, the abandoned
towns, the squalid country, the fields crowded with the dead, the
vast and dreadful solitude over the whole world."[1]

The Black Death showed itself in bleeding from the lungs, or
in swellings in groin or armpit, with the black blotches on the
skin that gave the disease its grisly name. "To the cure of these
maladies," says Boccaccio in the opening book of the *Decameron,*
"nor counsel of physician nor virtue of any medicine appeared
to avail or profit aught; on the contrary,—whether it was that
the nature of the infection suffered it not or that the ignorance
of the physicians (of whom, over and above the men of art, the
number, both men and women, who had never had any teaching
of medicine, was become exceeding great) availed not to know
whence it arose and consequently took not due measures there-
against,—not only did few recover thereof, but well nigh all

died within the third day from the appearance of the aforesaid signs. . . ."[2]

In Paris the medical faculty was asked what men could do to save themselves. These distinguished physicians answered in curious detail: for example, they held that "cold, moist, watery food is in general prejudicial. . . . Too much exercise is hurtful. . . . If it rain, a little fine treacle should be taken after dinner. Fat people should not sit in the sunshine. . . ."[3] Current opinion held that the infection was spread by and in the air, and to purify it a leading medical scholar recommended "large blazing fires of odoriferous wood"—a prescription which had not lost its appeal three centuries later when the plague swept London again, and found an echo in Philadelphia's efforts to combat yellow fever even as late as 1793. There were many notions as to treatment. Cautery of the boils, and bleeding, were favored. One notable physician was curiously selective in his choice of such methods; observing that most patients who were bled subsequently died, he "reserved this remedy for the plethoric; especially for the papal courtiers, and the hypocritical priests."[3]

How greatly Europe was demoralized by this experience it is hard after six centuries to say. In England so few men were left to work in the fields that wages nearly doubled. Lawyers thrived on the confusion of inheritances. Decencies were forgotten. The Jews were accused of poisoning the wells, and whole colonies of them were burnt alive. Religious fanatics, convinced that their sins had brought a fearful punishment, wandered from city to city scourging themselves in public places. Everywhere men were in panic, knowing no way to stem the tide of death except to flee before it.

## THE ENGLISH SWEAT

The singularity of the English is traditional, but it has never been more curiously demonstrated than by the appearance in the fifteenth and sixteenth centuries of a disease which, if contemporary accounts are to be believed, was so partial to Englishmen that at first it stopped short at the border of Scotland, and for the most part disdained to feed on lesser breeds without the law.

The Wars of the Roses were barely ended with the victory of Henry VII at Bosworth Field in August 1485, when an unfamiliar sickness frightened London. Unlike the plague, which flourished in the slums, the sweating sickness included among its victims the well placed and even the great. It came suddenly, as a doctor of the day recorded, "with a grete swetyng and stynkyng, with redness of the face and of all the body, and a contynual thurst, with a grete hete and hedache because of the fumes and venoms."[1] For five weeks it ravaged the city, killing two Lord Mayors in succession within a week, while the new king waited impatiently to be crowned. Twenty years later it struck again, and after another brief stay disappeared again. In 1517 Cardinal Wolsey had it three times, and Oxford felt its force. In 1528 it separated the ardent Henry VIII from Anne Boleyn, and the French ambassador saw people "as thick as flies rushing from the streets or shops into their houses" when they sickened. The next year the mysterious infection condescended to ravage Germany, where the outraged Catholics recognized it as just recompense for Luther's heresies. Pausing briefly at town after town, it traveled over much of eastern Europe and swung back into the low countries. In 1551 it showed itself once more in England, beginning at Shrewsbury, afflicting London for three weeks, and spreading through the eastern and northern counties.

When it struck, it struck with terrifying speed. "There were some dancing in the Court at nine o'clock that were dead at eleven," writes a minister. According to John Kaye, royal physician, the disease

. . . immediately killed some in opening theire windowes, some in plaieng with children in their strete dores, some in one hour, many in

6

two it destroyed, & at the longest, to them that merilye dined, it gaue a sorowful Supper. As it founde them so it toke them, some in sleape some in wake, some in mirthe some in care, some fasting & some ful, some busy and some idle, and in one house sometyme three sometyme fiue, sometyme seuen sometyme eyght, sometyme more sometyme all, of the whyche, if the haulfe in euerye Towne escaped, it was thoughte great fauour.[8]

A soberer account, that of the papal nuncio in London in 1517, declares that the attack lasted about twenty-four hours. So peremptory was its challenge to the robust and fashionable that the people called it "stop-gallant."

The German historian Hecker, writing in 1832, contrasts the sober good sense of the English laity in dealing with this "English" disease with the fantastic treatment seen among his own countrymen. The English custom was

. . . not to resort to any violent medicines, but to apply moderate heat, to abstain from food, taking only a small quantity of mild drink, and quietly to wait for four-and-twenty hours the crisis of this formidable malady. Those who were attacked during the day, in order to avoid any chill, immediately went to bed in their clothes, and those who sickened by night did not rise from their beds in the morning; while all carefully avoided exposing to the air even a hand or a foot. Thus they anxiously guarded against heat and cold, so as not to excite perspiration by the former, nor to check it by the latter—for they well knew that either was certain death.[8]

But in Germany in 1529, where the alarm "bordered upon maniacal despair," things were ordered differently:

The unfortunate delusion existed, that whoever wished to escape death . . . *must perspire for twenty-four hours without intermission.* So they put the patients, whether they had the Sweating Sickness or not, (for who had calmness enough to distinguish it?) instantly to bed, covered them with feather-beds and furs, and while the stove was heated to the utmost, closed the doors and windows with the greatest care to prevent all access of cool air. In order, moreover, to prevent the sufferer, should he be somewhat impatient, from throwing off his hot load, some persons in health likewise lay upon him, and thus oppressed him to such a degree, that he could neither stir hand nor foot, and finally, in this rehearsal of hell, being bathed in an agonizing sweat, gave up the ghost, when, perhaps, if his too officious relatives had manifested a little discretion, he might have been saved without difficulty.[8]

In time this Teutonic thoroughness was relaxed, and the sick were merely sewed into the covers instead of being buried under feather-beds. But it was thought dangerous to let them sleep, and one masterful physician was willing to go to such lengths as tearing out the patient's hair, or dropping vinegar into his eyes, to prevent it.

{Modern authorities identify the sweating sickness with influenza, and link it up both with other epidemics in England and with related outbreaks on the Continent} But the violence of its manifestations, the startling rapidity of its action, and the terror it inspired give it an outstanding place even in the curious history of that protean infection. Why these spectacular symptoms were so closely associated with the English we cannot say, but there are many other questions that epidemiologists have never been able to answer about influenza. Hecker thought the English dressed too warmly, took too many hot baths, used too little soap, and were too much influenced in their personal habits by the high price of linen. Perhaps these guesses are no wider of the mark than many others which have been made both before and after him.

"THE POORE'S PLAGUE"

While the English sweat snatched occasionally at the lords spiritual and temporal as well as the commoners, for three centuries after the Black Death the plague was a constant threat to the great masses of the London poor, living, as Bell says, in "low overhanging wooden houses, ill-kept, dark and congested" that "covered the ground in seemingly impenetrable rookeries of filthy courts and blind alleys." The rich could usually keep infection at arm's length, if not by cleanliness (which was none too dainty) at least by flight; (in 1563 Good Queen Bess had competently arranged that a gallows should be put up at Windsor, where she had taken refuge, "to hang all such as should come there from London.")

(Among the poor the plague made one last dreadful stand in the middle of the seventeenth century. It began to be noticed as the bitter winter of 1664–1665 came to an end. Its full force was not immediately recognized, for deaths, though they were recorded weekly in the Bills of Mortality, were reported not by physicians but by hags who for a small fee pushed their way into the houses where death had occurred and made a record of what they saw. Their testimony was not only incompetent, but often distorted by petty bribes. Even against such handicaps, however, the truth soon made itself felt.

Plague began in the slums and stews of St. Giles-in-the-Fields —an outparish then, though it lies close to the British Museum today. The magistrates tried to keep it there by posting sentinels on the main roads, but the effort was fruitless, and the pestilence spread. In Westminster it was seen in Long Ditch and Thieving Alley. Gradually it moved from the western to the eastern and southern parishes. By July it was in the City. It raged all summer. The deaths from plague (never fully reported) crept up to a thousand a week, two thousand, and in September passed seven thousand in a week. Then they began to lessen, but before the infection had disappeared the Bills of Mortality had recorded a total of 68,596. All this time the deaths ascribed to other causes had been far above normal levels, and probably the actual loss by plague was nearer 110,000—and this in a population of something like 460,000 when the epidemic began, or possibly 350,000 when those who could had left the city. )

"London"—to borrow Defoe's vivid phrases—"might well be said to be all in tears. . . . The shrieks of women and children at the windows and doors of their houses, where their dearest relations were perhaps dying, or just dead, were so frequent to be heard as we passed the streets, that it was enough to pierce the stoutest heart in the world to hear them. . . . Whole families, and indeed whole streets of families, were swept away together."[4]

Pepys' often-quoted letter tells of "little noise heard day or night but tolling of bells." In July a student in London writes that in St. Giles "they have a Bellman . . . with a cart; there dye so many that the bell would hardly ever leave ringing and so they ring not at all."[5] Delirious men and women screamed at the windows, burst into the streets to die. The dead-carts rumbled by, at first by night, then both night and day. The churchyards were filled; to this day they stand high above the streets; when they no longer sufficed huge pits were dug for the dead. "It is a greate mercy now counted," wrote one John Allin, "to dye of another disease."[5]

The court and the wealthy merchants fled. Sydenham, the finest doctor of his day, followed his patients into the country. The Lord Mayor and aldermen stayed at their posts, and did their best. The Privy Council ordered that houses in which plague was found be shut up for forty days, immuring the well with the sick. Watchers were posted at the doors. Nurses—sometimes more to be feared than the disease itself, for only the most miserable would accept such duty—took charge within. Poor relief was niggardly: parish officials hustled away men found sick in the streets to avoid the cost of burying them.

Public physicians were appointed, and others volunteered to care for the sick without pay. But what could they do? Defoe says the plague "defied all medicines; the very physicians were seized with it, with their preservatives in their hands." The College of Physicians issued their prescriptions, but they were still thumbing over the wisdom of the fifteenth century. A sharp smell was the favorite preventive; the rich burned brimstone, hops, pepper, frankincense; the poor, old shoes and horn. At Eton a schoolboy was flogged for not smoking. A physician who wrote of the plague gave his patients angelica, rue, veronica, scabious, pimpernel, ivy berries, balm, gentian, and juniper berries. For the buboes, or swellings, the College of Physicians advised that one "take a great onion, hollow it, put into it a fig, rue cut small, and a dram of Venice treacle; put it close stopt in a wet paper, and roast it in the embers; apply it hot unto the tumour."[1] In September, when all efforts seemed to fail, the authorities ordered fires built in the streets, one to every twelfth house.

In plain fact no man knew how the plague came or how to thwart it. The only safety seemed to lie in flight, in getting, as Wolsey had put it in an earlier epidemic, "into clean air." It was not human wisdom that drove the plague out of England, and kept it out for more than two centuries.*

### YELLOW FEVER AND THE FOUNDING FATHERS

It seems a far cry from Restoration London to the Philadelphia of Washington's day. Yet when yellow fever ravaged that city in 1793, six years after the adoption of the present Constitution of these United States, the fumbling measures taken to check the disease are strongly reminiscent of London in the plague year. Indeed some Philadelphians actually feared that the plague was among them, and Mathew Carey, whose little book on the epidemic became both a contemporary success and a classic of disease history, declares that "it is not probable that

---

* The epidemic here described marked the end of a long series. Plague left England in 1666, not to return until our own day. See page 322.

London, at the last stage of the plague, exhibited stronger marks of terror, than were to be seen in Philadelphia, from the 25th or 26th of August till pretty late in September." [6]

The fever first appeared in July on a street near the high-piled docks. As it began to spread, fear outstripped it. Before the end of August "the streets and roads leading from the city were crouded with families flying in every direction for safety to the country." Oliver Wolcott, Secretary of the Treasury, who stayed in town, minimized the danger at first, but by September 12 he was writing that "the apprehensiveness of the citizens cannot be increased; business is in a great measure abandoned; the true character of man is disclosed, and he shows himself a weak, timid, desponding and selfish being." [7]

The College of Physicians met to consider the danger and to give advice; they suggested isolation, marking of doors and windows where the sick lay, keeping the streets and wharfs clean, the establishment of an emergency hospital, prohibition of "the tolling of the bells," the avoidance of fatigue and excesses. Harking back to seventeenth-century London, the manifesto continued:

The college conceive *fires* to be very ineffectual, if not dangerous means of checking the progress of this fever. They have reason to place more dependence upon the burning of *gun-powder*. The benefits of *vinegar* and *camphor*, are confined chiefly to infected rooms, and they cannot be used too frequently upon handkerchiefs, or in smelling-bottles by persons whose duty calls them to visit or attend the sick. [8]

Their faith in gunpowder found a thunderous echo: the firing of guns was carried so far that the mayor had to prohibit it as dangerous. But none of these things stopped the fever, and "consternation . . . was carried beyond all bounds." "Dismay and affright," writes Carey, "were visible in almost every countenance. The smoke of tobacco being regarded as a preventative, many persons, even women and small boys, had segars constantly in their mouths. Others placing full confidence in garlic,

chewed it almost the whole day; some kept it in their shoes.
People hastily shifted their course at the sight of a hearse coming towards them. Many never walked on the foot path, but
went into the middle of the streets, to avoid being infected in
passing by houses where people had died. A person with a crape,
or any appearance of mourning, was shunned like a viper. And
many valued themselves highly on the skill and address with
which they got to windward of every person they met." [6] "The
hearse alone," writes another observer, "kept up the remem-
brance of the noise of carriages or carts in the streets." [8]

The panic spread. In New York bands of vigilantes were organized to patrol the streets lest fugitives from Philadelphia slip
into the town by night, and the newspapers hopefully predicted
that it would be unsafe for Congress to meet in Philadelphia in
December. A party of militia was stationed "at a pass on the
Philadelphia road, about two miles from Baltimore," to stop
travelers who lacked certificates of health. At Boston ships from
Philadelphia were held in the harbor for cleansing with vinegar
and exploding gunpowder.

The doctors labored earnestly to cure the sick and quarreled
violently over the means of doing so. Of some fifty physicians in
the city, ten died, and at one time so many were ill that only
three were able to visit the six thousand sick. Dr. Benjamin
Rush, sometime surgeon in the Revolutionary Army, professor
in the University, and one of the first physicians of his day, took
a leading part. Stricken himself and losing his sister and two students from his own household, he toiled devotedly and as devotedly preached the merits of bleeding, jalap, and mercury. On
September 11 he wrote his wife, "It is not yet five o'clock, and
I have had seven calls already." On another day he saw a hundred patients and thanked God that none of them died.

But even Rush realized at last that only the approach of
winter would end the disaster. In mid-October the disease began

to abate, but warmer weather seemed to revive it and it lingered into the next month. Though a third of Philadelphia's 50,000 citizens had fled the city, more than 4,000 were buried between August first and November ninth.

In November, when the government reassembled in Germantown, that suburb was still so crowded with refugees that Jefferson had to sleep in a corner of the public room of the King of Prussia tavern. Washington, back from Mt. Vernon, decided to stay in Germantown till the members of Congress gathered together, "merely," as Jefferson wrote Madison, "to form a point of union for them before they can have acquired information & courage." But by the appointed time Philadelphia was almost free of the fever, the hopes of New York were dashed, and the Third Congress met in its own proper place.

Meanwhile medical controversy still raged. Fisher Ames, sharp-tongued Congressman from Massachusetts, wrote to a friend that "every thing that ought to be called fact, is disputed, and all that should be modestly confessed to be ignorance, is affirmed." As for the doctors, "All vouch success. None had it." "I honor the zeal and heroism of the doctors," he continued, "but heaven preserve me from being the subject of their noble exertions." Alexander Hamilton, who had recovered from the fever, took a hand in the arguments which were set forth at great length in the daily press, and was obliging enough to mention his family physician's address in a postscript to his published letter. But the great Dr. Rush stuck to his guns, and haughtily defended his refusal to consult with opponents who had "slandered" him.

A Mahometan and a Jew might as well attempt to worship the Supreme Being in the same temple, and through the medium of the same ceremonies [he wrote], as two physicians of opposite principles and practice, attempt to confer about the life of the same patient. . . . The extremity of wrong in medicine, as in morals and government, is often

14

ADDRESS

OF THE CARRIER OF

# THE DESSERT TO

# The True American

## TO HIS PATRONS.

For the Year 1799.

Lo! Winter's come, with all his hoary train,
And drives with fury o'er the extended plain;
Keen blows the blaft, and loud the tempeft roars,
While Ocean's billows lafh the circling fhores;
The drifting fnow and rattling hail bare fway,
And dark'ning clouds obfcure the god of day:
Sad Nature ftruggles, but in vain contends,
His will is fate—and to his power fhe bends.

Not fo your News-boy, who with cheerful
mien,
Vifits your door, nor dreads the chilling fcene.
Ere the full morn has gilt the Eaftern fkies,
With eager hafte his daily round he flies;
Smiling at danger—when his duty calls,
Nor Wint'ry ftorms, nor peftilence appals.

Think when of late, difeafe's horrid form,
Stalk'd thro' thefe Streets, and hurl'd the fatal
ftorm;
How thoufands fled, how thoufand victims fell,
How few were fpar'd the mournful tale to tell!
What horror lowered, what glooms on glooms
arofe,
And how the Dæmon dealt his deadly blows.

Think then, ah! think, how 'mid this dread-
ful fcene,
Your faithful boy, undaunted and ferene,
His lengthy round continued ftill to go,
Tho' often threaten'd with the mortal blow:
Think how he firmly at his poft remain'd,
And think how all thofe horrors he fuftain'd;
'Twas duty bade—in hopes of pleafing you,
He fmil'd at dangers as they thicker grew!

But now, when other fcenes the mind employ,
And rofy health fpreads round an heartfelt joy,
When feftive mirth your plenteous board attends
And pleafure revels 'midft furrounding friends.
Your News-boy comes—to afk but not demand,
"Some little bounty from your liberal hand?"
Some little recompence for duty fo fevere,
Something to cheer him thro' the coming year.
So may your pleafures with your years increafe,
And all your days be pafs'd in tranquil peace.
May you thro' all the varied fcenes of life
Know fweet content, nor 'gage in wafteful
ftrife:
But calmly glide to age's rev'rend flate,
And there your laft great change with joy await.

New Year message from a Philadelphia newsboy to his customers after one of many local epidemics of yellow fever. The "Dessert" was a weekly literary supplement to "The True American"

a less mischief, than that mixture of right and wrong which serves by palliating, to perpetuate evil.[8]

One misses that accent in medical writing today.

As to the cause of the infection, Dr. Rush, with some of his confreres, held that it was produced "by a general constitution of the air, cooperating with miasmata," and sprang immediately from a cargo of spoiled coffee dumped on a pier and rotting there. In support of his theory he asserted that "cabbage, onions, black pepper, and even the mild potatoe, when in a state of putrefaction," had been "the remote causes of malignant fevers." The College of Physicians found, sensibly, after formal deliberation, that infection had been brought to Philadelphia by vessels arriving in midsummer.

But imported or domestic, no one knew how to stop it, and for another century yellow fever continued to harass American ports.

ASIATIC CHOLERA ON THE MARCH

I have just asked several people what they thought of when they heard the word *cholera*. The first said "hogs," others "India" and "the South Sea islands" and "people dying in the streets and carried off in two-wheeled carts." Only one answered "that awful disease." Yet our great-grandfathers and even our grandfathers knew cholera as an immediate and terrifying menace. Hardly more than half a century ago the New York State Board of Health issued a warning that began "Asiatic cholera is again on its deadly march." In 1854 liverymen driving out of St. Paul, Minnesota—a long way from the Ganges—used to put a bottle of "cholera medicine" under the seat lest passengers be stricken on the road. In 1849 visitors to a Mississippi plantation, where the infection was killing half the Negroes, found a doctor entrenched behind bowls of calomel, camphor, and capsicum, spooning out doses for all comers. In New York in the same year schoolhouses were turned into emergency hospitals, and there were five thousand cholera deaths.

The rise and fall of cholera as a world disease belongs to the story of a single century—the nineteenth. Before 1817, except for occasional minor excursions, it was a local disease of India. In that year, no one knows why, it started a slow march which carried it over most of India in 1817, over the frontier in 1818, and by 1823 eastward to Japan and westward to the threshold of Europe. In 1826 it traveled again with traders and pilgrims, found its way overland to Russia in 1830, to Germany and England in 1831, to Ireland in 1832, took ship that year with hungry Irish emigrants, crossed to Canada and the eastern states, and pushed into the western states in 1833. This march was over in 1836, and for ten years the disease remained at home. In 1846 it was abroad again, moving more quickly, and for the next sixteen years it was present intermittently in Europe, North America, and part of South America, reaching its height in the United States in 1849 and 1850. In 1865 it crossed by sea from India to Mecca and the Mediterranean, reaching Halifax, New York, and New Orleans the next year, and spreading twice through the Mississippi basin before it retreated in 1874. Cholera never ranged so far again. Between 1884 and 1887 it visited France, Spain, and Italy. In 1892 it swept across Russia and killed eighty-five hundred in Hamburg. Later waves of infection for the most part fell short of western Europe, and except for a few centers of persistent infection, cholera continues to afflict only its Indian home. There, however, it killed more than seven million people in twenty years of the present century.

With the radio at the elbow and glib talk of bacteria in every common school, it is hard for us to put ourselves in the place of the men and women who watched cholera creep slowly toward the western world a century ago. "Our citizens had heard and read much of this Asiatic scourge," writes a New York physician in 1833, "and all we knew of it had impressed us with a sense of its mysterious character, its rapid and erratic course, its unmanageable and incurable nature, and its certain and dreadful fatality. Its fearful devastation in India and elsewhere had filled the mind with horror at the bare recital of its ravages, and the rumor of its appearance on the shores of the St. Lawrence threw our population into consternation . . . which, in some instances, became so intense as to dethrone reason itself, and impel to suicide."[9]

When the disease struck New York, it fastened on the slums. In the wretched houses north of Canal Street "the dying and the dead were literally strewed about, like slaughtered victims on the field of battle." Cholera the world over has been predominantly a disease of the poor, and the comfortable classes were able to temper their distress at the disaster by those moral reflections so often associated with charitable impulses (at least in the nineteenth century). Thus in 1833 a New York physician notes that of the thousands who died of cholera in the three-month epidemic less than five hundred were not "habitually intemperate," and in 1849 it was observed that many deaths occurred in a section "occupied to a considerable extent by a filthy, degraded, and vicious population."

But the conditions favorable to the spread of disease from the alvine* discharges were not found in the city slums alone. For all their florid names, gilt paint, and blaring bands, the Mississippi river boats in epidemic years were "moving pest-houses." Infection ran riot among the poor travelers between decks, driven incessantly to the stool by the cruel purging which marks the disease. The *Peytona* lost fifty passengers between New Orleans and Louisville on one trip in 1849. Among the boats tying up in a single week at the Cairo docks, there were seven deaths

* If the reader is unacquainted with this polite and useful word it is worth a trip to the dictionary.

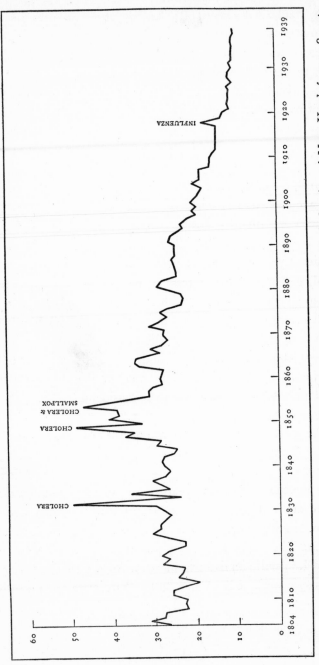

I. Pestilential peaks in the death rate (deaths per 1,000 population) of the city of New York from 1804 to 1939. At the beginning of this period the population was less than 100,000, at the end, 7,500,000. From a chart prepared by Charles F. Bolduan, M.D., for the New York City Department of Health on the *Bride,* three on the *Uncle Sam,* eight cases each on the *Belle Key,* the *Seraph,* the *Gladiator.* The primitive sanitation of the overland trails played its part too in the spread of disease. By a curious coincidence it is said to have been the steamer *Sacramento,* carrying emigrants up the Missouri on their way to California, that touched off a long train of infection that wound across the plains and mountains from St. Joseph to Sacramento itself. Half the population of the future capital of California fled when the cholera came in 1850, and a quarter of those who remained died.

Meanwhile doctors disagreed as to whether the disease was contagious. Many held, with the Sanitary Committee of the Philadelphia Board of Health in 1848, that it was not communicable, but derived from a "peculiar morbific poison in the atmosphere, which renders cordons and quarantine restrictions useless, sanitary arrangements being the only safeguard." To be sure, it was hard to judge the effectiveness of maritime quarantine when travelers who seemed well but, as we know now, were carrying the infection slipped through the gates unsuspected. It is surprising, however, to find that as late as 1876 an army surgeon detailed to study the situation felt obliged to defend the notion that American cholera was imported.

Organized public health service, still in its infancy, was in some instances nourished on the fear of cholera. Even the most conscientious boards and committees, however, had pitifully few facts to work on. Observing that the disease flourished in the dirtiest parts of the cities, they tried to prevent its spread by sporadic cleaning up, supplemented often by broadsides urging the public to live sensibly and keep calm. In Philadelphia in 1849, for instance, 2,970 privies were cleaned and 510 "purified," 918 hogpens were removed, 10 rag-and-bone shops closed (this gave the board special satisfaction), and altogether 6,573 nuisances were abated. In St. Louis when the authorities faltered a voluntary committee not only cleaned up the town and burned tar and sulfur but, for good measure, had bonfires lighted in the streets —without, however, preventing the death of 4,568 people.

In 1854 Dr. John Snow demonstrated brilliantly in London that the infection was carried by water, but his findings were not fully accepted at home and seem to have had little effect on contemporary American practice. In 1865 the Citizens' Association of New York was still content to make its anti-cholera slogan "Cleanse! CLEANSE! CLEANSE!" and even in 1885 the New York *Medical Record* was counting on the "extra cleanliness produced by the cholera scare" to prevent deaths from "other filth diseases."

No doubt some good was done by the promiscuous use of brooms and shovels. But the disappearance of cholera from America (the last reported death was in 1911) must be ascribed to more pertinent health measures, of which more will be said later, and perhaps to some as yet unexplained alteration in the dispersive power of the disease itself.

### YELLOW FEVER IN THE HEADLINES

The year 1878 was in some ways modern enough. Congress was tinkering with money; a Civil Service Reform Association was at work in New York; Louisiana, after the anomalies of Reconstruction, was safe in the hands of the Democrats; and the American Public Health Association was five years old. The *Times* lay on the breakfast tables of well-regulated New Yorkers. On July 24, on an inside page, it carried a small note reporting four deaths in forty-eight hours from yellow fever in New Orleans. On July 28, the news went, Mobile had established a rigid quarantine against New Orleans. On July 29 a fever story reached the front page: "The Memphis Board of Health and physicians generally are sanguine of security to Memphis, since they claim they are perfectly prepared for any emergency." The next day the most important medical news was an item on page two about horses with hay fever.

So, casually, the story of the great wave of yellow fever that swept up the Mississippi began. Before it was fully told a hundred thousand victims had been stricken and twenty thousand had died under the puzzled eyes of state and local boards of health and in defiance of their earnest efforts.

On August 11 a Memphis despatch mentioned the deaths of six persons at Grenada, Mississippi, and as the fever mounted and its ravages took one, two, three full columns on the sedate front page of the *New York Times* the story of Grenada leaped into prominence and brought the whole disaster into focus. A telegrapher sent vivid daily despatches from this little town, where the disease was swift and deadly. The first cases had been dismissed as "bilious fever," but on August 11 the board of health had reluctantly admitted the presence of an epidemic. Three days later all but seven hundred of the twenty-two hundred whites had fled; only the drug stores and the undertakers' shops were open; the jail was unlocked and the prisoners free. Trains sped through at thirty miles an hour, windows shut fast. Except for doctors and nurses from Memphis and New Orleans, the city was cut off from the world. Not all who fled were safe; one physician taking refuge in a nearby town had to bury his child with his own hands, for no one dared help him. On the fifteenth there were three hundred white people left, and half of them were sick. On the seventeenth there were two hundred, and only thirty or forty were well. "Surely," wired the correspondent, "the end cannot be far, and the chapter must soon be closed." A few days later: "No one has dared to enter the town for several days. When we are gone, God only knows what will become of the stricken." On the twenty-second Grenada heard that the War Department was sending tents for refugees. But who would put them up? "There are not twenty active men in town. . . . The *Times* specials are written in a house where there is one corpse and four persons sick with the fever." The despatches grew briefer. On August 29 there was little more than a list of the newly dead—twenty-two in twenty-four hours —and the telegrapher signed off with the despairing comment "In spite of all the doctors can do death seems to reign supreme." Two days later he too was dead. The story still told in Grenada is that he died at his key.

In mid-July, while the epidemic was gathering force in New Orleans, a handsome new towboat, the *John D. Porter,* put out from that port with a string of barges for Pittsburgh. As she chugged slowly up the brown river she too came to epitomize for newspaper readers the threat of the fever. At Vicksburg she put back to bury an engineer and a fireman, and shipped a substitute engineer. At Memphis she was already marked as a fever ship and barred from the docks. Beyond Cairo the substitute engineer left her and found his way home to die. At Cincinnati, after four deaths which everyone but the ship's officers ascribed to the fever, she was boarded by two federal physicians who stayed with her to care for the sick. Near Gallipolis, Ohio, the fever-ridden crew refused to go farther; all who could went ashore and, brushing aside the guards thrown out by the frightened hamlet, seem to have carried death to thirty-one of its citizens. When the boat finally reached her destination, it is said, twenty-three men had died on her and she had "distributed poison through a journey of more than 1,000 miles."

Meanwhile Memphis, which had been so sure of itself, felt the full blast of pestilence. Twenty-five thousand people fled from the city in ten days; five thousand more were evacuated to tent colonies; of those who remained (not quite twenty thousand) nearly a third paid for their daring with their lives. Shops, wharfs, depots were deserted; except at noonday, when a rabble of Negroes swarmed around the relief stations, the silence everywhere was "painfully profound"; death fires burning in the streets traced the course of mortality from one quarter to another; corpses were found in public parks and deserted buildings.

While New Orleans, Vicksburg, and Memphis suffered most severely, nearly a hundred cities and villages felt the fever. Communications were cut and trade halted throughout the lower valley; New Orleans estimated that she lost $5,000,000 in the stoppage and diversion of commerce. Refugees choked the trains to the north; travel between southwestern cities was paralyzed by innumerable local quarantines, enforced often at the point of a shotgun. Little Rock turned more than a hundred persons out of a train from Memphis and held them twenty-one days. Cincinnati infuriated its rival Louisville by quarantining against it on the strength of unverified rumor. Throughout the North funds were raised for the relief of the sick, the homeless, and the unemployed; Longfellow and Whittier sent autographs to be sold for this purpose. Congress appointed a commission to settle all the important questions as to the origin, spread, and control of both yellow fever and cholera.

The American Public Health Association deferred its annual meeting to hear the conclusions of this commission. Health officers generally were convinced that yellow fever was imported, but many people still thought this disease, like others, could rise spontaneously from filth. A prevailing compromise opinion was that the exotic infection became most dangerous in "foul and fetid conditions of the atmosphere." Yet the professor of medicine in the University of Louisiana, who was also quarantine officer for New Orleans, wrote candidly that "it was disheartening to the enthusiastic sanitarian, to drive along the filthy open canal in the center of Melpomene street, and contrast the comparative exemption of that thoroughfare from sickness, with the frightful decimation which occurred in the clean and beautiful residences about the intersections of Euterpe with Carondelet and Baronne streets."[10]

The commission found that the poison of the fever was specific and organic. It urged more study of chemical disinfectants; sprinkling the streets from watering carts filled with carbolic acid, and other devices, had not been too effective. Quarantine, for all its difficulties, seemed essential, and sanitation was also held important. There was some disappointment because the commission was unable to give categorical answers to the questions put to it. In point of fact, a disease which clearly was not transmitted *directly* from person to person and which nevertheless spread from one place to another with human travel was too puzzling to handle in any logical way until, years later, the mosquito was identified as middleman.

One can find a strong likeness between the ways in which a man in Genoa in 1348 and a man in Memphis in 1878 met the threat of epidemic death. Both put reliance first on shutting out disease and then, when that failed, on running away from it. Neither one knew what to shut out or what to flee. There was, however, one significant change. In 1878 medical men, knowing that yellow fever came somehow in ships from Havana, were not satisfied with the gesture of quarantine: they wanted to know *how* it came—even to the point of studying under the microscope an infusion made of the rock dust which the ships brought as ballast! That particular inquiry, of course, was futile. But it marks progress. Medicine had learned to ask more searching questions; in another generation it would know where, when, and how to defend men against many of the epidemic diseases.

### THE "SPANISH" INFLUENZA

So far in this chapter we have dealt with plagues that seem remote. But the influenza of 1918 and 1919 is too close for comfort. While all Christendom bent its energies to the killing of

24

young men, nature outstripped the statesmen: influenza killed more victims in a few months than all the armies in four years. In the United States perhaps half a million died. In India six months of influenza accounted for nearly as many deaths as twenty years of cholera, and the mortality in October topped all records of pestilence. Because the outlines of the disease were blurred, and disorder was general, one can only guess at the sum of all the deaths: estimates of world-wide mortality run from ten to twenty-one million. Probably not less than 200,000,000, possibly as many as 700,000,000, were sick. The pandemic of 1918 and 1919 ranks with the plague of Justinian and the Black Death as one of the three most destructive outbreaks of disease that the human race has known.

Yet we are struck by the absence, in 1918, of the degree of panic and desolation which is reported for comparable waves of death in earlier years. Of course there was little opportunity to run away from a disease which reached its peak simultaneously in Berlin, Paris, and New York. But even when one adds up the evidences of dislocation in normal living—the suppression of public gatherings, the hurried mobilization of doctors and nurses, the shattered households, the neglected sick, the unburied dead—it seems clear that human composure was not so shaken by this disaster as it had often been before by those of smaller compass.

The fact is that in 1918 the world was deeply preoccupied, and all perspectives were distorted. The Allies were pressing toward victory. Germany was desperate, Russia in labor. Years of war had dulled human sensibility to death. Regimentation was universal, and the epidemic made fresh demands on it: there was much to be busy about. Shocking though it was at close range, influenza may even have served (in this country, at least) to drain off current tensions by putting new groups of volunteers to work.

Moreover disease was no longer so mysterious, so portentous an experience as it had once been. After a generation of research, infection was comprehensible, even though this particular infection still proved baffling. And influenza came as a wolf in sheep's clothing; nobody feared a cold in the head, and "grippe" was a household word. Perhaps if one just took care of oneself the danger could be averted. There were no swellings or horrid blotches as in plague, no exotic associations as in cholera, no black vomit as in yellow fever, to give a macabre twist to the fear of death.

True, the death-roll was enormous, but that was because something like one person in every four (in the United States, at least) fell sick. The chance of surviving the disease was good. The Black Death killed nine out of ten whom it attacked; cholera sometimes four out of five; influenza in 1918, only two or three out of a hundred.

Influenza is hard to define and therefore hard to recognize until it has shown its hand in a large group of cases; that is, until an epidemic is well under way. It is impossible to say where or when the pandemic of 1918 began. Chance named it for neutral Spain rather than for one of the belligerents in the war that so greatly fostered its spread, but though eight million Spaniards sickened, that country seems not to have been the first point of attack.* There had been much influenza in the United States in 1915–1916. There was a "purulent bronchitis" in British army bases in the winter of 1916–1917, and the worst cases showed the bluish pallor later recognized as a grave sign in influenza. Various outbreaks of nervous diseases in America and Great Britain and on the Continent between 1915 and 1918 may or

* This is not the first time that influenza has been fathered on foreign parts. In 1889 and 1890 it was "Chinese influenza" in Russia, "Russian influenza" in Europe, "European influenza" in America, and "American influenza" in Japan.

may not have had something to do with the approaching pandemic.*

Early in 1918, ill-defined acute respiratory disorders were observed here and there in Europe, Asia, and America. By April and May such disorders, spreading among troops and civilians in France, were generally recognized as influenza, and the first wave of the pandemic was taking shape. During the late spring and summer influenza was seen widely in Western Europe, in India, and elsewhere as a "three-day fever," striking suddenly, bringing an aching lassitude, but soon giving way to an uneventful convalescence.

As this wave was subsiding in France, ominous changes were noticed. Graver complications appeared. The death rates in Paris began to climb. In September, at both ends of the busy Atlantic sea lanes, sickness began to multiply and deaths increased explosively. This was true at Brest, crowded with eager American doughboys, and in the naval stations around Boston. The autumn influenza was a very different matter from the disease of the preceding spring and summer. Most of those who were sick suffered the familiar aching fever and recovered without serious effect, but a significant minority (perhaps one out of five in English experience) were stricken, often without warning in the course of an apparently mild infection, with a severe pneumonia. This was chiefly what caused death, and if the lips and ears turned an ashy purple, with the face pallid, death was almost certain. At autopsy the lungs would be found to show varied and widespread damage quite unlike what is looked for in pneumonias of other origin.

As these sinister changes in the behavior of the disease began to be apparent, the impulse to brush it aside as merely "grippe" gave way to bewilderment and anxiety. In the United States,

* Certain left-wing epidemiologists have considered this association of diseases significant.

New England first felt the pressure of a major emergency. Three thousand cases developed in eight days at an army training camp. In the second week of October Boston was seriously affected. Public meetings were banned; the saloons were ordered and the churches requested to close their doors (Mother Eddy's followers dissenting). Many doctors and nurses had gone to war; those left at home were overwhelmed. Massachusetts called on the federal government for help. Emergency hospitals were set up in schools, churches, town halls, and (not least effectively) in the open air. A hospital train was rushed from Maryland to Massachusetts, and kept in service there till it was more urgently needed at home. So many operators were sick that use of the telephone was discouraged.

In the third week of October New York was in the thick of the epidemic, in the next week Washington and Chicago, in the next New Orleans and Los Angeles, in the next Seattle and San Francisco. Everywhere health authorities fired broadsides of advice at the public, then buckled down to the task of getting the sick cared for and the dead buried. The United States Public Health Service issued a terse bulletin summing up what little was known about the disease, asked and received a million dollars from Congress, recruited more than a thousand physicians for emergency duty, busied itself with current reporting, sent its own men to mobilize local resources. Volunteers visited the sick, cooked for the hungry, carried food to demoralized homes. In Detroit schools were closed so that the teachers might canvass their districts and report unattended cases. In Philadelphia when trained workers were lacking the local Council of National Defense advertised for "any person with two hands and a willingness to help." Harrowing situations were found—men and women dying without help; bedridden mothers and newborn babies sharing rooms with unburied corpses. In Philadelphia two hundred bodies were crowded into a morgue built for thirty-six; coffins gave out, and a street railway repair shop was turned into a coffin factory. In New York the mayor ordered street cleaners to the cemeteries to help dig graves. Even the elaborate organization for war had to yield precedence: fuel administrators relaxed their rules, and the movement of conscripts to the training camps was halted.

Meanwhile this second wave of influenza had spread eastward as well as westward and was covering the globe. By the end of October it was everywhere in Europe and North America, and at many points in South America. India, China, Persia, South Africa had been attacked early. In November influenza was ravaging the South Sea islands and pushing deep into the heart of Africa. Australia was able to hold off this wave of infection temporarily, but in January that continent too was invaded.

Everywhere the disease was far more fatal than it had been in the summer. American death rates soared to a peak which stands out like the Matterhorn in the curves for the present century.* In Philadelphia and Baltimore the deaths from all causes in the worst week of the epidemic were more than ten times those of the corresponding weeks in preceding years.

And the losses fell most heavily not on the weak but on the strong. In former years one thought of influenza as a disease that carried off those who were about ready to die, and especially the aged. But in 1918 the disease occurred most frequently among children from five to fourteen years old, and was more likely to strike at any age below forty than at any age above. Nearly half the deaths in the United States from influenza and pneumonia were among men and women in the prime of life— between twenty and forty—and the greatest losses in proportion

* See Chart II on page 252. Of course death rates had been sliding down for many years: in New York City, as Chart I on page 18 shows, the rates for the cholera years 1832 and 1849 make the influenza peak look like a foothill.

29

to population fell between twenty-five and twenty-nine years of age.

Public thinking about the nature of the disease was none too clear. Influenza was "the mysterious malady." A physician writing in the *Medical Record* suggested that it was really pneumonic plague, carried by coolies from China to France. A responsible officer of the Emergency Fleet Corporation thought the "germs" might have been released by "Huns sent ashore by Boche submarine commanders." North Carolinians were warned by their board of health that it was futile to wear "sulphur in their shoes, asafetida in their bosoms, cucumbers on their ankles, or potatoes in their pockets." But even solid business men carried camphor, and a mother wrote the United States Public Health Service that she dosed her baby with a mixture of asafetida and brandy.

More responsible ideas as to prevention differed in detail, but agreed on the fundamentals—diminishing crowd contacts, and keeping infection from the nose and mouth. Many cities closed their schools. New York decided against this course but tried to lessen rush hour congestion by staggering business hours. In Chicago the police were ordered to arrest those who coughed or sneezed without benefit of handkerchief. In San Francisco the wearing of masks was made compulsory. Vaccines were used in large quantity, and seemed to some authorities effective.

But when all was said and done, and the health men got together to compare their experiences, it was clear that no preventive measure, however respectable its scientific premise, could be shown conclusively to have checked the spread of disease. An officer of the Public Health Service admitted frankly at the annual meeting of the American Public Health Association that the federal government had been able to do little more than furnish sick relief, and added, "It is futile to talk of suppressing the spread of a disease of this character with our present knowledge." George Harvey declared truculently in his *North American Review* that public authorities had been guilty of "an exhibition of unreadiness, of ineptitude, of either apathy or cowardice or both, unrivalled in the history of the nation." He was manifestly unfair, but he was not alone in feeling that science and government had failed to cope with the emergency.

The truth is that no one knew enough about the disease to find its vulnerable spot. The huddle we call civilization was in 1918—and probably still is—defenseless against epidemic influenza.

REFERENCES

1. Creighton, Charles. *A history of epidemics in Britain.* Cambridge, England: University Press, 1891, vol. 1, p. 115, 177, 241, 673.
2. Boccaccio, Giovanni. *The decameron.* Translated by John Payne. New York: The Modern Library, 1931, p. 9.
3. Hecker, J. F. K. *The epidemics of the middle ages.* Translated by B. G. Babington. London: published for the Sydenham Society, 1844, p. 52, 61, 360, 186, 257–258.
4. Defoe, Daniel. *A journal of the plague year (London, 1722).* London: John Dent and Company, 1907, p. 22, 129.
5. Bell, Walter George. *The great plague in London in 1665.* London: John Lane, The Bodley Head, Ltd.; New York: Dodd, Mead and Company, 1924, p. 80, 260–261.
6. Carey, Mathew. *A short account of the malignant fever lately prevalent in Philadelphia: with a statement of the proceedings that took place on the subject in different parts of the United States.* 3d ed., improved. Philadelphia: printed by the author, 1793, p. 33.
7. Gibbs, George. *Memoirs of the administrations of Washington and John Adams.* Edited from the papers of Oliver Wolcott, Secretary of the Treasury. New York: printed for the subscribers, 1846, vol. 1, p. 110.
8. Rush, Benjamin. *An account of the bilious remitting yellow fever as it appeared in the city of Philadelphia in the year 1793.* Philadelphia: Thomas Dobson, 1794, p. 23–24, 125, 359.
9. Reese, David Meredith. *A plain and practical treatise on the epidemic cholera as it prevailed in the city of New York in the summer of 1832.* New York: Conner and Cooke, 1833, p. 23–24.

10. Bemiss, S. M. *Report upon yellow fever in Louisiana in 1878 and subsequently*. Reprinted from New Orleans Medical and Surgical Journal, August–September 1883, p. 21.

A NOTE ON SOURCES

My principal sources for the Black Death and the English sweat are Creighton and Hecker, both cited above. Creighton, though behind his times in medical theory, was a tireless historian and his two volumes will repay hours of browsing. Hirsch's *Handbook of geographical and historical pathology*, which Creighton translated (London: The New Sydenham Society, 1883), is lifeless by comparison but a mine of information too.

On the London plague of 1665 Bell's carefully documented study, which I have used freely, is of course far more scholarly than Defoe's apocryphal *Journal*, but one would not willingly give up Defoe's lively reconstruction of an event of which he had no personal knowledge.

Carey and Rush are natural sources for the Philadelphia yellow fever of 1793; few epidemics before our own day have been so well described in both medical and non-medical terms.

For cholera in the United States I draw on contemporary sources, including a report to the House of Representatives on the *Cholera epidemic of 1873 in the United States* (Washington: Government Printing Office, 1875) and some local histories. Greenwood's *Epidemics and crowd diseases* (London: Williams and Norgate, 1935), from which I have borrowed enthusiastically at all stages of my work, and Goodall's convenient *Short history of the epidemic infectious diseases* (London: John Bale, Sons and Danielsson, Ltd., 1934) put the pandemics in perspective. The latter is a useful introduction to the whole sweep of epidemiological history, yellow fever excepted.

For the story of the yellow fever of 1878 I have gone chiefly to contemporary records such as the New York Times, Harper's Weekly, local reports, the proceedings of the American Public Health Association for 1879 (published under the title Public Health, volume 4) and the *Conclusions of the board of experts authorized by Congress to investigate the yellow fever epidemic of 1878* (Washington: Judd & Detweiler, 1879). At Grenada in 1936 I had the good fortune to talk with Dr. Thomas J. Brown, who after nearly sixty years remembered vividly the outburst of fever in that unhappy city.

## A NOTE ON SOURCES

The *Report on the pandemic of influenza 1918–19* of the British Ministry of Health (London: H. M. Stationery Office, 1920) and an American study by E. O. Jordan, *Epidemic influenza, a survey* (Chicago: American Medical Association, 1927), give much information about the influenza of 1918. Some details are drawn from contemporary newspapers and magazines and from subsequent reports of the United States Public Health Service. Dr. Warren F. Draper of that Service and Dr. B. W. Carey of the Children's Fund of Michigan were helpful in correspondence on this matter.

# 3

## PAST THINKING

SIGNS in the sky, stinking mists, divine wrath, rotting coffee
—the curious causes which the human imagination has seized
upon in a desperate effort to explain pestilence are barely hinted
at in the stories just told. It would be easy to find abundant evidence of bewilderment, credulity, and ingenious wrongheaded-
ness in the history of epidemiological thinking. One is tempted
to set the crass ignorance of our ancestors over against our own
gratifying intelligence, letting Pasteur mark the turn of the tide,
and leave the matter there. But it would be a mistake to assume
that nothing of consequence was known or thought about communicable disease before Pasteur, or that what we know about
"germs" is all we need to know about epidemics. It might be
better to follow the human mind as it has gradually come to
grips with the ideas that are needed in the fight against epidemic
death, and to ask whether some of those ideas may not still elude
us.

It is not easy to keep a sound historical perspective in such a
task. For twenty centuries philosophers and physicians tried to
understand the strange phenomena of disease with only the evidence of their unaided senses to guide them: they saw, heard,
smelt what they could, and drew the best inferences they could
think of. It is not surprising that mistakes were made; the questions were hard, and the answers might have been even more

fantastic than they were. On the other hand, everyday medical practice may have been and probably was far below the level of the best surviving texts. Medicine rose and fell with the ground swells of culture: Hippocrates rode the crest of an intellectual wave, but for centuries after him men gave the lie to his clear pronouncement that all diseases have their natural causes. Ideas were prematurely born: Fracastor hinted in 1546 at the existence of a living contagion, but Pasteur still had to fight skepticism when he put this principle to work more than three hundred years later. In retrospect we can distinguish the logical implications of this or that notion, but we do so only at the risk of trimming its blurred edges to fit our own pattern of interpretation. Even those who had a glimpse of the truth had no way of knowing that it was the truth.

If we push back far enough into the primitive mind we shall probably find that all disease—from the pain in the painted warrior's belly to the epidemic that decimates the tribe—is an affair of magic. Evil spirits, human enemies in league with them, or the vindictive dead may cause it. Those who are wise in magic must deal with it. If in the process natural remedies happen to be used, their role is subordinate to that of the incantations.

No one can say when this sort of thinking began, and it would be equally hard to say when it ended—if it has ended. The civilized Romans put their gods to bed and feasted them as a means of checking pestilence. In the Middle Ages there was a devil to cause or a saint to cure each disease (St. Vitus' dance, for example), and medicine leaned on astrology. The scrofula was the King's Evil for centuries; the great Dr. Johnson submitted to being "touched" by Queen Anne. When cholera came to Ireland in 1832 runners darted from house to house distributing bits of smouldering peat, charging each householder to divide his bit among seven other houses and, while it burned, to offer up seven *paters*, three *aves*, and a *credo* in the name of God and the holy

St. John, to stop the plague. In 1935 a Negro orderly in a hospital built by the Commonwealth Fund surreptitiously slipped a pan of water under a patient's bed to stop her chills. How many persons still living had their ears pierced in childhood to prevent soreness of the eyes? And how many still murmur *Gesundheit* when they hear a sneeze?

## CONTAGION

Yet in very early times (if we limit ourselves to recorded history) one hard fact began to emerge out of the fog. Gods or devils might touch off disease, but once lighted up it often spread from person to person. It was "catching." Five or six hundred years before Christ the Hebrews had already learned, probably from the Egyptians or the Babylonians, to isolate the leper, and to give public warning when certain other diseases began to spread. They thought of pestilence as punishment of an erring people by an angry god, but contagion from case to case was a factor to be reckoned with in everyday terms.

Gradually the notion of contagion attached itself to a number of diseases, though it was often subordinated to a highly speculative system of remote and immediate causes. Hippocrates does not mention it, perhaps because it seemed to him to smack of that supernaturalism which he repudiated. But before the Christian era other Greek writers had come to consider phthisis, ophthalmia, and scabies contagious, and were puzzled because "fevers" and other ailments did not seem to behave in the same way. By the second century the contagious group included also plague, rabies, and elephantiasis.

The mumbling authorities of the Middle Ages tended to agree on a list of eight contagious diseases. We do not know what they all were, for names and symptom-pictures shift about, and there were vague categories like "plague," "leprosy," and "fever" which included a number of diseases now recognized as distinct. But lazar-houses were used throughout Europe for the isolation of "leprosy," and parents were warned, perhaps as early as the tenth or eleventh century, against exposing their children to smallpox. In the fourteenth century Basle barred those who were sick with certain specified diseases from all ordinary inter-course, and Venice, Genoa, Ragusa, and Marseilles established maritime quarantine against the plague. The contagiousness of syphilis seems to have been generally understood soon after the disease began to attract attention, late in the fifteenth century, though physicians paid their respects to the ecclesiastical view that it was a punishment for carnal sin, and one suggested po-litely that "an influence or corruption of the aire" might account for cases among the clergy.[1]

In the sixteenth century the Veronese Fracastor added mea-sles, the English sweat, typhus, and "pestilent fevers" to the contagious class. But about the same time, according to Hirsch, the doctors began to doubt whether leprosy was contagious, and only the public clung to the belief that it was. In the seventeenth century Sydenham gave little weight to contagion, though he recognized it in plague and syphilis. In the nineteenth, as we shall see, there was lively disagreement about the matter. But however uncertainly it was applied to particular diseases, the notion of contagion did play a significant part in early medical thinking about pestilence.

Experience, rumor, and tradition elaborated the notion. The Hebrew sanitary code dealt with both infected persons and in-fected houses. In the second century the breath as well as the bite of a mad dog was thought to be dangerous. In the tenth or eleventh century doctors warned the public to avoid things han-dled by a victim of smallpox, as well as his bed, his clothes, and his person. Boccaccio tells of seeing two hogs die in the street after mouthing the rags taken from a victim of the Black Death, and Guy de Chauliac declares that plague could be caught simply by looking at the sick. In a very long and very bad poem about the plague in London in 1665, cited by Bell, there is an amusing stanza about the precautions taken to avoid infection carried by money:

> All money is in water layd
> And basons now are purses made,
> And yet ye very water wch made clean
> All other things, it selfe began
> To be poluted now
> And was infected so
> That we had need to wash ye very water too.[2]

Fracastor in 1546 attempted to give a systematic account of the phenomena of contagion. It could, he said, occur by contact, through fomites (that is, neutral articles like wool or rags which were not themselves susceptible to the effects of contagion, but could receive it, hold it, and give it off unchanged), and at a distance through the air. Contagion was a sort of putrefaction passing from one thing to another; the *seminaria* or seed-pods which carried it could reproduce their kind, but Fracastor twice compares this process with the propagation of the vital spirits—whatever *they* were—and so falls short of identifying it clearly with anything we should recognize as the facts of life.*

In a cramped metaphysical way this was an ingenious guess. But the time was not yet ripe for translating it into simpler biological terms, or for putting it to the test, and it seems presently to have been forgotten. A century later in Prussia while the plague was abroad, the Jesuit Kircher, with the help of an early microscope, actually saw in the blood-stream and in decay-

---

* Goodall, however, finds it "difficult to resist the conclusion that in Fracastor's mind there was more than a glimmering notion that the *seminaria* [germs or seed-pods] were living in the present-day sense of the word." Goodall, E. W., Fracastor as an epidemiologist. *Proc. Roy. Soc. Med.*, 30: 341–350, February 1937.

ing matter small objects which he was bold enough to call the living carriers of contagion. These, he thought, could be thrown off into the air, and could creep into porous matter such as fabrics; when warmed by human contact, they entered the body like a "poisoned steam."[1] Kircher's glass was probably not good enough to show him what we now recognize as bacteria, but in the last quarter of the seventeenth century van Leeuwenhoek, in Holland, did see and describe both bacteria and the larger parasites called protozoa. Linnaeus made a place for bacteria in his eighteenth-century botanical system, though he had to lump them all together in a group called "chaos." Plague and "consumption" were ascribed to such living organisms by various writers, and about 1760 von Plenciz, in Vienna, suggested that contagious diseases generally were due to them.

A century before Pasteur, then, the fact of contagion was familiar and its nature had been guessed at. But there were other and highly seductive notions of disease to be reckoned with before medical thinking accepted the notion of bacterial invasion as a general theory.

## THE PHYSICAL ENVIRONMENT

We take infection by living organisms so much for granted that it presents itself as a possibility to be reckoned with whenever an unfamiliar disease process is first observed. But we also think of many ailments as arising spontaneously from some inexplicable alteration within the body or from some dietary deficiency or other failure of the environment. Progress in the understanding and control of the acute communicable diseases has come about through lifting them one by one out of the class of inexplicable or merely environmental phenomena into the class caused by the passage of specific living invaders from one body to another. To put ourselves in the place of medical thinkers before the latter part of the nineteenth century we must realize that relatively few diseases were believed to be invariably contagious; in the absence of strong indication to the contrary vague environmental influences reacting spontaneously with individual bodies were assumed to be the cause of disease.

Hippocrates, four hundred years before Christ, started from this point when he set about making a record of what he saw in his own practice, and particularly of the way in which certain diseases seemed to prevail at certain times and in certain places. At the beginning of the *First Book of the Epidemics* he writes, in a beautifully factual spirit:

> In Thasus, about the autumnal equinox, and under the Pleiades, the rains were abundant, constant, and soft, with southerly winds; the winter southerly, the northerly winds faint, droughts; on the whole, the winter having the character of spring. The spring was southerly, cool, rains small in quantity. Summer, for the most part, cloudy, no rain, the Etesian winds, rare and small, blew in an irregular manner. The whole constitution of the season being thus inclined to the southerly, and with droughts early in the spring, from the preceding opposite and northerly state, ardent fevers occurred in a few instances, and these very mild, being rarely attended with hemorrhage, and never proving fatal.[3]

Then he goes on to describe what even the layman can easily recognize as an epidemic of mumps. In the same vein he tells the story of several seasons and the diseases which he saw in them. In *Airs, Waters, and Places* he says explicitly that to investigate medicine properly one must take account of the seasons, the winds, the water supply, the orientation of the city, the topography, and the customs and occupations of the people under observation. All disease arises from natural causes; environment and regime have much to do with endemic (that is, continuously prevalent) diseases; epidemics seem to be associated in particular with climatic variations. Such is the tenor of his thinking.

It was thus the whole sweep of the environment that interested Hippocrates. But the "morbific" influence of the air came to play a special part in the theory of epidemics. It may have been one of Hippocrates' disciples who said in the treatise *On Breaths* that polluted air causes infirmities, and that fevers are common to many persons because they all breathe the same air. (The word *miasma,* meaning pollution, which was used in this connection, was revived with enthusiasm in the nineteenth century.) About the beginning of the Christian era, two historians wrote of epidemics caused by "poisonous exhalations from the damp ground," and in succeeding centuries the unhealthiness of swampy country—so common on the shores of the eastern Mediterranean—was a matter of frequent comment.*

In this simpler form the idea of atmospheric infection was sometimes a not unnatural misreading of data which still have significance for epidemiology. Marshes and malaria, for a quite sufficient reason, do often go together. But the theory was complicated by far more speculative elements. In his long poem *On the Nature of Things,* devoted to the atomic theory, Lucretius has this very interesting comment to make on the causes of disease:

And first I have shewn above that there are seeds of many things helpful to our life; and on the other hand many must fly about conducing to disease and death. When these by chance have happened to grow together and have disordered the atmosphere, the air becomes distempered. And all that force of disease and that pestilence come either from without down through the atmosphere in the shape of clouds and mists, or else do gather themselves up and rise out of the earth, when soaked with wet it has contracted a taint, being beaten upon by unseasonable rains and suns.[4]

The earth soaked with wet is a homely physical fact; the air distempered by an accidental disarrangement of the elements of

* The Roman writers Varro and Columella, in the second and first centuries B.C., even suggested that invisible animals or stinging insects bred in swamps could cause disease, but this idea seems to have been neglected for many centuries after them.

the universe is a concept of quite another order. For centuries the two notions move in and out of a puzzling *pas de deux*. Now putrefaction, now cosmic disorder poisons the air. An Italian discussing the great plague of the fourteenth century could bring together, among its causes, astral and terrestrial influences and the emanations from rotting heaps of locusts drowned in the sea and cast up on shore.*

Sydenham—the Roundhead physician, younger contemporary of Milton and friend of John Locke—drew a distinction between weather and the subtler offices of the air in causing disease. He divided acute diseases into two groups—"epidemic distempers" arising from "a latent and inexplicable alteration of the air, infecting the bodies of men," and others "arising from some peculiar indisposition of particular persons." The former occurred in particular years in more or less regular patterns called "epidemic constitutions," of which he wrote:

> There are various general constitutions of years, that owe their origin neither to heat, cold, dryness, or moisture; but rather depend upon a certain secret and inexplicable alteration in the bowels of the earth, whence the air becomes impregnated with such kinds of *effluvia* as subject the human body to particular distempers so long as that kind of constitution prevails, which, after a certain course of years, declines, and gives way to another. Each of these general constitutions is attended with its own proper and peculiar kind of fever, which never appears in any other. . . .[5]

Such familiar entities as moisture and temperature, Sydenham goes on to say, may have some share in producing the minor fevers which are always with us, and "may more or less dispose the body to the particular epidemic disease," but the major role in causing epidemics belongs to something far more elusive—an

---

* A Dane wrote in the fifteenth century that "every foul stink is to be eschewed," but plumbing, dentistry, and personal habits being what they were, this must have been difficult advice to follow.

A N

# ESSAY

CONCERNING THE

# EFFECTS

O F

# A I R

O N

# HUMAN BODIES.

By *JOHN ARBUTHNOT*, M. D.
Fellow of the *Royal Colleges of Phyſicians* of *London*
and *Edinburgh,* and of the *Royal Society.*

*L O N D O N:*
Printed for J. T o n s o n in the *Strand.*

M DCC XXXIII.

*Title page of Arbuthnot's contribution
to the discussion of a subject dear to
epidemiologists for twenty centuries*

imperceptible influence, perhaps material enough to be carried on the wind, but postulated only from its effect on mankind.*

The notion that infection in the air arose out of the bowels of the earth appealed strongly to Robert Boyle, the seventeenth-century chemist and philosopher who was interested in everything from the behavior of gases under pressure to the behavior of saints under martyrdom. Minerals and "mischievous fossils" in the fiery depths of the earth, sometimes stirred up by great convulsions, he thought, threw off emanations which might perhaps mingle in the air with those of the sun and planets. If bad, these emanations caused disease; if good, they checked it. When one man sickened of the plague and another escaped, the first must have had the misfortune to run into a bigger swarm of noxious air-borne "corpuscles" than the second. (But Boyle is better remembered, in this field, for the astute prophecy which Pasteur exactly fulfilled—that an understanding of ferments and fermentation would be the best road to the understanding of fevers and certain other diseases.)

In the next century the gentlemanly Arbuthnot, crony of Pope and Swift, leaned toward a more modest and plausible view of the relation between atmosphere and disease, concerning himself with problems of temperature and humidity and with organic matter in the air, in which he included the "Perspiration of Vegetables" and the "Steams of Animals, especially of such as are rotting." He believed in both morbific air and contagion, but he gave more weight to the air as the general cause of acute disease. There might be "invisible Insects" at work (this was

---

* There is no need to go here into the ramifications of the theory of the epidemic constitution. Some of them check with modern observation no better than the notion of the obscurely infected air fits modern epidemiological thinking. Sydenham's guesses at causation were poor, but behind his clinical generalizations there was, as Greenwood puts it, the valid principle that there is *order* in epidemiological phenomena. To that principle we must return later.

after Kircher and van Leeuwenhoek), though he was not convinced of it, and even if there were, the air must play a part by favoring their propagation.

At the risk of getting ahead of the story, a late flowering of Hippocratic curiosity about the physical environment in general must be mentioned here. In 1850 one of the most robust and admirable pioneers in American medicine, Daniel Drake, finished an ambitious job. He had observed that while some diseases were found generally, others—intermittent fevers, yellow fever, plague, pneumonia, and so on—seemed to occur in "certain climates, localities, or states of society" and, because of their local variations, demanded "some peculiarity of treatment." The climates, localities, and states of society which interested him were those of the great interior valley of North America, and he traveled from the Alleghenies to the Rockies, from the Great Lakes to the Gulf, making careful note of topography, climate, soil, winds, and of the people's occupations, habits, and domestic environment—even to the shade trees around the houses, and relating all this information so far as he could to the local prevalence of disease. In Germany a little later August Hirsch heaped up bit by bit a still more amazing compilation of data as to the geographical and meteorological incidence of disease, but he worked from books, Drake from thirty years of first-hand observation.

These men spoke to the earth in the hope that she would teach them; and sometimes they came very close to the truth, only to miss the essential clue. Hirsch's discussion of malaria is a beautiful picture of the conditions under which the disease occurs; it leads the reader up to the very heart of the problem, and there it stops. He felt sure the cause of the disease was specific, not a vague miasma; he favored the theory that it was a parasite; and he suggested further study to determine "what animal or vegetable forms the production of malaria appears to be associated with." But he did not suspect the mosquito. Nor did Drake, who knew malaria failed to appear in many places where current theories led him to look for it, liked the suggestion that some "vegeto-animal principle" was at work, and even guessed shrewdly that the familiar varieties of the fever might be due to different species of the same order—which later proved to be exactly true of the plasmodium.

Lacking scientific proof that any given agency was responsible for a given disease, such scholars were sound in their effort to gather up and set down every scrap of information they could get about environmental factors. Their industry, it is true, was largely fruitless so far as etiology was concerned, and their methods have all but disappeared into limbo along with phlebotomy and the town crier. And that is a pity, for we may yet have much to learn about the geographical—not to mention the temporal—variables in the rise and spread of epidemics.

### THE HUMAN FACTOR

So much for external influences. As to the human factor in disease, early thinking, if it be stated in the most general terms, seems to be right in principle though magnificently wrong in detail. The Greeks saw that some men became sick and others under like external conditions did not, and rightly inferred that the make-up or physical condition of the individual had something to do with his susceptibility to disease. Though they defined the human constitution in terms that seem childish to us— the four "humours" (blood, phlegm, yellow bile, and black bile) have little relation to physiology as we know it—the central notion has persisted throughout the subsequent history of medicine.

Aristotle remarked that fatigue brought on fever. Galen, the second-century Greek whose writings became the bible of medicine for many centuries, explained disease systematically in terms of individual constitution, individual ways of life, and atmospheric influences, and said soundly that "no cause can be efficient without an aptitude of the body." If the atmosphere carried "seeds of pestilence," the healthy body was less likely than the unhealthy to be injured by them. The distinguished Arabian physician Rhazes, about the year 900, pointed out bodily differences which seemed to make one person more susceptible to measles, another to smallpox. Guy de Chauliac, commentator on the Black Death, who thought the stars were the primary cause of the disaster, reckoned that corruption of the bodily fluids, debility, and obstruction of the natural passages played a part in the selection of the victims. John Kaye, whose vivid reference to the English sweat has already been quoted, wrote that "our bodies can not suffre any thing or hurt by corrupt & infectiue causes, except ther be in them a certein mater prepared apt & like to receiue it, els if one were sick, al shuld be sick. . . ." Like many other physicians before and after him, he urged his readers to set their minds as well as their bodies in order, if they wished to avoid the disease. His excursion into mental hygiene is worth quoting if only for the incidental ironic values the passage of time has given it.

Al these thinges duely obserued, and well executed, whiche before I haue for preseruation mencioned, if more ouer we can sette a parte al affections, as fretting cares & thoughtes, dolefull or sorowfull imaginations, vaine feares, folysh loues, gnawing hates, and geue oure selues to lyue quietly, friendlye, & merily one with an outher, as men were wont to do in the old world, when this countrie was called merye Englande, and euery man to medle in his own matters, thinking them sufficient, as thei do in Italye, and auoyde malyce and dissencion, the destruction of commune wealthes, and priuate houses: I doubte not but we shall preserue oure selues, bothe from this sweatinge sicknesse, and other diseases also not here purposed to be spoken of.[6]

Such counsel may be poor protection against the virus of influenza, and the opposite view, so far as animate contagion was concerned, was neatly put two centuries later by Arbuthnot when he pointed out that "invisible Insects would bite or sting whether a Person was in a Passion or Calm." John Snow, who thought so clearly about cholera in the mid-nineteenth century, ridiculed the classic preoccupation with the predisposing cause. It was, he said, "nothing visible or evident: like the elephant, which supports the world, according to Hindoo mythology, it was merely invented to remove a difficulty" [7]—the difficulty being that though all men breathed the air which seemed to carry disease, only some men sickened. Yet we are not sure enough of our ground today to dismiss entirely the possibility that emotions have something to do with systemic health, that systemic health has something to do with resistance, and that resistance has something to do with the spread and intensity of infection. At least we still believe that what the body is and does plays a significant part in the reaction which we call disease, making some (for whatever reason) more resistant than others. By devious ways, the ancients reached the same generalization.

## CHRONOLOGICAL DIGRESSION

By the end of the eighteenth century, medicine had come to some such assumptions as these: disease is a natural process; some diseases are contagious, or may become so under certain conditions, but others arise spontaneously when morbid influences from the earth or sky, transmitted through the air, find human bodies responsive to them; epidemics are more plausibly explained in terms of such "miasmatic" influences than in terms of contagion; contagion is perhaps the work of living organisms. Among the indubitably contagious diseases, smallpox alone could be prevented: Jenner had just shown the way to the general use of vaccination.

So we come to the nineteenth century—the century of our own grandfathers, of the devoted (and inadequate) sanitarians, of

Pasteur and Koch. The main streams of epidemiological think-ing began to flood new channels. For a time the brilliant deduc-tions of Fracastor, Kircher, and their eighteenth-century succes-sors were largely forgotten or neglected. Neither cholera nor yellow fever, which terrorized the old world and the new, could be fitted into the familiar pattern of contagion laid down by plague, smallpox, and syphilis. A New York doctor asked in bewilderment whether cholera was "contagious, meteoratious, or infectious." Meanwhile the leisure classes discovered the poor; well-born noses were outraged by the smells of the slum; the pioneers in public health grew impatient of etiological specula-tion when there were so many "unhealthy" drains to fix. But a few investigators were fascinated by the unfolding world of microscopic life; its swarming complexity reminded one of them of the Milky Way. Some acute minds leaped to assumptions about the nature of infection which, however doubtful at the moment, were dramatically confirmed before the century ended. Doctors learned to count, and their inferences were subjected, almost for the first time, to statistical criticism. For epidemiology it was the great century.

Great—and also turbulent. The controversy over miasma and contagion lasted most of the century, though the speculative miasmatists gave way to the sanitarians, and the proponents of the *contagium vivum* were succeeded by the early bacteriolo-gists. Even in the last quarter of the century, which in the main belongs to modern medicine, some strongholds of old thinking still held out.

## MIASMA VS. CONTAGION

When Philadelphia suffered from yellow fever in 1793 the local physicians decided officially that the mischief came from imported infection, not from local putrefaction. But the lexi-cographer Noah Webster was not satisfied, and he ushered in the new century with a *Brief History of Epidemic and Pestilential Diseases* designed to put an end to the nonsense about infection. With a rhetorician's instinct, he rebelled at the idea that "invisible animalcules" could cause plague, or contagion carried in old clothes could touch off great conflagrations of disease. Epidemics were natural phenomena on a grand scale; their causes must be correspondingly profound. He ascribed them to disturbances of the electricity or internal fires of the earth, due perhaps to the passage of comets, and signalized by striking manifestations of many sorts—earthquakes, droughts, floods, hail, "extraordinary intumescence of the ocean," "sickly and tasteless" oysters, enormous hauls of shad. Though his credulity led him into anticlimax, he did amass a prodigious quantity of historical data, and his work was still quoted with respect by a loyal miasmatist ninety years later.

More than rhetoric was needed, however, to settle the controversy. Knowledge of life under the microscope was slowly piling up. A Frenchman and a German, Cagniard de la Tour and Schwann, had watched minute vegetable cells multiplying in fermenting liquids, and an Italian and a Frenchman, Bassi and Audouin, had studied muscardine, a contagious fungus disease of silkworms. While neither yeast nor fungus, as we know now, offered an exact analogy for the behavior of bacteria, the findings were very suggestive at a time when the role of microorganisms in disease was known by surmise rather than observation. They greatly interested the German anatomist Jakob Henle, whose essay on miasma and contagion, published in 1840, wrestled sturdily with the confused concepts of his day. Where so many of his predecessors had been credulous or bumptious or both, he showed himself cautious and critical, aware of the limitations of his own thinking, and sensitive to the difference between theory and demonstration.

Contagion, Henle thought, was the work of living organisms

49

which like yeast entered the host in minute quantities and multiplied parasitically. It could be carried through the air like the spores thrown off by the fungoid growths which muscardine produced on the silkworm's skin. If it passed from one diseased body to another, either directly or through the air, it was obviously contagion; if it seemed to originate elsewhere it might be called miasma; but the two were essentially identical. In malaria miasma alone might be at work; in some diseases only contagion could be observed; but in many others the infective material might first appear as miasma and then be spread as contagion. Miasma was to be postulated only when contagion could not be demonstrated. While he was certain that the *contagium* was alive, he was not sure whether it lived "independently"—that is, as a distinct species—or was an abnormal modification of human or animal tissue thrown off by the diseased body.

Similar views were expressed in a similar spirit at about the same time by Sir Henry Holland, who took cholera as the special problem on which to hang his speculations about the cause and transmission of contagious diseases. None of the current theories about cholera satisfied him: neither electrical nor physical changes in the atmosphere could be expected to wander all over the globe as cholera did; local exhalations or living conditions could hardly be identical at widely different times and places; the notion of an epidemic constitution seemed "vague and doubtful in import." It seemed much more probable to him that some form of animal life, migrating, striking here and there, flourishing under favorable circumstances and dying out under unfavorable, behaving in general like "the insect swarms which inflict blight upon vegetable life," was at work. He knew the toxic effect of animal and insect secretions, and thought smaller organisms might be similarly poisonous.

Both men regretted the necessity of arguing by deduction and analogy. Holland carefully set off his speculations from his chapters of clinical observation. Henle despaired of the possibility of a clear-cut identification of the disease-bearing organisms in the blood or tissue; he had labored at the microscope himself, and confessed that he could not tell the stuff of contagion from other cells. But he set the stage for further experimentation when he asserted that microscopic forms, to be regarded with certainty as the cause of contagion, must be found not occasionally but regularly in the infectious stuff, must be separated from it, and must be tested to determine their potency. These early thinkers were thwarted by the lack of techniques—staining and culturing, for example—which would have put a firm foundation under their deductions.* It is always an interesting question how far logic can go in science without the parallel development of ingenuity in the manipulation of material. Yet the very paucity of factual details in which to clothe their conceptions makes the logical initiative of these men—and of their like-minded predecessors—the more admirable. Their conclusions were not mere guesswork. They reasoned that if, as in smallpox, a minute quantity of infectious stuff increased in the body till it was thrown off at many points on the skin, and then repeated the process in another body, it must have the power of multiplying itself—and only living matter could do that. The lapse of time between exposure and the appearance of symptoms suggested, not the action of an inert poison, but a period of growth or reproduction of the infectious agent. Noxious stuff produced spontaneously should affect the body in the same way no matter how many times it was inhaled or ingested, but smallpox and measles left some permanent change behind them so that reinfection did not occur; was not some adjustment taking place between biological forces? Miasma or electricity should act uni-

* Holland seems to have foreseen the utility of staining when he suggests that "coloring matter, suitable to animal organisation," might be applied to natural or artificial dew condensed from miasma.

formly over a given area, but disease showed the chance distribution characteristic of living things; fevers were scattered about like bees or thistles. This was ingenious thinking.

In America about this time and in like vein John Kearsley Mitchell (whose papers were edited by his better-known son, S. Weir Mitchell) was telling his students at Philadelphia that if malaria were caused by heat and moisture, or by a poison given off by decaying vegetation, or by some chemically recognizable gas, it should occur wherever these stimuli were present. Since it did not, he ascribed it to an organic agent, probably spores thrown off by mouldy growths in damp places, carried short distances on the wind, and multiplying where they fell. Mitchell too was working toward the truth by substituting a lesser misunderstanding for a greater.

But this was still theoretical, and there was much naive thinking in humbler quarters. Hirsch reports that when cholera was first prevalent in Europe "peculiarly-tinted, mist-like obscurities in the air" were thought to be "dense swarms of lower organisms—'cholera-animalcules'—that had been carried from India by the wind." An enterprising layman of Lancaster, Pennsylvania, shared with the world in 1855 his surprising observations on a cloud of "dust-colored flies," which appeared simultaneously with the cholera. "When inhaled by persons whose systems are disordered by disease or improper diet," he wrote, "their poison is deadly as the viper's sting."

Until someone found out just how contagion passed from one body to another, in the diseases still thought to be miasmatic, the theory of the *contagium vivum* was hardly convincing. In the forties and fifties two notable pieces of work accomplished just this for cholera and typhoid fever.

John Snow was a shy and studious physician who, as a medical apprentice, had seen the cholera of 1831 in the coal-mines of Newcastle and had later been especially interested in respiration and anesthesia. Clinical observation convinced him that the poison of cholera was not inhaled but swallowed, and in 1849 he published a pamphlet expressing the opinion that the contagious matter was thrown off from the diseased intestine and might enter the system in polluted water. The great waves of cholera which were sweeping over England gave him an opportunity to confirm his theory by first-hand investigation, and as his biographer says, "wherever cholera was visitant, there was he in the midst."

In the late summer of 1854 there was a shocking neighborhood explosion of the disease in London: more than five hundred people died in ten days within two hundred and fifty yards of the corner of Broad and Cambridge Streets. Snow hurried to make a house-to-house canvass of the early cases; suspected a "much-frequented street-pump in Broad Street"; convinced himself that "there was no other circumstance or agent common to the circumscribed locality in which this sudden increase of cholera occurred"; and (knocking modestly at the door of the room where they sat in consultation) persuaded the vestrymen of the parish to take the handle off the pump. Then he elaborated his findings. Of eighty-three persons who died in the first three days of the outbreak, sixty-one had been accustomed to drink the water from the suspected well either constantly or occasionally. Adequate controls were at hand: a brewery and a workhouse, both in the immediate vicinity, but both with private wells, escaped the extraordinary mortality. Striking cases supported Snow's conclusions: a woman who had moved away from the neighborhood, but still had water fetched from the pump, died in the West End, and her niece who had visited her and drunk of the same water died in Islington. A visitor from Brighton who had spent only twenty minutes in his dead brother's house near Broad Street, but had drunk the water mixed with brandy, died the next day. It was a beautiful piece of epidemiological

*53*

induction. Snow himself found no clue to the way in which the well had been infected, but other investigators the next spring discovered seepage about the well from a cesspool and drain serving a house in which there had been suspicious illness before and four recorded cases of cholera during the epidemic.

Meanwhile Snow was busy at a broader inquiry. The registrar-general had made in 1853 a comparative study of cholera mortality among the customers of various private companies supplying water to London, and by similar methods in 1854 Snow found in one quarter of the city evidences of an involuntary experiment "on the grandest scale." The mains of two competing companies ran side by side through many streets, serving one house or another indiscriminately. One company drew its water from the Thames above London, the other from the heart of the city. "No fewer than 300,000 people of both sexes, of every age and occupation, and of every rank and station, from gentlefolks down to the very poor, were divided into two groups without their choice, and, in most cases, without their knowledge; one group being supplied with water containing the sewage of London, and, amongst it, whatever might have come from the cholera patients, the other group having water quite free from such impurity."[7] Again tramping the streets, interviewing householders, and even making his own analyses of water samples when necessary, Snow found that in the first four weeks of the epidemic the mortality rate from cholera among the users of the foul water was fourteen times as high as that among the control group. The method here is as significant as the results. Sydenham had tried to generalize from his own practice; Webster and many other commentators generalized from masses of historical information and misinformation uncritically heaped together; Snow generalized from groups of cases accurately counted and classified.[*]

* This was possible only because the recording of deaths had been recog-

Snow was no superman: he suggested that not only typhoid fever (in which he was right) but also yellow fever and plague (in which, of course, he was wrong) could be "communicated by accidentally swallowing the morbid excretions of the patients." His remedy for the excessive use and fouling of water supplies by sewage-disposal systems was, in part, to discourage the use of water-closets among the poor! He did not entirely rule out the possibility of the spontaneous origin of disease. But his basic position was sound: the direct transmission of infection from patient to patient was the only important means of spreading what he was the first to call the "communicable" diseases. And he was sure that no "emanation" could originate any specific disease.

William Budd seems to have come independently to Snow's conclusions about cholera, and perhaps did so first, but his great contribution to epidemiology was to trace the route by which typhoid was transmitted. His early practice in a Devonshire village had shown him that until a case of typhoid occurred, there might be much smell but no fever, but that once the infection was present it traveled from person to person along the route taken by the dejecta of the sick. It was fairly easy to trace this route in the village, but more difficult in the city, where the sewer became "the direct continuation of the diseased intestine" and the contagious stuff might do its work far from the original case. When there was definite typhoid infection in the drain, the effluvia were dangerous, as well as the water which the drain polluted. But without this specific infection emanations were harmless: Budd

nized as a public function. The clumsy Bills of Mortality in London had run annually from 1532; John Graunt in 1662 had begun to analyze them and to develop some of the inferences which they yielded up; the General Register Office had been set up in 1836; and William Farr, appointed to the staff of the registrar-general in 1839, had devoted himself to organizing vital statistics in such a way as to make them really informing. The value of clinical statistics, moreover, had been demonstrated by Louis (who described and named typhoid fever in 1829).

called attention to the fact that in an historic summer when the Thames stank there were fewer fevers and diarrheas than usual.

Budd drew on his own sound observation for the premises and application of his theory: he knew the pathology of the diseased intestine, he had traced water-borne epidemics at various places, and he had checked the spread of typhoid in particular instances by rigorous disinfection of the patient's excreta. He was forthright in his insistence that contagion was no "accident or epiphenomenon," but an essential and invariable attribute of communicable disease—"the *master*-fact in its history." [8] And as for spontaneous origin—what doctor, he asked dryly, ever listened to a patient who offered that as an explanation of a case of syphilis? This was all a tonic influence on the thinking of a generation still inclined to juggle alternative causes and contingencies. Yet even in 1873, when he gave full expression to the views he had begun to offer in the medical journals in 1856, Budd still felt himself to be in the minority, and it is curious to see how often he compares typhoid with smallpox, as if to borrow strength for his theory from the acknowledged contagiousness of the latter disease.

Snow and Budd did something for medicine that generations of speculation about causes had failed to do: they showed the way to practical methods of preventing the spread of infection. For this it was sufficient to be convinced that the disease was caused by a living agent, thrown off by the patient, which could reproduce itself. Yet neither of these men knew just what the agent was. Budd, indeed, had the unhappy experience of announcing the discovery of a cholera organism only to have other investigators prove a few weeks later that he did not know what he was talking about.

On the other side of the fence miasma was undergoing a metamorphosis. The notion that some subtle distemper of the air, unrelated to local influences, was essential to the spread of disease faded gradually as attention was centered more and more on sewers and smells. But it did not disappear for a long time. In 1850 the vigorous and sensible report of the state commission headed by Lemuel Shattuck, proposing a sanitary survey of Massachusetts, discussed contagion in this groping fashion:

> Some diseases can be communicated only by actual contact with another person, or with the poison of the disease of the person; as itch, syphilis, necusia, &c. This is *personal contagion*. Others may be communicated either by contact with the air of the locality where the diseased person is or has been; as small-pox, measles, &c.; or with the poisonous emanations from decomposing animal or vegetable matters, or from other substances; this is *local contagion*. Others may be communicated by contact with the atmosphere while in a peculiar condition; as influenza, dysentery, cholera, &c.; this is *atmospheric contagion*.[9]

Atmospheric contagion, he added, was "generally harmless unless attracted by local causes," and it was to the local causes that public health effort was naturally addressed. The idea that local noxious influences might predispose to infection was the logical bridge between the old cosmology and the new sanitation.*

It was, however, the immediate effect of foul air that stirred the sanitarians into action. In London Southwood Smith tramped the slums to collect evidence of the need for housing and sanitary reform; his shocking testimony led to a huge report on the *Sanitary Condition of the Labouring Population of Great Britain*, prepared by the Poor-Law Commissioners in 1842, and when Parliament created a General Board of Health in 1848 he was made a member of it. Believing that filth and overcrowding were the "predisposing and localizing" causes of the ordinary fevers, while no one knew their precise and ultimate cause, Smith thought it "mischievous" to put undue weight on contagion.

* A Michigan doctor writing in 1853 considered typhoid fever a "nosological hybrid, its paternity being traceable to malaria [i.e., bad air] on one side, and epidemic meteoration on the other."

Edwin Chadwick's report for the Poor-Law Commissioners took the charmingly unscientific position that "the medical controversy as to the causes of fever . . . does not appear to be one that for practical purposes need be considered, except that its effect is prejudicial in diverting attention from the practical means of prevention."[10]

This was notably to put the cart before the horse. Yet European thinkers, if Smith interprets them correctly, had for half a century been losing faith or interest in the contagiousness of most epidemic diseases, and after all (except perhaps in smallpox and syphilis) there was nothing much one could *do* about contagion without more knowledge than these earnest souls had. As Snow pointed out a little later, contagion was an irritating topic because the logical defense against it was quarantine and that ran afoul of "pecuniary interests." Moreover it seldom worked. In all conscience, the domestic environment of the English needed attention: the congestion in the tenements passed belief; cesspools were still numerous in London; open drains ran through Edinburgh and Glasgow; one held the nose while walking the leafy lanes about Inverness. Sewers discharging their contents into the rivers whence the growing cities drew raw water for drinking were a questionable blessing. In the hot summer of 1858 it was all but impossible to transact public business on the banks of the odoriferous Thames. It was a national disgrace: "India is in revolt, and the Thames stinks," wrote a jeering foreign correspondent.

It was orthodox to believe that bad air caused fever. Lancisi in the previous century had formulated the doctrine of the miasmatic origin of the intermittent fevers.* Murchison, a prominent clinician, did a similar task for the continued fevers in a monumental treatise published in 1862. Typhus and typhoid had but

* Recalling Varro and Columella, Lancisi also mentioned mosquitoes as possible carriers of poison.

recently been distinguished. Murchison thought the former, though contagious, was fostered by intemperance, fatigue, fear, previous illness, overcrowding, destitution, and "recent residence in an infected locality," and immediately caused by concentrated human exhalations. In this connection he borrowed a vivid picture from one William Grant:

If any person will take the trouble to stand in the sun and look at his own shadow on a white-plastered wall, he will easily perceive that his whole body is a smoking dunghill, with a vapour exhaling from every part of it. This vapour is subtle, acrid, and offensive to the smell; if retained by the body it becomes morbid; but if re-absorbed, highly deleterious. If a number of persons, therefore, are long confined in any close place, not properly ventilated, so as to inspire and swallow with their spittle, the vapours of each other, they must soon feel its bad effects. Bad provisions and gloomy thoughts will add to their misery, and soon breed the seminium of a pestilential fever.*[11]

Typhoid he thought communicable "to a limited degree," but he preferred to think of it as "pythogenic fever," that is, fever bred of decay, commonly produced by poisons contained in the emanations from sewers. This of course meant that it occurred spontaneously.† In the hands of a doughty propagandist like Florence Nightingale, the notion that diseases might originate spontaneously was carried to greater extremes. She declared roundly, on the evidence of her own eyes and nose, that she had observed smallpox "growing up in first specimens, either in close rooms or

---

* This sort of argument, of course, did not go unchallenged. A Dr. Edward N. Bancroft had pointed out in lectures before the College of Physicians in London as early as 1806 or 1807 that the natives of "Kamstchatka, Oonalaska, Greenland, and Russia" lived in such fashion that they were subjected to overpowering mutual exhalations (in the vernacular, stewed in their own juices) without any perceptible ill effect.

† It is odd to find this contemporary of Snow and Budd arguing that since Moses said nothing of such diseases in his account of the Creation they must have appeared spontaneously later, and that if that had happened once it might happen again!

in overcrowded wards, where it could not by any possibility have been 'caught,' but must have begun."[12] Yet smallpox was and had been for years the very paradigm of contagion.

## BACTERIA

From this murky confusion we turn to Pasteur, the first scientist in history glamorous enough to be exploited—and successfully too—by Hollywood. The tender-hearted pugnacious chemist, alternately despairing and exultant, brandishing his flasks and his test-tubes, slaying the dragon of "hydrophobia," is in a fair way to become a folk-figure. His triumphs are familiar, his place in medical history secure. Here we need only try to place him in perspective with relation to the long and slow development of medical thought.

His first important demonstration in this field was that fermentation resulted from the life process of specific organisms; thus he confirmed and developed the theories of de la Tour, Schwann, and Helmholtz. Moreover, he found one organism produced lactic acid, another alcohol. Each tiny creature belonged to its own species; had its own work to do; bred true. This did not seem consistent with the still-surviving doctrine of spontaneous generation: if living things just happened, why the regularity in the way they happened? There had been much argument over such questions. Pasteur, devising more rigorous experiments than those of his predecessors, proved that "organized corpuscles" were present in the air and appeared in a sterilized liquid only when it was freely open to the air, or in contact with unsterile objects. They entered the liquid from outside; they did not arise spontaneously. Other savants disputed his conclusions, and the controversy was fought out, with the Academy of Sciences as arbiter, in a fashion which would have delighted a tabloid reporter.

From these inquiries it was a short step to the use of heat—we still call the process pasteurization—to kill the organisms that made wine spoil. By 1875, though he had not yet turned his attention definitely to human diseases, Pasteur had put a firm foundation under medical thinking about bacteria, and this is a convenient date at which to interrupt his story for a glance at some of his contemporaries.

Pasteur was not alone, of course, in the exploration of this new world. The German Pollender and the Frenchman Davaine had observed the "bacteridium" of anthrax and Davaine, after becoming acquainted with Pasteur's work on ferments, maintained that this organism was the sole cause of the disease. Robert Koch was soon to work on the same microbe. Klebs and other Germans, in the sixties, had seen pus-forming organisms in various clinical conditions. Lister, experimenting in England with antiseptic surgery, was glad to acknowledge his debt to Pasteur for establishing "the germ theory of putrefaction." The new ideas were becoming familiar, even though some conservative physicians ridiculed them.

The annual reports of Sir John Simon, the leading authority on public health in Great Britain, reflect the gradual change in medical opinion. In 1853 Simon had given the "retention and soakage of organic refuse" a dominant place among the causes of cholera, for which a "migratory ferment," most likely to work in the presence of filth, was responsible. The next year he was somewhat troubled by evidence that cholera passed over some filthy places, but his faith was strong that they would suffer sooner or later. In 1863 he discussed the spread of "zymotic" diseases—that is, diseases operating like a ferment—in deliberately equivocal terms, for, he said, the conclusiveness of Pasteur's "very interesting experiments" connecting fermentation or putrefaction with specific living agents was "still a matter of the warmest scientific controversy." In 1865 he noted a family

61

epidemic of cholera in which the discharges from the first patients gave "an additional and peculiar taint" to a polluted water supply, and asserted as "an elementary truth of medicine" the fact that "many of our worst diseases acquire diffusion and local perpetuity by means of specific infective influences which the sick exercise on the healthy." But while he emphasized the contagiousness of cholera he thought (with Pettenkofer) that the discharges were comparatively non-infective at first and ripened in the soil. Even if it was only specific cholera-excrement which was infective, he said in 1868 in his typically pragmatic way, the job of public health was to keep excrement "indiscriminately" from "fouling us with its decay." By 1869 he was setting his research staff to study living contagion and the chemistry of organic decomposition, both of which seemed important. In 1874 he was ready to formulate "general conclusions" to the effect that

the characteristic-shaped elements, which the microscope had shown abounding in various infective products, are self-multiplying organic forms, not congeneric with the animal body in which they are formed, but apparently of the lowest vegetable kind; and . . . such living organisms are probably the essence, or an inseparable part of the essence, of all the contagia of disease.[13]

This being so, he pointed out that one might put an end to a stink without at all checking infection. He had gone far beyond Chadwick and Southwood Smith.

There was still much ground to be cleared, in the seventies, before preventive medicine could make effective use of the "germ theory." When yellow fever invaded New Orleans in 1878 the plan of disinfection was based on the hypothesis that living germs—probably "wingless animalcula"—were traveling through the air near the surface of the ground. Thinking was confused until parasites and saprophytes (the organisms feeding on dead matter) were distinguished: Simon and others were convinced that the common bacteria of putrefaction could act alike on living or dead tissue, and this notion died hard.* One still heard of miasma: a Louisville physician quoted in the *Lancet* of London in 1879 maintained that the ships from a yellow fever port brought "something from the climate, and not from the sick." The best minds in medicine, however, found an enormously fertile field for inquiry in the "germ theory." They were not unready for the astonishing progress of the eighties.

This brings us back to Pasteur and Koch. Robert Koch was a well-trained young physician who had studied with Henle at Göttingen and knew his stimulating theories of the *contagium vivum*. In 1875 he was practicing medicine as a government employee (*pace* state medicine) in a small town in German Poland. Here, with a curtain stretched across one end of his office to mark off a laboratory, he gave all the time he could spare to research, and here he grew the anthrax organism that Pollender and Davaine had observed. He watched the tiny rods lengthen and under certain circumstances bead out into spores which presently left the parent stalks. Under suitable conditions, again, he saw them develop once more into rods. Whether spores or rods were present, the culture carried anthrax and death to the frogs, mice, and rabbits which he inoculated. For the first time in history the whole life cycle of an organism known to produce a given disease had been observed and recorded.

Even so, there were skeptics. Perhaps the infection was carried not by the bacteridia—they might be mere by-products—but by some poisonous "virus"† which was no separate organism but part of the very blood of the first diseased animal. Koch had seeded his first culture with a drop of blood or a bit of tissue, the second with a drop from the first, the third with a drop from

---

* Even today Hollywood puts in Pasteur's mouth, in the picture based on his life, the statement that the germs causing puerperal fever "breed in filth." When apartment-house employees struck in New York, tenants feared that uncollected garbage would somehow spawn an epidemic.

† Not, of course, virus as we use the word today.

the second, and so on through a series of eight cultures. A virus present in the original drop must have been sadly diluted when this stage was reached, and it took a good deal of imagination to suppose that it could still have killed the experimental animals. But the germ theory was very much on the defensive and bore a heavy burden of proof. Pasteur met this challenge by prolonging the series of successive cultures—a task for which his technique was then better than Koch's—and proving that a culture a hundred times removed from the original blood still had power to cause anthrax. By that time "the original drop of blood," as Pasteur's associate Duclaux puts it, had been "drowned in an ocean." It was inconceivable that the death-dealing effect of the final culture should be due to anything but the multiplying organism itself.

The next step shows Pasteur at his best. An old culture of chicken cholera, which he had been studying, was injected into fowls and failed to kill them. It occurred to Pasteur to inoculate the same chickens with an active culture, which, surprisingly, they resisted. They had become immune. Such a discovery hangs on the knife-edge between accident and the intuition of a genius; Pasteur quickly grasped the principle, threw himself into the new task of deliberately weakening disease organisms to make them immunizing agents, and presently had a vaccine against anthrax. This was demonstrated to the sheepgrowers of France in the dramatic experiment at Melun, and became as important a resource in the sheepfold as Pasteur's precisely described bacteria had been in the vinegar and beer vats and his methods for controlling infection had been in the silk industry.

The best known of all Pasteur's discoveries was still to come, but he was already collecting mad dogs for its preliminary stages. How their foaming saliva was drawn into pipettes and eagerly studied, how the malignant stuff was finally obtained from the diseased brain, how the dried spinal cords of inoculated rabbits seemed to be effective as a vaccine, and how, with cruel doubts and brilliant success, Pasteur applied his new technique to the mangled Alsatian boy—all this has become one of the classics of medical history. But the essential principles had been worked out in the less glamorous study of anthrax.

Stripped of this glamor, what was Pasteur's contribution to our knowledge of communicable diseases? Essentially this, that where other men had surmised, Pasteur experimented, and where other men had experimented inconclusively, Pasteur had the wit and ingenuity to devise and carry through experiments which left no room for doubt. And he did not hide his light under a bushel.

His contemporary Paul Bert summed up his discoveries under three heads: "(1) each fermentation is produced by the development of a special microbe; (2) each infectious disease [so far as the studies of Pasteur and his associates carried them] is produced by the development within the organism of a special microbe; (3) the microbe of an infectious disease, cultivated under certain detrimental conditions, is attenuated in its pathogenic activity; from a virus it has become a vaccine." [14] In other words, Pasteur established the fact that specific microscopic organisms were responsible both for fermentation and for certain animal and human diseases, and learned how to control some of these diseases through artificial immunization. Jenner, it is true, had vaccinated against smallpox, but that lesson was learned far more casually. Pasteur's vaccines owed their discovery to the methodical laboratory investigation of known pathogenic organisms.

In developing the new techniques of bacteriology, Koch took the lead. We have seen that he was first to trace the metamorphoses of a single bacillus—that of anthrax. Henle had been unable to distinguish bacteria from body cells; Weigert in the early seventies learned that cellular bodies differed in their capacity to absorb aniline dyes, and so had thrown bacteria into relief, in the tissues, by staining. Koch worked out a method of presenting bacteria in a thin heat-dried film on a bit of glass, and staining them with Weigert's dyes for study and comparison at leisure. Pasteur had grown his bacteria in liquid media—broths and the like—in which it was difficult to separate one kind from another. Koch devised gelatinous media, mixed with animal juices on which the bacteria could feed, which could be used either solid or liquid. When they were solid, a droplet of liquid containing bacteria could be spread over their surface so thin that individual colonies of a single organism were separated from groups of other organisms and could be studied by themselves or transplanted like seedlings to other plates. When they were liquid, they could be poured out in a thin film in which the groups were similarly distinguishable. Thus bacteria were grown in "pure culture." Koch himself thought these and other contributions to method his most important achievement.

With his feet firmly planted on this foundation of technique, Koch was able to move forward to the discovery of the tubercle bacillus, searching out and identifying, by a new stain, the organism which was always present in tuberculous lesions, distinguishing it from those which happened to accompany it in particular instances, growing it in pure culture, and inoculating it into laboratory animals to be sure of its infective power.

This was a decisive step in the checkered history of the disease. As we have seen, the Greeks thought phthisis contagious and the Mediterranean savants took this for granted for many centuries, though the English were surprised and shocked when Budd asserted it even in 1867. As knowledge of anatomy increased and the varied lesions of tuberculosis became known, there was much uncertainty whether what we call tuberculosis was one disease or many. Laënnec, early in the nineteenth century, pulled all the phases of the disease together by clinical induction and taught that tuberculosis was a unit. But after him the Germans insisted

66

on breaking this unit down into a series of discrete pathological changes. Villemin, following Pasteur's lead, again proved, this time by inoculation, that the disease was a specific entity. But Pidoux, spokesman for the conservatives in French medicine, ridiculed this notion and insisted that tuberculosis was "the common result of a quantity of diverse external and internal causes." The effect of Koch's discovery was therefore to settle a long controversy, and we read that when he presented his findings in 1882 the Physiological Society of Berlin received them with the silence of complete conviction.

This is an outstanding example of the effect of bacteriology on nosology—the classification of disease. Disease is of course an abstraction. As Crookshank points out, doctors create a disease by agreeing to call a certain group of observed changes in the stuff and behavior of the physical organism by a given name; from time to time they discard old diseases or create new ones by altering conceptual patterns, and the names of diseases may be no more than "current and fashionable terminological inexactitudes." We have noted the early confusion over the nature of the great group of diseases characterized by fever. Sydenham tried to classify such diseases in terms of their epidemic occurrence, but this method failed to stand the test of later clinical observation. The refinement of physiology gave a better basis for clinical differentiation, but the identification of a specific cause—a peg to hang the symptoms on—clinched the definition of the communicable diseases.*

About this time Koch carried the thinking of his master Henle a step farther and laid down the criteria which must be satisfied

* Fever plus diarrhea plus the cholera vibrio is obviously a much neater set of identifying facts than fever plus diarrhea alone. Cause, however, is a porcupine word, and those who handle it carelessly are likely to get hurt. We are still far from understanding the subtle factors which shape the interaction of an invader and an invaded body, and do well not to talk loosely of a single link in the chain—the germ—as *the* cause.

in order to prove that a given organism caused a given disease. As "Koch's postulates," these principles did much to standardize investigation during the fertile decades that followed. Variously stated, they run as follows in an address made by Koch in 1890 (translated by Rivers):

> However, if it can be proved: first that the parasite occurs in every case of the disease in question, and under circumstances which can account for the pathological changes and clinical course of the disease; secondly, that it occurs in no other disease as a fortuitous and non-pathogenic parasite; and thirdly, that it, after being fully isolated from the body and repeatedly grown in pure culture, can induce the disease anew; then the occurrence of the parasite in the disease can no longer be accidental. . . .[15]

Or as summarized by Topley:

> 1. The organism should be found in all cases of the disease in question, and its distribution in the body should be in accordance with the lesions observed.
> 2. The organism should be cultivated outside the body of the host, in pure culture, for several generations.
> 3. The organism so isolated should reproduce the disease in other susceptible animals.*[16]

By such methodical steps Koch proceeded, as head of the German Cholera Commission, to fasten responsibility on the cholera vibrio and by isolating the organism from drinking water and food to show how effective control must be established. He went on to urge the filtration of water supplies to prevent water-borne epidemics of this and other diseases.

\* Such an attempt to impose rigorous logic on investigation marks a great advance. Indeed the postulates were rather too rigorous. They assumed, for instance, not only that a given organism would be found wherever a given disease was present, but would not be found where that disease was absent—a corollary that ceased to fit the facts when the carrier state was discovered. Technical difficulties often block the way to the complete satisfaction of the postulates, notably in the case of the viruses, which cannot be cultivated in the absence of living tissue.

Both Pasteur and Koch in their later years were surrounded by pupils and associates who formed a nucleus for a great galaxy of investigators. The names of Roux and Yersin from Pasteur's group and Gaffky, Löffler, Behring, Flügge, Pfeiffer, and Wassermann from Koch's are closely associated with many of the brilliant discoveries which succeeded one another in a burst of enlightenment during the last two decades of the nineteenth century and the early years of the twentieth. The bacterium of leprosy had been found before 1875; that of gonorrhea, in 1879. In rapid sequence in the eighties the organisms of typhoid fever, lobar pneumonia, glanders, erysipelas, diphtheria, tetanus, Malta fever, and cerebrospinal meningitis were isolated. Roux discovered that the bacillus of diphtheria puts out a poison or toxin which causes the pathological changes in this disease, and Behring found the antitoxin which neutralizes it. Manson, by showing in 1879 that mosquitoes carry the parasites which cause filariasis, opened the door on a wide new range of interpretations for some of the puzzling phenomena of infection through the air, while others were clarified in 1898 when Flügge made note of the infectious droplets thrown off from the mouth of tuberculous patients. Malaria, the paradigm of miasmatic infection, was traced to a blood parasite by Laveran in 1880; the parasite was found in the mosquito by Ross in the nineties. Meanwhile Pfeiffer's bacillus (*particeps criminis* though not the sole author of many respiratory infections) and the organisms of bubonic plague and dysentery were discovered, while those of syphilis, typhus, and whooping cough had to wait the turn of the century. Theobald Smith's discovery in 1893 that ticks spread Texas fever among cattle paved the way for significant work on other non-flying insect vectors.

All this mass of new knowledge was not at once digested. The Johns Hopkins Hospital, opened in 1889, was built with a thick layer of asphalt to insulate the basement against exhalations from the soil. Charles Creighton, who published in the early nineties a scholarly history of epidemics in Great Britain, clung stubbornly to the idea of miasma and insisted that it was not incompatible with the current ideas of contagion. For practical purposes, however, the experimentation of these two or three decades eclipsed the theorizing of twenty centuries.

In retrospect the turning point in human understanding of communicable disease seems to have been in large part a matter of technique. There was painstaking observation before Pasteur, much of it competent and acute. There was ingenious thinking, some of it very near the truth. Clinical watchfulness was enough to establish the fact of contagion. Systematic curiosity built up a great store of information about times and places in the occurrence of disease. Even the existence of microscopic alien entities in the sick body was demonstrated. But men worked in the dark. Real progress began when they learned to pluck the disease principle out of the body and watch it by itself. The study of bacteria in the laboratory—though no complete substitute for first-hand knowledge of what went on behind the curtain of the skin—was enormously illuminating. When disease could be caused at will in laboratory animals the way was open for an endless series of clarifying deductions. So Pasteur and Koch, their pupils and their successors, were able to prove what men before them could only hint at, and to carry the theory of disease forward to hypotheses previously undreamed of. To those hypotheses we now turn.

REFERENCES

1. Major, Ralph H., editor. Classic descriptions of disease, with biographical sketches of the authors. 2d ed. Springfield, Illinois: C. C. Thomas, 1938, p. 20–21, 7–8.
2. Bell, Walter George. The great plague in London in 1665. London: John Lane, The Bodley Head, Ltd.; New York: Dodd, Mead and Company, 1924, p. 349.

# REFERENCES

3. Hippocrates. *First book of the epidemics. In* The genuine works of Hippocrates. Translated from the Greek with a preliminary discourse and annotations by Francis Adams. London: The Sydenham Society, 1849, p. 352.

4. Lucretius. *On the nature of things.* Translated by H. A. J. Munro. London: G. Bell and Sons, Ltd., 1913, p. 260. [This translation first published 1864.]

5. Sydenham, Thomas. *The entire works of Dr. Thomas Sydenham, Newly made English from the Originals: Wherein the History of Acute and Chronic Diseases, and the Safest and most Effectual Methods of treating them, are faithfully, clearly, and accurately delivered. To which are added, Explanatory and Practical Notes, From the best medicinal Writers.* The Second Edition, Revised, Corrected, and Enlarged with several Additional Notes. Edited by John Swan. London: Edward Cave, 1749, p. 5.

6. Hecker, J. F. K. *The epidemics of the middle ages.* Translated by B. G. Babington. London: published for the Sydenham Society, 1844, p. 375.

7. *Snow on cholera: a reprint of two papers by John Snow.* New York: The Commonwealth Fund, 1936, p. 159, 75.

8. Budd, William. *Typhoid fever: its nature, mode of spreading, and prevention.* London: Longmans, Green and Company, 1873, p. 35, 61.

9. Shattuck, Lemuel. *Report of a general plan for the promotion of public and personal health, devised, prepared and recommended by the commissioners appointed under a resolve of the Legislature of Massachusetts relating to a sanitary survey of the state.* Boston: Dutton and Wentworth, 1850, p. 152.

10. Great Britain. *Report to Her Majesty's principal secretary of state for the Home Department, from the Poor-Law Commissioners, on an inquiry into the sanitary condition of the labouring population of Great Britain.* London: H. M. Stationery Office, 1842, p. 148.

11. Murchison, Charles. *A treatise on the continued fevers of Great Britain.* London: Parker, Son, and Bourn, 1862, p. 111.

12. Nightingale, Florence. *Notes on nursing: what it is, and what it is not.* New York: D. Appleton and Company, 1860, p. 32–33.

13. Simon, John. *Public health reports.* Edited for the Sanitary Institute of Great Britain by Edward Seaton. London: Office of the Sanitary Institute, 1887, vol. 2, p. 534.

14. Vallery-Radot, René. *The life of Pasteur.* Translated by R. L. Devonshire. New York: Doubleday, Page and Company, 1923, p. 375.

15. Rivers, Thomas M. *Viruses and Koch's postulates.* Journal of Bacteriology, 33:1–12, January 1937.

71

16. Topley, W. W. C. *An outline of immunity.* Baltimore: William Wood and Company, 1933, p. 29.

## A NOTE ON SOURCES

The list of citations given above, though already cumbersome, is inadequate for this patchwork chapter. I have leaned heavily on Garrison's *Introduction to the history of medicine* (3d ed. Philadelphia: Saunders, 1924) and have drawn on Goodall; Greenwood; Jones' *Malaria and Greek history* (Manchester: University Press, 1909); Newsholme's *Evolution of preventive medicine* (Baltimore: Williams and Wilkins, 1927); and Osler's charming *Evolution of modern medicine* (New Haven: Yale University Press, 1921).

The reader may be interested to know that Fracastor's *De contagione* is available in English translation by W. C. Wright (New York: Putnam, 1932) and Henle's brilliant essay *On miasmata and contagia* in one by George Rosen (Baltimore: Johns Hopkins Press, 1938). Miss Hildegard Nagel was kind enough to translate parts of the latter for me before the English version appeared. Other interesting original sources not clearly identified in the text or foregoing list are these:

Arbuthnot, John. *An essay concerning the effects of the air on human bodies.* London: J. Tonson, 1733.

Boyle, Robert. *The works of the Honorable Robert Boyle in five volumes to which is prefixed the life of the author.* London: printed for A. Millar opposite Catharine-Street, in the Strand, 1744.

Drake, Daniel. *A systematic treatise, historical, etiological, and practical, on the principal diseases of the interior valley of North America, as they appear in the Caucasian, African, Indian, and Esquimaux varieties of its population.* Cincinnati: Winthrop B. Smith and Company, 1850, 2 vols.

Holland, Henry. *Medical notes and reflections.* 3d ed. London: Longmans, Brown, Green, and Longmans, 1855.

I have used both the standard biographies of Pasteur, the Vallery-Radot cited in the references and Duclaux' *Pasteur: the history of a mind,* translated by Smith and Hedges (Philadelphia: Saunders, 1920). For Koch, about whom not so much has been written, I draw chiefly on a brief sketch by Ford in the Bulletin of the Johns Hopkins Hospital for December 1911 (22:415–425). Crookshank's unorthodox and engaging views are set forth in the volume he edited on *Influenza: essays by several authors* (London: William Heinemann, 1932).

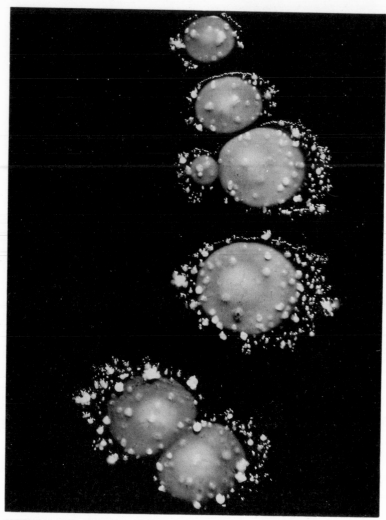

*Bacteria in the laboratory: Staphylococcus aureus iso-lated from a fatal throat infection and grown for a week on blood-and-agar jelly. There are probably from one to eight billion bacteria in each of the major colonies, which range from two to four hundredths of an inch in diameter. The small daughter colonies, new growth in a filmy mantle about the aging mother colonies, are only occasionally seen in such cultures*

# 4

## THE SICK MAN

WHEN the sniffling shopgirl turns to her companion in the subway and says, "Gee, the bug's got me all right," she is, to that extent, wiser than Hippocrates. She is epitomizing a theory of infection which, as the last chapter indicates, it took the race more than twenty centuries to work out.

We know today that germs are alive, that they pass from the sick to the well and reproduce the sickness, sometimes in epidemic waves, that the body has ways of resisting them, that we can sometimes aid the body in this effort. Behind these everyday generalizations lies a world of intricate observation—two worlds, in fact, one the microcosm within us, the other the macrocosm built up by the statistician. The sick man is broken down into a complex of infinitesimal entities; sick men are totted up together into mathematical formulae and epidemic curves. Only the well taught can penetrate far into either world, but one must at least look into both to trace the outline of present thinking about communicable disease.

First the one-man world. It begins with the familiar concepts of schoolbook physiology—skin, blood, liver, respiration. But the anatomist breaks it down into cells and sera, the chemist into proteins and carbohydrates and oxidation-reduction systems, the physicist into electrical charges and surface tensions and the mutual attractions and repulsions of microscopic masses. The body becomes then chiefly a congeries of fluids and semifluids, end-lessly interacting, endlessly creating and losing and recreating a fragile balance of opposing forces. When this balance is upset by certain invaders from outside the body, we sicken. If it cannot be regained, we die.

What happens in this world in communicable disease? What sort of creature invades the body, how does it get in, what response does the body make to it, and how at long last is the issue resolved?

THE PARASITE

We are not concerned here with the gaudy drama of invasion by relatively complicated organisms, such as the tapeworm, the hookworm, or their relatives. These invaders come from the world known to the naked eye—the tapeworm being measured in feet and the hookworm in major fractions of an inch, and even the tiny worm that causes trichinosis reaching a length of a milli-meter. The diseases with which this book is chiefly concerned owe their origin to creatures from the microscopic world and be-yond. They are by no means all of the same kind, and they vary in size as strikingly as the animals do. If the organism that causes amebic dysentery* were as large as a basket-ball the streptococcus that often makes throats sore would look like a big marble and the virus of influenza would be about the size of birdshot. In fact if one could blow the cysted ameba up to the size of the perisphere at the New York World's Fair the smallest things known to cause infectious disease, such as the virus of poliomye-litis, would be no bigger than billiard-balls.† But this is deceptive. It is better to stick to the sober truth: a fingernail would accom-modate a hundred million streptococci side by side, but it would

* This comparison is based on the cyst or dormant form of *Endamoeba histolytica*.
† Assuming that they are spherical: some viruses are not.

take something like ten or twenty *billion* units of poliomyelitis virus to cover the head of a common pin.

If one takes a bit of blood from a man sick with malaria, or a bit of feces from a patient with one variety of dysentery, and smears the material, properly prepared, on a slide, one can see under the microscope the one-cell creatures which cause these diseases. In malaria there will be a dot or crescent or loop inside a red blood cell, perhaps moving slowly about: it is the plasmodium.* In amebic dysentery there will be a vague blob of protoplasm oozing its way across the field of vision with a curious flowing motion, and perhaps a red blood cell will be carried along inside the blob. This is *Endamoeba histolytica,* the most dangerous member of the ameba tribe.

If one gently scrapes the surface of the throat of a child sick with diphtheria, or takes a bit of the sputum coughed up in tuberculosis or pneumonia, one can by standardized technical procedures isolate and see single-cell organisms of another sort, the bacteria. No less than 1,200 different species of bacteria have been recognized and named. Relatively few of them cause disease, and it is a complicated process to distinguish one from another. Sometimes (as in tuberculosis) the organism can be seen directly if a suitably stained smear of sputum is put under the microscope. More often the material containing the organism must be greatly diluted and spread thin in or on a suitable medium so that the individual cells may have a favorable opportunity to divide and multiply and form colonies. These aggregations are then identified by a process of elimination in which many characteristics may be taken into account. Some bacteria will grow in air, others only in airless places; some at one tem-

* The test is more conveniently made (as is usually the case in such diagnostic procedures) after the specimen has been dried and stained with a specified dye, which shows the organism in color against a colorless or differently colored background. But then, of course, the organism is dead and no longer in motion.

75

perature, some at another; some prefer acids, others alkalis; some thrive on simple food, such as blood in seaweed jelly, or a slice of potato, others require elaborate mixtures, or favor fluids drawn from sick bodies. Some bacteria can move independently (but only at top speed, which in relation to their size is sometimes astonishing), some cannot move themselves at all. Some cause fermentation or other changes in test materials, others are inert in the same situations. The clinching test of disease-producing power is to inject the micro-organism into a healthy animal living a controlled life in the laboratory and watch the results; bacteriological research is a composite epitaph of uncounted billions of mice, guinea-pigs, and rabbits.

The authors of malaria and amebic dysentery are protozoa, belonging to the animal kingdom. The bacteria are classified as plants.* The protozoa, like higher animals, can take food in whole—as witness the red blood cells to be seen inside the ameba. The bacteria depend on matter in solution which seeps through the cell wall. The cycle of reproduction is usually more complicated in the protozoa than in the bacteria: the plasmodium of malaria, for instance, goes through an elaborate sequence of sexual and asexual phases, while the bacteria just divide, or put out rudimentary buds like the yeasts. But it is convenience rather than strict logic which justifies the distinction between one-cell animals and one-cell plants: it is quite sufficient to think of both as bits of protoplasm bounded by something like a wall.†

Typhus (along with spotted fever and some other persistent fevers-with-rash) is traceable to a kind of organism so small and

* The spirochetes, twisted cells which writhe about in a distinctive way, are more like animals than plants in this respect, but are closer to the bacteria than the protozoa in other respects. They cause syphilis, yaws, relapsing fever, infectious jaundice, and some other diseases.

† Like the wall between Pyramus and Thisbe, the boundary of the cell is remarkable quite as much for the communication it permits as for the separation it enforces.

nondescript that it was for a time confused with cell debris. The rickettsiae look like very small bacteria, but unlike bacteria they are at home only within the cells of the host. They seem to be primarily parasites of insects, and until a way was found to grow them in carefully adjusted tissue cultures, they were planted for this purpose in the rectum of the louse—a satisfactory environment because, as Topley and Wilson remark with the precise and beautiful gravity of the scientist, "the intestine of the louse is practically free from ordinary bacteria." In the hierarchy of agents of disease the rickettsiae stand between the bacteria and the viruses to which we must presently turn.

The disease-producing protozoa, bacteria, and rickettsiae have one thing clearly in common: their place in the biological scheme of things is to live the parasitic life, which according to the definition quoted by Theobald Smith is "the finding of lodgment and food by one organism on or in another." Man is inevitably a boarding-house: he sickens when he entertains the wrong guests.

There are all degrees of intimacy in this relationship. There are bacteria which, indifferent to living bodies, guzzle the massive wastes of life and death. The micro-organisms that feed on decay do not ordinarily multiply in living tissue, though some of them (such as the tetanus bacillus) may seize an opportunity to exploit damaged or dead cells in a wound and then shed poisons into the body. Some of the potential parasites are beggars on the doorstep, making shift to live on what the host discards; such are the bacteria that busy themselves with the slough and sweat of the skin. Some throng the corridors of the body and snatch a share of what is carried by; such are the numerous inhabitants of the lower intestines. Characteristically the bacteria that produce disease push their way into the inmost tissues and crowd the body cells, and the rickettsiae even find lodging within the cells.

77

None of the parasites thus far described accounts for yellow fever or smallpox, rabies or poliomyelitis, mumps, warts, influenza, or the common cold. Each of these diseases is caused by something called a virus.

This tough old word, in the Latin, meant a slimy liquid or poison. In English, though its connotations have changed with the fashions in epidemiology, it has been for hundreds of years a convenient generic name for disease-stuff. Much nonsense was cleared out of it in the nineteenth century, and the word was ready for a new lease of life when a disease agent differing from bacteria was discovered in 1892. A Russian found then that the sap of a plant sick with tobacco mosaic disease would carry the disease to other plants even after it had been passed through a filter that would hold back fungi or bacteria. A Dutchman in 1898 called this elusive disease-principle a *contagium vivum fluidum*—odd reversion to the language of 1840 and earlier— and for many years it went by the name of filtrable virus, which meant in effect disease-stuff of unknown composition that could not be separated by filtration from the liquids it was found in. Not till the last ten or twenty years, as many other disease agents fitting this loose description have been isolated and studied by new techniques, has the word virus begun to take on a more positive meaning.*

Today we think of viruses as particulate entities of very small but determinable size,† incapable of development or multiplica-

* Passage through a filter is not, in fact, a satisfactory criterion for distinguishing between viruses and bacteria. Bacteria small enough to pass filters that hold back the tobacco mosaic virus have recently been found in juices from tobacco and tomato plants.

† The size of viruses is estimated chiefly by passing them through collodion membranes with pores of known average size. It can also be computed (if certain assumptions are made) from the rate at which viruses are thrown down in the ultracentrifuge (see page 80) and, in the case of some large viruses, by ultraviolet photography. Findings arrived at by these three methods check reasonably well.

tion outside living cells, and causing either overstimulation or death (or both) of the cells in which they lodge. Most of them are invisible, but they are frequently associated with visible bits of extraneous matter or altered protoplasm inside cells: such "inclusion bodies" are reasonably puzzling in their own right, for some of them can be identified as clusters of individual units of virus and others appear in situations where there is no reason to suspect any virus at all.

Finding a virus is tedious work. One identifies it originally not by putting it in a vial of broth or on a slab of gelatine and watching it grow, like the bacteria, but by observing its power to make a laboratory animal sick in what seems to be a significant way. One looks for it in the raw stuff from a typical lesion of the disease, such as tissue from a pock in smallpox, or garglings in influenza, or tissue from the brain in encephalitis. One must be sure there are no bacteria about to confuse the issue: usually they are removed by passing the material through an earthenware or cellulose filter with pores small enough to hold them back; if samples of the filtrate are then planted on media congenial to bacterial growth and nothing happens, it is safe to assume that none are there. The bacteria-free filtrate is inoculated by what seems to be an appropriate route (or by various alternative routes) into what seems to be an appropriate animal (sometimes it takes years to find the right one) and the investigator waits to see what happens. If the animal sickens or dies, material from its diseased tissues is similarly inoculated into another animal, and so on until the results seem to fall into a consistent pattern. Even then one has, not the virus, but a mess of animal tissue or fluids containing the virus. To get the virus itself relatively free of extraneous matter requires further delicate manipulation, usually ultracentrifugation. This means whirling the mixture about at terrific speeds (the small virus of yellow fever "comes down" at speeds of the order of 25,000 revolutions per minute), which makes it separate into layers according to the relative weight of its constituent parts.* The concentrated disease-producing substance thus obtained can be kept for long periods in an inactive state, can be passed from animal to animal, or can be "grown" if suitable living tissue, such as chick embryo cells, is provided for it.

Work with invisible materials has its pitfalls. The clinical interpretation of symptoms in laboratory animals is often difficult—how is one to be sure of a slight sniffle in a white mouse?— and even the examination of tissues at autopsy† may be inconclusive. The creatures concerned have their own diseases, and if something the investigator does stirs up latent infection in supposedly normal animals, or if some virus already at home in their tissues is passed along with the experimental material, a fine state of confusion may result. If one happens not to use the right animal, or inadvertently puts the stuff to be tested through too fine a filter, or injures the fragile disease principle in the ordinary course of laboratory manipulation, the virus may stay in hiding. Many, no doubt, still elude the searchers.

Parasitism is a relation between two living things. How does virus infection fit this pattern? Virus multiplies as if it were alive, and virus diseases spread through a herd of animals or people like bacterial diseases. But no one has been able to find conclusive signs of biological organization in it, and it is hard to conceive of life on so small a scale. Some investigators have preferred to think of virus as a curiously gifted chemical having the power to set off, inside a cell, a chemical change that turns cell-

---

* The ultracentrifuge is a sublimated cream separator, revolving in an ingenious system of air cushions and vacuums which cuts resistance to trifling proportions, and driven usually by a stream of oil or a jet of air under moderate pressure.

† In the polite language of research one "sacrifices" the rat or guinea-pig that has failed to die but must be autopsied anyway.

stuff into more virus and perhaps goes on and on (like the nervous repetitive theme in *The Sorcerer's Apprentice*) till the available stuff is used up. The explanation slides over certain difficulties, but this way of thinking about viruses was strongly reinforced in 1935 by the discovery that the tobacco mosaic virus—which had precipitated the virus dilemma forty years earlier—gave every indication of being chemically homogeneous and was in fact a colossal molecule of nucleoprotein, capable of taking a crystalline form.* Now the biochemist can philosophically point out that "crystallinity, of itself, offers no evidence as to the living or non-living nature of a material"[1] but the notion of a crystalline creature is disturbing to the lay mind, and it is hard to attribute the degree of organization called life to a single molecule of nucleoprotein. What becomes then of the theory that contagion is always an affair of living organisms?

The difficulty may be verbal. There are no words in nature. *Virus, living organism, life* are just words, and perhaps not very precise ones. Virus may still stand for a job-lot of different things—the bigger ones virtually like bacteria, the smaller just molecules. That is not very satisfying, for the viruses whose size is known may be arranged in a series leading by easy stages from the size of the smaller bacteria down to that of the larger molecules of blood protein, and where would one draw the line? It is more helpful to give the word *life* a little more rope: perhaps life shades into not-life.

This is the theme of a bold hypothesis put forward by several workers in the virus field. Life as we know it requires tools: genes, enzymes, and the like—an assortment of chemical entities. The more complex the life, the more tools are needed; the more tools, the more space they occupy. Questions of space may not be important in a man or a jelly-fish, but in an organism meas-

* Tobacco mosaic virus has not been observed to form true three-dimensional crystals, but another plant virus does.

ured in millionths of a millimeter the case may be quite different. Parasitism is a way of simplifying life, of living at second-hand. What the host does, the parasite no longer needs to do. When a function is abandoned to the host, a tool may be dropped out of the tool-kit, and why should not the tool-kit shrink a little? When a parasite has reached that superb degree of parasitism at which it does nothing for itself but breed and breed true, it may well have diminished to something approaching the stature of a nucleoprotein molecule. Yet it would remain a biological entity and, in a sense, would still be alive. So virus may be either a sublimated molecule or a vestigial being, and it is well not to be too glib about it at present.

Whatever the chemist may have to say eventually about this and other biological problems, parasitism has been a fertile concept in modern thinking about communicable disease. Some of its implications must be left for discussion later. Here it is sufficient to point out that if the agencies causing disease are dependent upon living hosts the course of infection must be from one living thing to another.* It is needless to beat about the bush of cosmic influences; it is needless to agitate oneself about filth as filth; it is the living and not the dead who are to be watched and feared. Practical epidemiology consists essentially of the effort to trace the passage of the parasite from one living host to another and the processes of adjustment or conflict within the recipient, and to work out from these data some means of interrupting the passage or intervening in the conflict.

It is true that some micro-organisms whose proper home is in

* Of course this begs the question which so greatly agitated the nineteenth century: where did the first case come from, and how did it arise? The question has faded into unimportance, but has not been answered and cannot be answered until the mist which veils most of the biological ultimates has been cleared away. When we can point confidently to the mechanisms which produced the first cow or cat we may be ready to discuss the first pneumococcus and the first case of pneumonia.

or about an animal host are so widespread that it is beside the mark to try to trace their migration. Such are the staphylococci. Some members of this large family cause boils, pimples, and abscesses, and some can produce graver disorders. Like the streptococci they are ambulance chasers and lie in wait for the wounded. These bacteria, and many others which threaten health only occasionally or not at all, are always present: the sick man need look no farther than the back of his hand to find the source of his infection. But in most acute communicable diseases the parasite is far less widely distributed and the effort to trace its travel is more rewarding.

## APPROACH OF THE PARASITE

We come then to the first of the very practical questions which we must ask if we are to do anything about epidemics. How does the disease-producing organism get into the body? This is really a double question: how does the micro-organism reach the body, and how does it then effect an entrance?

The everyday name for the process by which a disease is passed from a sick body to a well one is contagion, and *contagion* is from *contingere*, to touch. Fracastor stated the general principle of contact infection in terms of a bad apple and a good one side by side, and the disease to which he gave a name, syphilis,* is the classic example of it. In this case the infective organism present in open lesions of one body can probably pass to another through unbroken skin or mucous membrane. The mad dog, if he breaks the skin when he bites, can plant the virus of rabies in or near the nerve tissue where it has its deadly effect. Promiscuous kissing at birthday parties in the season of colds and measles

---

* This euphonic term comes from the same literary tradition as that which gave us Daphnis and Chloe, Baucis and Philemon. *Syphilis* was the name given by Fracastor to the shepherd-hero of a narrative poem in which he described the disease at length.

83

spreads infection by the exchange of bacteria and viruses in the saliva; the micro-organism travels by a short route from the upper respiratory passages of one child to those of another.

From the kiss to the sneeze is an abrupt transition emotionally, a very natural one epidemiologically. Both may have the same result; the transfer of dangerous organisms from one person to another in saliva and fragments of mucus. Of the two, the kiss has been considered the more devastating. Spraying one's family with bacteria or viruses when one coughs, sneezes, or sputters is like spraying a tree with a garden hose: many droplets fall to the ground without effect. Drying and sunlight are thought to be generally destructive to the organisms which produce disease, and though some are more resistant than others, it is a question how many can survive dangerously in the air and dust.

Though Chapin's masterly argument in 1910 seemed to dispose of the ancient notion that the air itself might be an important vehicle of infection, recent experiments, bringing new techniques into play, reopen the question. Wells points out that while gravity makes heavy droplets fall quickly, very small ones —less than 0.1 millimeter in diameter—may evaporate before they reach the ground, leaving a solid residue so light that it floats in the air for hours or days and can be seen there as a cloud when a beam of light is thrown through a dark chamber. Some of the bacteria associated with these "droplet nuclei" may survive for a considerable time and will start new growth if they are caught on a suitable medium.* Thus pneumococcus and the diphtheria bacillus have been found alive after several hours of suspension, and the virus of influenza was infectious after half an hour in the air. Animals can be infected with tuberculosis by

---

* The cream-separator principle is put to work for this purpose, a sample of air being whirled about in a cylinder at such speed that the bacteria are carried to the wall of the vessel and settle there.

bacilli carried to them on the air well beyond the range of Flügge's* droplets. It is still uncertain how dangerous this situation is under ordinary conditions, but the range of air-borne respiratory infection—in both space and time—is clearly broader than scientists thought yesterday, even if it is not so broad as they thought day before yesterday.

But disease-producing organisms from the nose and throat can be distributed in other ways. "Who can doubt," asks Chapin, "that if the salivary glands secreted indigo the fingers would continually be stained a deep blue, and who can doubt that if the nasal and oral secretions contain the germs of disease these germs will almost as constantly be found upon the fingers?" He continues:

The cook spreads his saliva on the muffins and rolls, the waitress infects the glasses and spoons, the moistened fingers of the peddler arrange his fruit, the thumb of the milkman is his measure, the reader moistens the pages of his book, the conductor his transfer tickets, the "lady" the fingers of her glove. Every one is busily engaged in this distribution of saliva. . . .[2]

This salivary communism is bad enough, but the distribution of human excreta is even less pleasant to think about. The old masters in public health knew how to sketch these subjects vigorously; Chapin quotes Sedgwick on a Massachusetts mill town:

The families are of that grade in which food always stands upon the table; meals are irregular except for those who must obey the factory bell. The children play awhile, then visit the privies, and with unwashed hands finger the food upon the table. They eat awhile and return to play. Or, changing the order of things, they play in the dirt and eat and run to the privy, then eat, play, and eat again, and this in various houses and in various privies. For them, so long as they are friendly, all things are common—dirt, dinners and privies. . . .[2]

As we shall see in a later chapter, the transfer of feces by fingers

* See page 69.

to food is often a clue to the typhoid problem in communities where the gross contamination of drinking water has been brought to an end.

The fly may serve, under favorable circumstances, as an alternate to the human hand, transmitting micro-organisms mechanically on its feet and in its excreta. While the evidence for such transmission is strong enough to justify the popular belief that swatting the fly has peculiar sanitary merit, epidemiologists are rather less concerned about this mode of infection today than they were a few years ago. It takes a great many flies shuttling very busily between feces and food to create a really massive dose of infection, and the opportunities for such traffic are far less numerous in this motor age than they were when horses littered the streets and stables went with houses.

Under the general name of *fomites* (literally, tinder used to carry fire), things touched or handled by the sick and later handled by the well have long been held responsible for contagion. The truth of the matter hangs on the viability of the germ. To accept all the wild stories that have been told about infection from rags, clothing, bedding, and toys one must believe that organisms which are kept alive in the laboratory only by the most careful attention to their temperature, moisture, and nourishment are able to survive random transportation in an unfriendly environment. Some micro-organisms—such as those of anthrax and tetanus—can do just that; the damp bedclothing of a patient tortured by typhoid fever or cholera may carry living bacteria, and the moist rim of a drinking-glass hastily sloshed with tepid water at the soda-fountain is very likely to do so; but the general survival of infective organisms on inanimate things over long periods of time is inherently improbable and epidemiologically unimportant.

It is an accident when fingers, flies, or bedding carry feces from one person to another. Dumping feces and other wastes into water and then drinking the water, or eating raw shellfish out of it, was until recent years an accepted municipal practice. The organisms of typhoid fever, cholera, and certain dysenteries can survive in water for days or weeks. When the sewer (as Budd said in a passage already quoted) is "the direct continuation of the diseased intestine" and the public water system is the direct continuation of the public sewer the results are far more devastating than those of casual individual contacts with the sick.

The means of spreading disease so far discussed are alike in that they are chiefly mechanical extensions of human contact or of contact between a sick animal and a human body (as in anthrax and rabies), requiring only two parties to the transaction. This is not always the case. An intermediary may be necessary, and this intermediary itself may play host to the micro-organism. Some grave infections are carried by insects, either from animals to man or from one man to another. Usually the disease-producing organism is not only brought to the human body by the insect but is actually injected into susceptible tissues through the punctured skin, or deposited with such irritating accompaniments that the victim accomplishes the same result by scratching himself. Some of these diseases, limited chiefly to the tropics, need not concern us here, but others are of world-wide importance and deserve further discussion.

The micro-organisms brought to the human body by insects may be protozoa, as in malaria and African sleeping-sickness; bacteria, as in plague; rickettsiae, as in typhus and several related diseases; or viruses, as in yellow fever.

Malaria is a disease of human beings. But it is kept in circulation by mosquitoes—specifically, by female mosquitoes of the night-flying *Anopheles* family, distinguished by their habit of standing as nearly as possible on their heads when they bite. With a meal of human blood, if the blood happens to come from a malarious person, the mosquito swallows a number of minute males and females of the plasmodium, the parasite causing the disease. These, using the stomach of the mosquito as their nuptial chamber, unite to form cysts which eventually break and shed minute non-sexual forms which travel to the mosquito's salivary glands, to be thrust into a new victim's blood when he in turn is bitten. Between the bite that infects the insect and the bite that infects a man the plasmodium must have time and a favorable temperature to complete this part of its life-cycle. Once back in a human host, the plasmodium burrows into a red blood cell, matures, and divides asexually. The progeny burst out into the blood-stream simultaneously, causing the characteristic recurrent fever of the disease, and either enter new cells or pass through an adolescent change and wait for a visiting mosquito to enable them to set up housekeeping. The mosquito is not inconvenienced; the man aches and languishes and may die.

The mosquito which commonly carries yellow fever from man to man is an entirely different species from that which transmits malaria; it flies by day, and is essentially domesticated, breeding in odd bits of standing water around the house. The female does the biting: the male is a tame creature who eats only vegetables (like Bernard Shaw) and lacks the strength to puncture the human skin. The virus which travels in the mosquito must have a period in which to develop inside the mosquito before it can pass to a second human host. It was this latent period that suggested to Carter, an early investigator, that the infection must linger somewhere outside the human body, and so helped to pave the way for the demonstration of the mosquito's role.

Mosquito and man are thus equal partners in the spread of malaria and classic yellow fever. Plague shows a different pattern. This is a disease of rodents—wild or domesticated—caused by a bacillus which normally uses the flea as its vehicle between one rodent and another, and ranges farther afield only at the whim of its conductor. When the plague-ridden animal is bitten by a flea (males and females alike being aggressors) the bacteria enter the flea's body with the meal of blood. There they have a curious history. The flea, by what seems an excessive refinement of biological architecture, has two stomachs, or at least a stomach and an antechamber. When the bacteria get as far as the antechamber they settle down and divide busily till in time they block it completely. The starved flea goes on biting frantically, but the blood simply goes in, is dammed up, and spills out again, carrying a deadly load of bacteria with it into the circulation of the bitten animal. Not all the fleas that infest rodents will bite man, but just as rats leave a sinking ship fleas leave a dying rat, and hungry rat fleas leaping adventurously to human beings have more than once put civilization in peril. Once implanted in the human blood-stream the bacillus has other ways of perpetuating itself: in particular, it can adapt itself to residence in the lungs and be spread in droplets like the common cold without benefit of either rats or fleas. The Black Death, in its early stages, seems to have been predominantly of this pneumonic type, and this would help to account for its explosive and terrifying spread.

The dissemination of typhus also takes several forms. "The history of typhus," writes Hirsch, "is written in those dark pages of the world's story which tell of the grievous visitations of mankind by war, famine, and misery of every kind."[3] It has been retold with fascinating overtones by Zinsser in *Rats, Lice and History*. The typhus that correlates with human misery is the epidemic form of the disease, carried from man to man by the louse; recent investigation has revealed another form, endemic rather than epidemic, which seems to belong to the rat and is brought to man, not necessarily under conditions of want and squalor, by the flea. The louse, adequately described by Rosenau as a "degraded, wingless" insect, appears to suffer for its sins; its life may be cut short by the micro-organism which it receives

89

from one man and carries to another. And in this instance the female is no deadlier than the male.

ENTRANCE OF THE PARASITE

So much for the first of the two questions: how do disease-producing organisms reach the body? The second remains: how, once having reached the body, do they enter it? The answer has been touched upon in some special cases—those in which the biting insect penetrates the skin and implants a micro-organism in the blood—but it deserves more general statement. How is entrance into the body to be defined? The body is a bundle of variegated units of protoplasm done up in a tough homogeneous wrapping, the skin. It has various dead-end recesses and is traversed by one continuous canal. The recesses and the canal are lined with specialized cells which, if more permeable than the skin, are yet more resistant than the tissues beneath. In one sense, whatever is within the nose, ear, intestine might be said to be inside the body, but there is a further distinction to be made. The button swallowed by the infant passes through the body without incident; it never really effects an entrance, any more than a boatload of sightseers chugging through the Cape Cod Canal could be said to have entered Cape Cod. So the contents of the intestine, and even its walls, may harbor bacteria which, from the standpoint of pathology, are inside but not *in* the body. As a matter of fact we all have staphylococci on the skin, assorted micro-organisms in the nose and mouth, and what the bacteriologists call "a rich and varied flora" in the colon. These parasites are at home; some of the intestinal bacteria, at least, can be found almost immediately after birth; many are harmless, and it would be futile to try to oust them.

Infection takes place only when a potentially harmful micro-organism penetrates or is carried into tissue where it can multiply. This the body discourages. Experiments show that the skin

—so long as it is clean—rids itself rather quickly, by some mechanism not yet understood, of unwelcome bacteria that lodge upon it. Tears not only contain a bactericidal substance, but wash invaders through the tear-duct into the nasal cavities. The nose, in turn, is lined in part with cells whose minute waving fingers urge bacteria toward the pharynx. In the mouth suction and drainage operate to sweep foreign matter and bacteria into the gullet. In the stomach most bacteria find the strongly acid gastric juice destructive. Only the micro-organisms that survive these hazards remain harmful.

Some do. The influx of invaders may be too great to be held in check, or specific defenses may break down. The skin may be cut or torn, or punctured by an insect marauder. The mucous membrane, through which most of the harmful micro-organisms enter, may be weakened or injured at vulnerable points. Bacteria settling in folds or pockets of tissue may elude the cleansing streams that bathe the surface. The gastric juice is of variable acidity, and at best may fail to exterminate micro-organisms that are well shielded—like the waxy tubercle bacillus and the tough cyst of the ameba—or others that lurk in resistant food particles or mucus.

We speak of these organisms as invaders, but the word smacks too much of aggressive movement to fit the facts.* The ameba does seem to invade the intestinal wall, first putting out a solvent that damages the cells and then oozing into the breach. The bacteria seem to have a different technique; like hangers-on in the hotel lobby, they take care to be where things may happen and then make the most of their opportunities. But all these organisms are presumably pushed and pulled about by forces which,

* All the brisk useful words that describe the behavior of micro-organisms (and perhaps prouder creatures too) as though it were self-directed are unscientific and deplorable. The writer and the reader have a gentleman's agreement not to take them too seriously.

if we understood them better, could be expressed in kinetic formulae and chemical equations. These would be fairly complex by the time we had explained why the staphylococcus does its work in the immediate vicinity of a wound, and the diphtheria bacillus is content to multiply in the tissues of the throat where it first settles down, while the pneumococcus finds a resting place in the lung and the typhoid bacillus travels till it reaches intestinal lymph tissue. The affinity of particular micro-organisms for particular tissues is a cardinal fact of disease, but, in the words of the English bacteriologist Topley, "we are, at the moment, almost blankly ignorant of the factors concerned."

One can, however, recognize some of the gross mechanisms by which the process of invasion is carried through to its completion at the point where the micro-organism can multiply best. Chief among them is the circulation of body fluids—the tissue fluid that bathes individual cells, the lymph, and the blood. Lymph—about which the schoolbooks have relatively little to say—probably plays an important part in the transit of invaders from the point of entry to the blood-stream; it circulates freely and accessibly in the tissues about the nose and throat and intestines where so many micro-organisms effect an entrance, and the lymph nodes are important way-stations, at least, in the invader's travel. It has even been suggested that the bacteria of typhoid and cholera, both taken into the mouth in food or fluids, may not always have to run the gantlet of the acid stomach, but may be sidetracked in the neighborhood of the tonsils, picked up by the lymph, transferred to the blood, and so carried to the intestinal wall from the body side rather than from the channel. Such details are speculative, but it is obvious that no matter what part it plays in the destruction of bacteria, the blood-stream is a great highway, sometimes a speedway,* to all parts of the body.

* Pneumococci put up the nose of a mouse have reached the heart within a minute, the tail in less than ten minutes.

EFFECT OF THE PARASITE

This chapter began with the everyday assumption that germs cause disease. We have elaborated the notion of germs and traced their advance on the body without raising an obvious but often forgotten question; *how* do they cause disease?

The most general answer is that they poison the body. As Topley puts it, "the basis of all harmful effects of bacterial infection is quite certainly chemical." Yet there is mechanical injury to be considered too. What usually happens at the site of a bacterial invasion parallels what happens when one tears a finger: the place gets red, hot, swollen. Gradually the redness, heat, and swelling disappear and the flesh comes together again in a scar, or they continue and a viscous fluid oozes out. In other words, cells are hurt, the blood-flow is altered, white blood cells accumulate in the damaged area, serum fluids saturate the tissues, and eventually either the fiber-forming elements of the blood harden and close the break or the cells go on breaking down to form an abscess. This is inflammation; it is usually painful; and it gives rise to many of the characteristic symptoms of disease. Think of all the disease names that end in -*itis*, meaning simply *inflammation of*. Pneumonia is an inflammation of lung tissue and the flooding of the air-sacs by fluids that ooze out of the inflamed tissue is a sort of interior drowning.

Inflammation, none the less, is a defense measure. Its effect may be to wall off the invader in the injured area and hold him there instead of letting him roam all over the body. Like the boy with his thumb in the dike, the local tissues may suffer to protect the body as a whole. When infection kills, it is usually because this intervention is unsuccessful, and the trouble cannot be confined to the area of primary inflammation. Bacteria may escape into the blood-stream and settle in tissues where grave physiological consequences follow secondary inflammation—in the kidneys, for instance, where local damage may result in backing up poisonous products of normal metabolism.

There may be poisoning of another sort. In diphtheria the inflamed cells lining the throat may break down and coalesce into a tough membrane which may shut off breathing altogether. But even if a child escapes suffocation by breathing through a tube which the surgeon inserts, he may still die of diphtheria because the bacilli in the throat put forth a powerful toxin which travels far beyond the inflamed area and cripples the heart or nervous system. The power to release toxins (or poisons) into the circulation is a more dangerous attribute of many parasites than their power to invade tissues.

Not much is known about the part that toxins play in the life of the bacterium; some appear only as the bacteria die. Nor is their chemical composition clearly understood. They appear to be proteins. The more active toxins are so fragile that they are hard to study in the laboratory, but their existence can be demonstrated by filtering them away from the bacteria which produce them. Unlike the common inorganic poisons—arsenic or bichloride of mercury—they are usually not harmful when taken by mouth.* One could drink a glassful of cholera toxin with impunity, but when it is released within the sick tissues of the intestinal wall it contributes to the deadly effect of the disease. Some toxins act specifically on certain tissues: that of tetanus, for example, damages nerve cells and so "locks" the jaw or causes more general paralysis. Toxins readily released by bacteria stimulate the body to produce antitoxins or neutralizing substances.†

The viruses make the host "sick" in a characteristic way. As

---

* There is one notable exception: the poison produced by certain bacteria living in spoiled food. In this instance the micro-organism itself is harmless in the body but its toxin is extremely dangerous when swallowed.

† This is one of a group of defensive reactions to be discussed more fully in the following section.

has been said, the virus typically stimulates the cell in which it operates to abnormal growth, or kills it, or first stimulates and then kills it. When the virus works slowly as a stimulating force the result is a wart or a species of tumor. When it works quickly as a lethal agent the result may be death of nerve cells, as in rabies and poliomyelitis, or death of liver cells, as in yellow fever (*yellow* because the damaged liver releases excessive amounts of bile into the blood), or similar manifestations in other groups of cells. In smallpox the cells of the skin are probably first over-stimulated and then killed, and the "pock" results. Inflammation may be associated with these fundamental cell changes.

The body is sick, then, at those points where bacteria are multiplying and causing inflammation or where their toxins are at work, or where viruses are busy inside tissue cells. These points are determined by the way the micro-organism enters the body, by its adaptation to certain tissues, and by the accidents of distribution through the blood-stream. Thus the pneumococcus is usually inactive in the mouth, multiplies vigorously in the lungs, and sets up a fatal infection if it happens to be carried to the sheath of the brain.

Is the blood itself sick? Free bacteria are found in the blood when they spill over from local lesions or from the internment camps—liver or spleen—to which they have been carried. They are unlikely to multiply in the blood-stream. Though certain toxins attack red blood cells and so cause a true blood-poisoning, the presence of bacteria in the blood is usually important chiefly as an index to the degree or prevalence of infection in other tissues.

What of fever? This is so familiar that it was long thought to be a basic disease process, and doctors classified their patients' ills as "continued fevers" or "remittents" or "intermittents" for centuries before they had any better means of distinguishing them. We still speak of "scarlet fever," "spotted fever," "yellow fever." In family medicine we turn habitually to the thermometer to determine whether or not the doctor must be called. The physiologists can tell us now how fever is produced in terms of a disturbance—which can be plausibly connected with toxic influences—in the normal heat-regulating system. But they do not know yet whether it usually supports or hinders the body in fighting off invasion. In some diseases, it is true, fevers artificially induced either by a secondary infection or by external heat have been found beneficial. This is particularly true of gonorrhea (the parasite being killed at temperatures which men can endure) and general paralysis, a late form of syphilis (the mechanism in this case being still uncertain). It is too soon to infer that all fever is a blessing in disguise.

Trying to follow a war through cracks in the censorship is child's play compared with trying to follow the war inside the body when bacteria or viruses invade it. The observer is a long way from the battlefield. Clinical observation has been much elaborated since Hippocrates drew his classic picture of a man about to die, but it is still sharply limited. The doctor must draw what inferences he can from what goes on at the body surfaces, what he can feel or hear beneath the skin or see dimly through it with the aid of the x-ray, what the body gives off (sometimes in terms of what it takes in), and what he can conveniently get at by artificial means (as for instance by tapping the spinal column or slicing a superficial growth). Much remains hidden from him. If the sick man dies or the laboratory animal is killed, the pathologist can then select specimens of tissue freely for study under the microscope; he has broadened and sharpened the concept of disease by associating specific tissue changes with the clinical picture. Sometimes, in retrospect, he can trace the progress of a disease from stage to stage. Yet he too is studying results, and process largely eludes him. At best we know little of the earliest beginnings of disease within the body.

In late years a curious new attack on this problem has been made by way of the unhatched chick. This is an admirable laboratory animal, for it is plentiful, needs no feeding, and comes to the work-bench sealed against contamination. Its past is a clean page, its present under full control, its future a matter of indifference even to the man who pays the bills. When a window is carefully cut through the shell (and shell-lining), the underlying membrane, rich in blood vessels and visibly pulsing with life, is exposed, and here or at a deeper level the chick can be inoculated with bacteria or virus. For a week or so after it is strong enough to stand such handling and before it is ready to hatch, the chick embryo is vulnerable to a number of infections which both the mature chick and other laboratory animals resist. During this time the investigator can study disease in a pocket edition which is often surprisingly like the human version in its effect on specific tissues.* It is even possible to graft fragments of human skin on the membrane and keep them alive through a series of transfers from one egg to another; if infection can be maintained in such transplanted cells the watcher will get a better view than ever before of the disease process in living human tissue.

RECEPTION OF THE PARASITE

The body does not merely fall sick: it fights back. Some of the symptoms of disease, we have seen, are incidental to this fight. There are also general measures of defense and counterattack that operate whether or not the body becomes perceptibly sick, and sometimes fend off sickness. Since it is easier to follow the fortunes of the visible bacteria than those of the invisible

* The bacillus causing whooping cough, for instance, clusters about the cilia or thready protuberances of the cells lining the windpipe and deeper air-passages in the chick embryo (if it is old enough to have such cells), just as it does in the child.

viruses, most of what is known about these measures relates primarily to the fight against bacteria, though much of it has been extended, apparently with full validity, to the fight against viruses too. Naturally the processes that can be seen (under the microscope or in the test-tube) have held the center of the stage, and as they are described the reader must bear in mind that others not yet clearly recognized may be of equal or greater importance.

Within the body, then, the phagocytes lie in wait for the invading parasite. The phagocytes are cell-eating cells—savage survivors in a highly organized community, which unlike their more specialized neighbors have kept the primitive power of swallowing and digesting living prey. Such cells are found in the liver, spleen, bone-marrow, and lymph glands; there they eat what is brought to them in blood or lymph. They rid the blood-stream of red cells which have outlived their usefulness, and in malaria so many cells injured by the parasites are sent to the disposal works that the spleen is characteristically enlarged.

Similar cells are scattered through the intervals of tissue generally, and these, together with the majority of the white cells of the blood, have the astonishing property of being as footloose* as the ameba. They go where the invader is, oozing through capillary walls or slipping through networks of tissue to do so. Sometimes the larger phagocytes are the first to swallow up bacteria. More often the white cells pour out of the blood-stream (where they are found in greatly increased numbers when invasion occurs)† and eat the invaders, only to be

* No wandering gypsy ever had so loose a foot as the tentative jelly-like protrusion that serves the purposes of locomotion in the ameba and in these body cells which resemble it.

† The number of white cells which can be counted in a unit sample of blood is thus a useful index to the degree of infection. This is why a surgeon asks for a white blood count before deciding whether to operate in appendicitis, for instance.

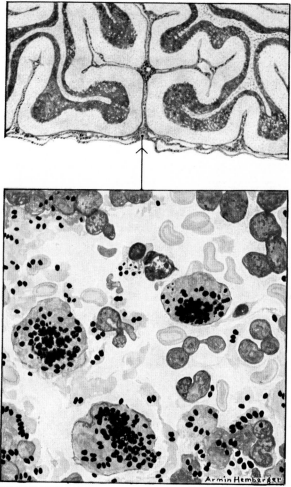

*Bacteria in the body. The upper drawing shows a section across some convolutions of the brain and, along the lower edge, the meninges which sheath it. The dot to which the arrow points marks an area which, in the lower drawing, is seen specially stained and magnified to 1800 diameters. Meningococci (shown in blue-black) have invaded the meninges in great numbers; many have been swallowed by large phagocytic cells (shown in pale red). Other blood cells of various types, brought to this area by the inflammatory process, are also to be seen. Drawn at the microscope by Armin Hemberger*

eaten in turn—invaders included—by the larger mobile or stationary phagocytes. The invader does not necessarily die; it may travel unharmed like Jonah in the belly of the whale, and may even poison its whale en route. This seems to be true in particular of the tubercle bacillus, which has a waxy indigestible coat. The gonococcus and meningococcus, apparently, go on multiplying inside the cell which has eaten them. In such cases it is a question whether phagocytosis (that is, what the phagocytes do) is helpful or harmful to the host, since the wandering cell actually provides transportation to deeper tissues for an invader with which it cannot cope. But the invader, if not destroyed, may be at least interned; most of us, for example, have small stony lumps in our lungs where a few tubercle bacilli were walled off in a lymph node before they could multiply and spread infection. Phagocytosis is a maneuver—usually effective if the invasion is not too heavy—to rid the more vulnerable tissues of dangerous intruders.

But this is only part of the story. The phagocytes do their work better if their prey is chemically prepared for them,* and sometimes cannot work at all until repellent substances emitted by the invader are neutralized. Phagocytosis is thus sometimes dependent on certain reactions between the invader and the body fluids which, taken together, make up another main line of defense. Here we come to hard going: the theory of these subtle and peculiar reactions is well beyond the scope of this book. It began by giving names to things which were assumed to exist because something was seen to happen and there must have been something to make it happen. In recent years this unsatisfactory state of affairs has given way to more exact knowledge; some of the substances concerned have been isolated and one can

---

* Or, as Shaw puts it rather broadly in Act I of *The Doctor's Dilemma*, "The phagocytes won't eat the microbes unless the microbes are nicely buttered for them."

see them in a bottle, and the mathematical principles which they obey are coming into view, but the field is still one in which everyday experience offers no guidance and any simple explanation is probably wrong.

The nub of the matter seems to be this: in the bacterial invader there are chemical constituents called antigens which stimulate the host to make other substances called antibodies, and when antigen and antibody interact they produce a variety of striking results which may have an important bearing on the outcome of the invasion.

Antigen and antibody, like right and left, can be defined only in terms of each other. Of the two words antigen, being wholly abstract, is the better for the layman: antibody calls up confusing mind-pictures. Both are chemical substances, usually proteins, and one is no more corporeal than the other. Antigen is always the foreign element, the stimulus; antibody the home product, the response. Like a seal pressed into soft wax, the antigen stamps a distinctive character on something native to the body; like the image in the wax, the antibody fits only the antigen to which it owes its pattern.* The metaphor is misleading in many

* These statements are generally true, but need some qualification. The definition of antigen should be broad enough to include all substances (bacterial and other) which "in contact with the animal body," as Zinsser, Enders, and Fothergill put it, "lead to a specifically altered reaction capacity," whether or not recognizable antibodies are produced. Antigens may sometimes elicit antibodies in series, one part of the antigen acting at a time, so that it is not always possible to squeeze what happens into a one-antigen-one-antibody formula. Antigens are usually proteins, extravagantly complex molecules built up mainly of some twenty different amino acids. Arithmetical computation suggests that these units could form 2,432,902,008,176,-640,000 different combinations. Even if the geometrical requirements of molecular structure should cut down the possible alternatives, there would still be plenty of room for occasional overlapping between a part of one antigenic molecule and a part of another. If such overlapping occurs, the antibodies produced in response to invasion by organism $a$ might give some protection against organism $b$ and vice versa.

ways: take it merely as underlining the peculiar correspondence between two causally related substances that is basic to the concept. This correspondence is so exact that if one part in a million of a given solution is a particular antigen the solution will give a characteristic reaction with its own proper antibody and no other. It is so exact that generally speaking the body has antibody-defenses only against the particular antigens it has met: against those of the pneumococcus and not the meningococcus, for instance, or against one type of pneumococcus and not another.

The antigen is not the same thing as the bacterium: it is a chemical component of the bacterium. A single organism may contain several antigens: the pneumococcus has perhaps half a dozen or more, one of which is peculiar to its type. The smaller viruses may be more nearly simple antigens, but that is another story. Chemical exploration of the pneumococcus revealed some years ago the fact that carbohydrates as well as proteins have antigenic effect, for the sticky stuff exuded by the parasite to form its capsule is technically a sugar, and differences in the composition and molecular architecture of this sugar make one type of pneumococcus unlike another.* Type differences have been found in other organisms too, but the chemical factors that determine them are not all of the same kind.

About antibodies one can be more categorical: they are proteins. Not only that: they are modified forms of certain identifiable proteins normally found in the liquid part of the blood and going by the name of globulins. Just where the ordinary serum globulins are put together in the body no one knows, but presumably the custom-tailored globulins which function as antibodies are made in the same places. A pretty piece of recent work strengthens the impression that this goes on primarily in a class

* I hope Avery and Heidelberger will one day tell general readers the story of this brilliant work.

of cells already known to be associated with phagocytosis. When a red dye-protein—an antigen that can be traced under the micro-scope—is injected into rabbits it finds its way to the larger phago-cytic cells in the liver, the spleen, the regional lymph nodes, and the tissues about the point of injection. It is held visibly for a time in these cells, apparently occupying cavities in the proto-plasm which are thought to be the site of intracellular digestion, and then disappears. As it disappears, evidently into the stuff of the cell, the cell seems to slough off pieces of surface film and at about the same time antibodies can be demonstrated in the blood-stream. These cells, the macrophages or "big eaters,"* may be regular Pooh-Bahs, not only turning out normal serum globulins as an everyday job but in emergency saucing the bacteria with antibody and eventually eating them up.

Most of what is known about antigen-antibody reactions has been learned from endless experiments *in vitro* (that is, in glass, in the test-tube, as distinguished from *in vivo*, in the living body). Immunology is a laboratory science flowering impres-sively like a hothouse dahlia on a slender stalk of clinical obser-vation. Only *in vitro* can the reactions be measured accurately enough to throw light on their nature, and so to reveal the fact that they follow the mathematical laws proper to chemical phe-nomena. It is in the laboratory that the basic reactions have been observed and described. Bacterial cells have been seen to swell and lose their contents by seepage through the cell wall: that is lysis. Bacteria visible one by one only under a powerful micro-scope come together into clumps large enough to be seen with the naked eye: that is agglutination. Flakes of stuff derived from the antigen-antibody mixture settle visibly out of solution: that

* Etymology by Florence R. Sabin, whose work is here roughly sum-marized. Landsteiner has more recently reported (*Journal of Experimental Medicine*, 71:231–236, February 1, 1940) an experiment indicating that "connective tissue can produce proteins which are identical with, or closely related to, serum proteins."

is precipitation. Other reactions are demonstrated by animal experimentation: poisons thrown off by bacteria are neutralized (the toxin playing the part of antigen, the antitoxin that of antibody), and viruses are made inactive.

Such reactions, occurring with extraordinary specificity, have been of great practical importance in the identification of disease-producing agents and the discovery of means to circumvent them. With a known antigen in one test-tube and serum of unknown properties in another, one can test the serum for the presence of antibodies that react with that particular antigen. The Wassermann test for syphilis, so familiar in public health work, is a roundabout application of this principle. With known antibodies in one test-tube and unknown antigens in another, it is possible to solve the equation the other way around: to test for the particular antigen (and hence the particular disease agent) whose presence is suspected. The matching-up process is far more sensitive than ordinary methods of chemical analysis and has been useful in extending biochemical knowledge generally, besides paving the way for the development of modern serum therapy.

What goes on in the laboratory is dependent on what goes on in living bodies. Antigens the investigator can sometimes build up artificially; not so antibodies: when he wants them he must turn to an animal to make them. Nothing he can do in his test-tubes duplicates what the guinea-pig does automatically when the proper stimulus is applied. Moreover some reactions involving antigen and antibody require also a *tertium quid* derived from normal unheated blood serum—a substance or property called complement which is essential to the destruction of bacterial cells by lysis and may encourage their being swallowed up by the phagocytes.

What goes on in the laboratory, however, is only inferentially a picture of what goes on in the human body. Some of the things that can be made to happen in the laboratory and are very illuminating there—such as precipitation—may have no particular significance for the host fighting off disease. On the other hand antibodies that favor phagocytosis (sometimes by modifying the defensive capsule of the bacterium), or kill the bacterium directly, or neutralize its toxin, must be of great biological value. Even agglutination may be helpful to the body if bacteria are bunched together at points where the phagocytes can conveniently attack them.

The practical effect of such reactions in disease is limited by considerations of quantity (is there enough antibody?) and of place (can the antibody get at the invader?). Generally speaking antibodies can be discovered only in the blood-stream. If bacteria are there too, antibodies, or antibodies and phagocytes together, can clear them out; if toxin is there antitoxin can neutralize it. This is the place where the action of antibodies is most often and most clearly evident. If bacteria or toxin are in the tissue spaces, between the cells, antibodies may reach them there also.* If toxin has entered cells, however (the nerve cells in tetanus, for instance), antitoxin seems unable to deal with it; if virus has entered cells—and virus characteristically works inside cells—the neutralizing substances which the virus elicits in the blood-stream seem to be similarly powerless.

Why antibody should not work inside these cells (if such be the case) is not wholly clear. Other things being equal, antibody is not too big to go where viruses go (though size is not the only factor that affects passage through the cell wall). Perhaps antibody does enter cells but finds the chemical environment resulting from their prior invasion by the virus forbidding: perhaps when virus has begun to increase inside a cell there is just not

* It is possible to give an experimental animal so much antibody that some of it works through the tissue spaces and appears in the lymph, where, however, it does not seem to be very effective.

room enough for effective amounts of antibody. Perhaps, on the other hand, experimenters have been too niggardly with antibody to be sure of what it can do. At all events in some diseases, particularly of nerve tissue, the antibodies in the blood-stream seem to have no appreciable effect on the course of the infection and no close relation to the resistance the host can muster. Apparently they can work only while the virus is in transit to the tissue of its choice, which may be a very short time indeed, or when the virus is being spilled over into the blood-stream from damaged tissue—which is too late to do any good. At best antibody formation is only one factor in resistance, and its importance should not be exaggerated because in an oblique sort of way this factor can be measured while others cannot.*

Some tissues, we know, put up mechanical and general barriers to invasion. Whether tissue cells generally also have apparatus for reacting in specific ways to specific invaders is a knotty question. Conceivably some of them may store antibody, which might account for some of the resistance that cannot now be traced to the circulating antibodies, but so far this cannot be taken as proven. Some signs point to the possible existence of purely cellular defenses or reactions which have nothing to do with the antibodies we know about; here too information is fragmentary and inferences speculative.

Possibilities of this sort, however, lend piquancy to the difficult problems of hypersensitivity and immunity. While these two concepts are tied together too subtly for unraveling by the layman, hypersensitivity may be whittled down to the observa-

---

* The antibodies ordinarily measured are those circulating, unused, in the blood-stream, and these are either an untried reserve or an oversupply. Those that have done their work, whether in the blood-stream or elsewhere, have combined with antigen and disappeared. This may help to explain some of the discrepancies which are found when one tries to correlate the concentration of antibodies in serum with the host's capacity to throw off even bacterial infection.

tion that the response of the body to a given antigen may be disproportionately greater at a second invasion, if a suitable interval of time has elapsed, than it was at the first. This may work either to the advantage or to the disadvantage of the host: think of hay fever and asthma. What we ignorantly call "allergy" may be a significant factor in a number of bacterial diseases. Immunity may be thought of as a beneficial consequence of hypersensitivity: the body retains over long periods (often throughout life in the case of virus infections) the power to respond so promptly and effectively to a given antigen that repeated invasions are checked before they can cause disease.* So we have measles or yellow fever only once. If, as seems probable, the machinery of immunization is set in motion in reasonably resistant bodies by stimuli too slight to be noticed, we may even acquire as we go through life a large assortment of protective responses to diseases we do not remember having.

The mystery here is that the cells and sera that react to disease today may not be those that must react to disease another day. The body is made up of stuff that changes constantly, yet for a considerable time the pattern of the reaction is somehow preserved. This difficulty has less weight in the protozoal infections, in which the responses made by the body—amounting as a rule to some degree of tolerance rather than complete suppression of the invader—probably operate only so long as the parasite is actually present. In the virus diseases, too, the antigen-antibody reaction may be continuous; some viruses linger in the tissues so long and so unobtrusively that man becomes not only a boarding-house but a haunted house. The surprising persistence of im-

* This is a very rough definition of immunity: it has a teleological flavor which the word has begun to shed in current medical thinking. The "immune reaction," for instance, may have nothing in particular to do with the drama of disease. But one can't feel very guilty about oversimplification when so distinguished an authority as Topley calls immunity and immunology "misleading names for an ill-defined subject of study."

munity to bacterial invaders (which often seem to disappear entirely from the body) may be no stranger than the persistence of memory, but there is mystery enough in all the phenomena of biological organization to give pause to the stoutest imagination.

## FATE OF THE HOST

Through all this curious detail runs one central theme: the conflict between parasite and host. The body has walls, the parasite breaches them. The body counterattacks, the parasite defends itself. From the point of initial inflammation the parasites may escape into the blood-stream or launch their poisons into it; or the injury may be localized and the blood-stream cleared. But again, the parasites cleared from the blood-stream may be killed and disposed of, or merely transported to other tissue where colonization starts afresh. If the parasites are able to spread in a second sortie from these new colonies, and sweep unchecked through the body, the host is in grave danger.

The general term for the capacity of a given organism to cause disease is virulence. Now disease occurs when the attacking forces are strong enough either to overpower the defensive ones or to force the body to physiological maneuvers which are themselves disturbing to normal function. Virulence is therefore not an absolute quality, but the net result of a clash of opposing forces—a plus sign on the invader's side of a complicated algebraic equation. It is usually measured by the mortality among a group of animals infected in the laboratory, animals whose capacity for resistance may vary considerably.*

Yet there are demonstrable differences between bacteria which justify us in calling some more virulent than others. Some spe-

* Often both the dosage and the means by which organisms are forced into the body differ widely from the circumstances of natural infection. The measurement of virulence is thus a thoroughly artificial procedure. The careful investigator seeks to compensate for individual variations by the use of large numbers of animals.

cies are more apt at spreading within the body, some more prolific of toxins. More significantly, some strains within a single
species show more disease-producing and death-dealing power
than others, or a single strain may be more lethal at one time
than another. Sometimes one strain seems more subject than
others to this sort of fluctuation. Sometimes, but not always, differences in virulence are associated with differences in appearance. Bacteria which can surround themselves individually with
a coating or capsule of distinctive chemical composition, and
which grow in colonies made smooth and glossy by this or similar stuff, are usually more dangerous with such a covering than
without it: it tends to protect them from attack.

Virulence, then, may be one critical factor in the conflict. Dosage is another. In the laboratory it has been found possible to
infect guinea-pigs with as few as two tubercle bacilli apiece, and
white mice with a single pneumococcus. But more commonly in
experimental work doses run up into the thousands or millions of
bacteria, and in practical experience stray organisms do not cause
disease. The number of micro-organisms reaching a given host
at a given time depends, of course, on the rate at which they are
being shed within range of him by sick persons or carriers—who
form the reservoir of infection—and the efficiency of the means
of transmission. But time is also at work: the effective dose need
not reach him all at once, but may be built up day after day or
week after week by a succession of invasions each of which leaves
in his body a few more micro-organisms than his defense forces
can dispose of before the next lot reaches him. This is the characteristic mode of infection in tuberculosis.

Team-work between attacking organisms of different kinds
may also affect the fate of the host. This is seen in a simple form
when bacteria follow the ameba into the damaged tissues of the
intestinal wall. Recent work with respiratory infections suggests
that in some instances the relationship between two agents may

be more intimate. Bacteriologists think now that the common cold is caused by a virus, but that the more unpleasant symptoms which appear as the infection progresses are due to bacteria which, in varying number, are frequent or habitual tenants of the nose and throat—particularly streptococcus, pneumococcus, and Pfeiffer's bacillus (long supposed to be the cause of influenza and now called *Hemophilus influenzae*). In the chimpanzee, which sniffles like a man, the virus of the common cold seems to stir up the "influenza bacillus," so that less virulent "rough" forms turn to more virulent "smooth" forms. This is not known to occur in human colds, but it is plausible to assume at least that the activity of the virus paves the way for bacterial invasion by damaging the lining of the nasal passages. In hogs a disease called swine influenza* has been traced to a virus and the "influenza bacillus" working together; it is much more severe than the slight infection produced by the virus alone. Though the virus of influenza by itself causes pneumonia in mice and ferrets, and human cases with abrupt fatal damage to the lungs were reported in 1918, death in epidemic influenza is usually the result of cumulative invasion by virus and bacteria.

Incidental factors, such as the presence of chemicals which themselves irritate the tissue, may also work against the host by favoring bacterial invasion. So wounds gotten about the garden are the more dangerous because calcium salts, common in cultivated soil, encourage the activity of the tetanus organism. Silica dust in the lungs fosters the development of tuberculosis.

On the one hand, then, we have a micro-organism capable of multiplication with extraordinary rapidity,† naturally adapted to

* This is much like human influenza, and there are even some indications that the virus may have passed from man to hogs during the pandemic of 1918.

† In the laboratory, under the most favorable conditions, the cholera vibrio produces a new generation every half-hour. In the body the rate of multiplication is much slower, but still rapid.

growth in the human tissues, quick to take advantage of any flaw in the host's defenses, and endowed by nature with chemical attributes which gravely threaten the host once the barriers are down.

On the other side is the human body, a complex of physical and chemical forces whose subtlety we have only just begun to suspect, with cells qualified to deal with invaders, with an elaborate system of physical and chemical defenses, and with an astonishing capacity to memorize and repeat successful defense tactics.

Resistance is the obverse of virulence. If the parasite is such as to gain the upper hand, we call it virulent. If the host is such as to win out against the parasite, we call him resistant. But this is a matter of degree; we cannot think of immunity and susceptibility as white and black; they shade into each other. One host may be just resistant enough to escape death by confining an infection to a limited tissue area; another may throw off the parasite at the gates of the body and escape infection altogether; and there are many stages between these extremes.

The measurement of resistance is usually a rule-of-thumb procedure, for just as virulence is tested against variable living hosts, resistance is tested against variable living organisms. In human disease there is ordinarily no way to measure either the attacking or the defensive forces. One can, it is true, detect antibodies by sampling the blood, and antibodies are undoubtedly part of the apparatus of resistance. But one cannot foretell the issue of battle by counting rounds of ammunition before the fighting begins. No one can be sure that Jones is fully resistant to pneumonia till he has come unscathed through an attack by a sufficiently large number of sufficiently virulent organisms to have downed him if he were not resistant! The variables chase each other around a circle.

In the laboratory, though the facts are still slippery, one can be a little more definite. If the epidemiologist studies mice in cages rather than men roaming over the face of the earth, he can stop the merry-go-round of variables and draw a base-line from which to work. He can control the parentage of his mice, their diet, their climate, their associates, and within reasonable limits their exposure to disease. Moreover in seven or eight years he can accumulate a sheaf of data which it would take more than two centuries to duplicate in human experience, since a day in the life of a mouse is worth a month in that of a man. What Webster describes as the effort "to bring to light through experiment the general mechanisms underlying the spread of infectious diseases" helps to bridge the gap between field epidemiology and bacteriology, the one embarrassingly complex, the other, at times, artificially simple. Experimental epidemiology is a technique for studying the sick crowd rather than the sick man, but one phase of it is much to the point here.

In a caged epidemic some animals sicken and die, some sicken and recover, some apparently escape infection altogether (though even this last group, at autopsy, usually shows evidence of tissue invasion, and few, under the conditions of cage-life, go scot-free). In other words, all degrees of resistance are exhibited. Why these differences? There are two possible explanations; British workers have stressed one and Americans the other.

Topley and Greenwood, working with unselected strains of mice in London, made tables of life expectancy for their caged herds and observed that old-timers who had lived through the early stages of an epidemic were more resistant thereafter than newcomers. Then by moving small herds about in various combinations and drawing mathematical inferences from the results they came to the conclusion that the immunity built up by gradual exposure to infection was more influential than any innate quality in lengthening the lives of the survivors. They thought that differences between mice reflected, chiefly, differences in experience with immunizing micro-organisms, the "size and spacing of the doses of the parasite received" being of critical importance. Both innate and acquired resistance, they felt, were feeble reeds, for most of their unselected mice died eventually of the current infection. After a certain point, indeed, it appeared that repeated exposure might lessen resistance.

Webster, working with mice at the Rockefeller Institute, noted that "individuals submitted to precisely the same risk of infection, under identical conditions, where every known factor was controlled, exhibited profound differences in response."[4] Selecting mice on the basis of these differences and inbreeding them, he was able to develop two strains of the same species, one so susceptible that approximately nine out of ten mice would succumb to a fixed dose of certain bacteria, the other so resistant that approximately nine out of ten would survive the same infection given in the same way.* Decisive tests ruled out the possibility that resistance in these mice was due to the progressive effect of repeated immunizing infection. If mice from the susceptible and resistant strains, both tagged for identification, were put together in a cage and subjected to the same hazards of infection by natural routes, the tagged susceptibles would be taken out dead and the tagged resistants would triumphantly survive. Innate qualities seemed to determine the issue.

Now resistance may be both innate and acquired, and the British workers go so far as to say that the capacity to react to antigens "briskly and effectively" may be an inborn quality, so that one animal might make better use than another of the same sequence of exposures to infection. But this seems insufficient to explain the sweeping differences shown in Webster's mice. It

* Other strains were bred for resistance or susceptibility to certain virus infections. In some cases a given strain was resistant, or susceptible, to a number of different infections, but this overlapping seemed due to chance: what the mice inherited was a tendency to respond in a specific way to a specific infection, not just a good or bad "constitution."

may be more pertinent to ask whether relative values may not shift as one moves from the extremes of resistance and susceptibility to the middle ground where the common run of mice and men are found. For Webster's highly selected mice—more susceptible or more resistant than any mixed breed would be—innate qualities may be all-important. The hyperresistant host has so much resistance to start with that the increment gained by chance contact with infection is negligible, though he may go through life building up immunity in strict accord with the biblical formula "To him that hath shall be given." The hypersusceptible host has so little to start with that he can never build his dikes high enough to fend off even a small flood. But for the average host the level of innate resistance may be so near the threshold of safety that the bit more or the bit less that he gets for himself by accidents of dosage may really help to decide whether he survives or goes under. At the least, innate differences must be one of the factors, along with pure chance, that shape the course of individual experience. At the most, they may tip the scales decisively toward immunity or death.

Webster could not find any anatomical or physiological differences between his resistant and susceptible mice; resistance was clearly inherited, but he could not tell how. There is some evidence to suggest, vaguely, that the seat of this resistance is in the tissues which in the susceptible host would suffer most—in encephalitis, the brain.* It is clear only that the curious mechanisms of acquired immunity may be merely one, and not the most important, of the instrumentalities by which we defend ourselves, and that the basic defenses may still be hidden from us.

* Efforts to find the site of resistance in completely refractory species also point generally to the cells. It must be remembered that the differences in resistance within a single species are less marked than those between one species and another; for instance, one cannot give a mouse measles, or a man the disease called cattle plague. Nothing is known of the essential mechanisms of such complete resistance.

Granted that the pattern of individual resistance is laid down partly by birthright and partly by contact with infection, it is still possible that extraneous influences may warp it, or that it may change from time to time in response to physiological rhythms and local vicissitudes. Diet almost certainly plays a part in it, though more work is needed before that part can be defined. Under certain circumstances the death rate from a specific infection in experimental colonies of mice can be raised or lowered by changing their food. Vitamin A has been shown to influence the defense mechanisms; the lack of it weakens them, but there is no proof that the assiduous consumption of extra milk or cod-liver oil will raise resistance above normal levels. Recent investigations suggest a relation between the intake of ascorbic acid (the cabbage and orange-juice vitamin) and the chemical defenses in the blood-stream. It is generally agreed that good nutrition is a defense against tuberculosis, though the healthy host may not escape infection so much as put a brake on it, confining it to a limited and clinically unimportant lesion.

The passing years give opportunity for a succession of immunizing experiences, but this may not be the only significance of age in the pattern of resistance. Old mice are better able than young ones to keep certain viruses, injected by various routes, from reaching the vulnerable nervous system. The machinery for producing antibodies seems to get under way slowly, and is less efficient in babies than in their elders. Once out of the egg, chickens are not affected by a number of diseases one can give them before they are hatched. Here too more facts are needed before those we have can be sorted out and put together.

One has to reckon also with transient changes. Hot moist weather seems to affect the production of the gastric juice which guards the alimentary canal against the passage of bacteria from the mouth to the vulnerable intestines, and there are other seasonal variations whose effect is more obscure. Chilling after exposure to warm moist air sets up conspicuous changes in the mucous membrane of the nose, changes which might well affect its resistance to the entry of micro-organisms, though statistical evidence to that effect is lacking. Healthy tissues are in general more resistant than sick ones, and yet certain damaged tissues go through some alteration in the process of recovery that makes them for the time being resistant to invasion. Vicissitudes that seem to have nothing to do with a specific infection may touch off disease. Cold sores or fever blisters, for instance, are caused by a virus that may linger idly in the tissues till some general disturbance—a cold, an attack of malaria, vaccination with a foreign protein, or treatment with artificial fever—stirs it into activity.

Folk wisdom has long held that a healthy body and a quiet mind are good defenses against disease. Only in a limited sense can this be proved; sometimes it is quite untrue. Everyone has measles; influenza sometimes seems to prefer the young and vigorous. There is reason to believe that once invasion is under way a "good constitution," rest, and suitable nourishment aid the body to meet it without going under. Beyond these meager consolations, the problem becomes speculative; we must take our chances.

## FATE OF THE PARASITE

Turn now and look at disease from the other side. Protozoa, bacteria, and perhaps viruses are living things. Like other living things their end is to be fruitful and multiply. To accomplish this they seek food and a congenial environment in or on the body of some other living thing. But in doing so some of them— quite incidentally to their main business in life*—irritate or in-

* Biologically blameless, risking all for posterity, doing their duty as they see it, the bacteria might share the poisonous King Gama's plaint in *Princess Ida:* "I love my fellow creatures—I do all the good I can: Yet everybody says I'm such a disagreeable man: And I can't think why!"

jure the host and stimulate him to reprisals. An unkind fate may lurk behind the most inviting tonsil. If the host kills the parasite there is an end of its biological career; if the parasite kills the host, it may perish with him like Samson in the temple, and fail posterity no less completely.

The invader succeeds in life only when it accustoms itself to a roving existence, flitting rapidly from one host to another, or when it establishes such relations with the host that it can live and multiply in him without serious conflict. It thrives in the situation described by the London physician who (as Creighton tells us) rubbed his hands one sniffly April and exclaimed, "Best thing I ever had! Quite a godsend! Everybody ill, nobody dying."

So biological adaptation—a broad principle which discreetly covers our ignorance of ways and means*—acclimates the invader to those parts of the host's body which it can reach by an available route and from which in turn it can readily escape to repeat the process in another host. The tubercle bacillus settles in the lungs to which the air-passages and other avenues give access and from which its descendants can easily be coughed out again. The typhoid and cholera bacilli, perhaps by a more circuitous route, find lodging in the intestinal wall and slip out of the body in the feces. The virus of smallpox, entering perhaps by the nose, settles in the skin and is shed again from the pustules. If on the other hand the parasite wanders from the beaten

* The biologist interprets the changes which may take place in the parasite in terms of random variation *plus* a progressive adaptation to the environment, the adaptable variants living and the stiff-necked conservatives dying off according to the law of natural selection. The mechanics of such changes are better understood in the protozoa than in the bacteria. Inheritance is supposed to be controlled by the chromosomes in the nucleus of the cell. But it is doubtful whether the bacterium has a nucleus, and even if it has something like chromosomes one must look to the raw cell-stuff (cytoplasm) as the principal determinant of the character of the offspring. This makes the bacterium, genetically, a maverick.

path, and in so doing loses its way out of the body, as the tubercle bacillus may do when it lodges in the brain sheath, it may set up a variety of curious disease processes and still defeat its own racial purposes.

Adaptation, moreover, may bring about a state of things in which the parasite produces no ill effect, or so little that the host offers no serious resistance to its permanent residence. The virus of lymphocytic choriomeningitis, a disease of the nervous system, can establish itself so firmly and suavely in a strain of mice that all the mice are infected before birth and remain immune throughout life, none shows any symptoms, and the virus can be revealed only by transfer to a non-immune strain. In lower forms of life the parasite may even become useful to the host; the termite seems to need the help of its parasites in digesting the wood which it inconsiderately devours. The human body ignores the parasites which normally inhabit the intestine and share its food supply. The staphylococci on the skin are tolerated by the police forces which quickly sweep away unfamiliar trespassers. Meningococci and pneumococci in the nose and throat probably do cause some defensive reaction, but not enough to dislodge them. After an attack of typhoid in which the host and the invader have fought it out to a finish bacilli may linger for years in the gall-bladder, powerless to do further damage in this particular body, but ready for a reproductive spree if they are carried to another. Peaceable relations may thus range from "commensalism"—the sharing of a common table—to what is known as the "carrier state," the carrier being a host who harbors disease-producing organisms which are not at the moment producing disease,* but which can be shed in saliva or feces or otherwise to carry infection to other hosts. We may suppose that some species, over a long period of time, become less virulent because

---

* The carrier state may be either the aftermath of frank disease or a limited invasion which never reaches that stage.

the more virulent strains among them kill their hosts and so commit racial suicide, while the others come to terms with their hosts and make the world safe for parasitism. In diphtheria non-virulent bacilli have been known to supplant virulent ones within the brief span of a given infection in a given host.

The natural trend of parasitism is toward such adjustments. "Parasitism," Theobald Smith writes, "is in a sense a compromise or truce between two living things, accompanied by predatory processes whenever opportunity is offered one or the other party. . . . The pathological manifestations are only incidents in a developing parasitism."[5] And Frost suggests that we may classify communicable diseases in terms of the degree of adaptation which the parasite has reached. Thus the virus of measles is so ill adapted to the human host that it causes, almost universally, a flare-up of disease at its first entrance into the body. The bacillus of diphtheria, on the contrary, is so well adapted that it lives all but harmlessly in the throats of many human beings and causes disease in relatively few. If we could afford to be as patient as nature herself we *might* some day find that all our microscopic enemies were similarly tamed.

### REFERENCES

1. Stanley, W. M. *The architecture of viruses.* Physiological Reviews, 19: 524–556, October 1939.
2. Chapin, Charles V. *The sources and modes of infection.* 2d ed. New York: John Wiley & Sons, Inc., 1912, p. 189, 169.
3. Hirsch, August. *Handbook of geographical and historical pathology.* Translated by Charles Creighton. London: The New Sydenham Society, 1883, vol. 1, p. 544.
4. Webster, Leslie T. *Experimental epidemiology.* Science, 75:445–452, April 29, 1932.
5. Smith, Theobald. *Parasitism and disease.* Princeton: Princeton University Press, 1934, p. 3–4.

A NOTE ON SOURCES

The little book by Theobald Smith which closes the list of citations above is an elegant statement of the broad biological aspects of parasitism and an agreeable introduction to the field of this chapter. I have drawn freely both here and elsewhere on the following texts:

Cecil, Russell L., ed. *A textbook of medicine, by American authors.* 4th ed., revised. Philadelphia: W. B. Saunders Company, 1938.
Rosenau, Milton J. *Preventive medicine and hygiene.* 6th ed. New York: D. Appleton-Century Company, 1935.
Stallybrass, C. O. *The principles of epidemiology and the process of infection.* New York: The Macmillan Company, 1931.
Topley, W. W. C. *An outline of immunity.* Baltimore: William Wood and Company, 1933.
Topley, W. W. C., and Wilson, G. S. *The principles of bacteriology and immunity.* 2d ed. Baltimore: William Wood and Company, 1937.
Zinsser, Hans, Enders, John F., and Fothergill, LeRoy D. *Immunity: principles and application in medicine and public health.* 5th ed. New York: The Macmillan Company, 1939.

I also found interesting material in Frobisher's *Fundamentals of bacteriology* (Philadelphia: Saunders, 1937) and H. G. Wells' *The chemical aspects of immunity* (New York: Chemical Catalog Company, 1929). On viruses I have drawn chiefly on Rivers' many contributions to the journals and textbooks; the Harvard symposium on *Virus and rickettsial diseases* (Cambridge: Harvard University Press, 1940); and the fascinating short summary by Laidlaw, *Virus diseases and viruses* (New York: Macmillan, 1939). W. F. Wells' important work on air-borne infection, still in progress, was originally reported in the American Journal of Hygiene during 1934, 1935, and 1936. The English work on experimental epidemiology is reviewed in a monograph (Special Report Series No. 209) of the Medical Research Council, 1936; Webster has summarized his own work very briefly in the Scientific Monthly for January 1939 (48:69–72); his most dramatic experiments thus far are reported in the Journal of Experimental Medicine for August 1939 (70:193–208).

In trying to understand the broad issues of communicable disease and in writing this chapter I have been greatly helped by interviews and correspondence with Dr. O. T. Avery, Dr. Thomas M. Rivers, and Dr. Leslie T. Webster of the Rockefeller Institute; Dr. Michael

Heidelberger and Dr. A. R. Dochez of Columbia; Dr. E. W. Goodpasture and Dr. G. John Buddingh of Vanderbilt; Dr. John E. Gordon and Dr. J. Howard Mueller of Harvard; Dr. Thomas Francis, Jr., of New York University; Dr. Howard A. Howe of Johns Hopkins; and Dr. R. F. Parker of Western Reserve.

# Health Reporter.

## Sunday, July 29 1832 10 o'clock.

The Board of Health reports 122 CASES OF CHOLERA & 39 DEATHS, since July 28, at 10 O'clock.

| | | | | |
|---|---|---|---|---|
| 420 Pearl | | 98 Catherine | | dead |
| 27 Oak | | Lewis near 6th | | |
| 130 Forsyth | dead | 66 Lewis | | |
| 242 Mulberry | | 9 Tomkins | | |
| 154 Elim | | Monroe cor Rutgers | ; | |
| 111 Anthony | dead | 19 1-2 Orange | | |
| 5 Jacob | dead | 56    do | | dead |
| 2 at 90 Madison | | 5 Little Water | | |
| Convales. Hospital in Orange | dead | 11 Pell | | |
| 151 Chambers | | 63 Orange | | |
| 49 Lewis | dead | 59    do | | |
| 269 Delancy | | 93    do | | |
| Orange near Walker | | 11 Mulberry | | |
| 71 Cliff | dead | 89    do | | |
| 8 Chesnut | | 47 Mott | | dead |
| 63 Walker | | 292 Broadway | | dead |
| 4 Cross  2 cases | ; | 127 Amity | | |
| 125 Anthony | | 16 Dominick | | |
| 55 North Moore | | 545 Broom | | |
| 59 Crosby | dead | 509 Wrshington | | dead |
| 36 Mulberry | | 33 watt | | dead |
| 89 Cross | | 79 do | | |
| 13 Orange, | dead | 549 Broome | | dead |
| 275 Spring | dead | 298 Stanton | | |
| 124 Ridge | dead | 94 Willett | | |
| 234 North | | 261 Stanton | | |
| 233 North | dead | 88 Sherriff | | |
| 131 First—rear | | 2 at 101 Pitt | | |
| 47 Mott | | 87 Goerck | | |
| Bank near Bleeker | dead | | | |

## HOSPITAL REPORT.

| | Remaining at last Report. | New Cases. | Dead. | Cured. | Remaining |
|---|---|---|---|---|---|
| Park Hospital, | 23 | 18 | 6 | 9 | 25 |
| Greenwich, | 11 | 7 | 2 | 6 | 10 |
| Crosby-Street, | 8 | 9 | 4 | 6 | 7 |
| Rivington-Street, | 84 | 16 | 1 | 13 | 86 |
| Corlaer's-Hook, | 22 | 8 | 2 | 8 | 20 |
| Bellevue, | 32 | 1 | 2 | 17 | 14 |
| Yorkville | 6 | 2 | 3 | 0 | 5 |
| Harlaem | | | | | |
| PRIVATE DWELLINGS, — | | 61 | 19 | — | — |
| ☞ TOTAL, | | 122 | 39 | | |

☞ Total, since the commencent of the disease, Cases, 3506 Deaths 1435.

Interments during the Week, ending on Sunday, 10 A·M.

Monday, 135 persons generally, by Cholera, 108—Tuesday, 140, by Cholera 106—Wednesday, 135, by Cholera, 110—Thursday 106, by Cholera 73; —Friday, 89, by Cholera 63,—Saturday, 98, by Cholera, 70,—Sunday;

Printed an Published, by A. Ming, No. 9 Canal-st. corner of Elm-st    §

*"Total, since the commencement of the disease, Cases, 3506, Deaths, 1435": handbill reporting the progress of New York's first great cholera epidemic*

# 5

## THE SICK CROWD

DISEASE is personal and death the most solitary of all experiences. But certain diseases and the deaths they cause crowd together in time and place. An epidemic literally is something that comes upon the people—the *epi* is the same as in *epitaph* (upon the tomb), the *demos* the same as in that old-fashioned word *democracy*. Greenwood defines epidemiology as "the study of disease, any disease, as a mass phenomenon," and has given a book the happy title *Epidemics and Crowd-diseases*. Here we confine ourselves to diseases which are spread from person to person, and this is the common usage, but the word might apply also to disorders like pellagra, which may occur simultaneously in masses of people whose diet has a common deficiency.

We are so well accustomed to the notion of epidemics that we probably use the word at times when it is not statistically justified. It takes only a slight increase above the average display of poliomyelitis in a given summer to terrify newspaper-reading parents, although the epidemic in this case is mostly psychological, and the danger, though real, is mathematically unimportant. The definition changes, moreover, in accordance with medical perspectives. In Massachusetts today the simultaneous appearance of three or four cases of typhoid in a single community is enough to start the state's epidemiological machinery working, but it is hard to reconcile the use of the word *epidemic* for such trivial phenomena with the tidal waves of yellow fever and cholera which swept America during the nineteenth century.

Yet, whatever its scale, the epidemic offers the curious mind a problem which is distinct from that of the causation of disease in the individual. Nothing that has been said of the sick man in the last chapter explains adequately the sudden concatenation of sickness in many men and its almost equally sudden subsidence. One is not wholly satisfied to be told that droplets and droplet residues may carry influenza. One wants to know also why at some times and in some places so many droplets carry influenza to so many people, while at other times and other places the disease is negligible.

Epidemics are like waves: they rise and fall. Sometimes they seem to be spaced at fairly regular intervals of time. Measles may rise to a peak every second or third year. Some diseases seem always to be present in certain places; this persistent unspectacular prevalence is called endemic. Topography and climate seem to have something to do with both epidemics and endemics; we have seen how Hippocrates and, in our own country, Daniel Drake wrestled with this problem. Ophthalmia is traditionally associated with Egypt, malaria with the Mediterranean shores, plague with the East, yellow fever with the tropics of America. Moreover some diseases spread and become threatening at one season of the year, some at another. Pneumonia is a winter disease, measles seems to reach its peak in the spring, babies die of diarrhea in the hot months, and one fears poliomyelitis most in the late summer. Some diseases, again, fall upon people of all ages, some upon children, some most severely on the old.

These variations can hardly be due to raw chance, and good minds have sought for explanations of all of them. Until the usual mechanisms of disease began to be clear, however, men groped in the dark for the unusual ones, and until accurate counts replaced qualitative impressions, theory was bound to be loose-jointed. Bacteriology and vital statistics give the epidemiologist a springboard; statistical method helps him to come down with both feet on the ground.*

~

It is no part of our task to trace the intricacies of statistical method, but one must know what it is about. Its fundamental notion can be stated very briefly, and the classic way of doing so is to make use of the old game of pitching pennies. In this field (though we may cling to the notion that shooting craps or playing the races offers more latitude for the individual operator) most of us will agree without argument that the number of times heads come up in a long series of tosses should be equal to the number of times tails come up. This is the way pure chance works. What the statistician does in epidemiology is to determine whether or not what has happened with respect to sickness and death in a given community is significantly different from what would have happened if only the laws of chance had been at work. Of course throwing heads and tails is a simple matter, and the chance that ten of the hundred people on Jones' milk route will have typhoid while only two of Brown's fifty customers have it is harder to compute, but the same theoretical principles are involved in both problems.

Around this fundamental notion a thicket of mathematical techniques has grown up. Thus the statistician can measure roughly the *degree* to which what has happened differs from what would have happened in obedience to pure chance; he can compute the chances that two or more events which seem to be related really are related; and he can figure the probability that

* All he needs now is the willingness to jump—a quality by no means universal among scientific workers, and perhaps a bit more characteristic of British than of American epidemiologists.

the particular sample of events which he has to work with is representative of the whole group of events. Incidentally he can draw pictures of the waves which represent the rise and fall of disease or death in the community and sometimes, by analytical geometry, find the algebraic equations which fit the curves. But his equations and curves, his sigmas and Chi-squares, boil down to the fact that by fastening his eye on the group—not the individual—he can impose a certain unity and clarity on the record of what has happened, and at some few points, within narrow limits, foretell what probably will happen to a given group under given conditions.

In his abstract analytical fashion the statistician describes, but he does not explain. His function is to sharpen the facts and then to assess the probability that some other man's explanations of them may mean something. And as that engaging statistician Greenwood says:

> The statistician, however mathematical, has no magic spell which forces Dame Nature to treat him differently from other men. She always answers truthfully the question you ask her, not the question you *meant* to ask but the one you *did* ask.
>
> Anybody, I think, who has patiently applied the statistical method to the complex data of recorded human experience in the hope of finding the laws of epidemic happenings will reach the same conclusion, viz., that he does not know enough of the elements of the subject to be fit to ask questions; that until he has studied something simpler than the palimpsests of human experience, it is hopeless to expect to learn much from them about the fundamental laws. That does not mean that their study is either uninteresting or useless—far from it—but it does imply that at present with all our knowledge of detail, we shall not reach the general "laws" which Sydenham failed to discover.[1]

~

Yet many words have been spilt since Sydenham's day in the effort to find some formula that explains epidemics. It is not hard to make a beginning on such a formula. It is the nature of communicable disease to be communicated, that is, to spread.* So disease tends to increase: the wave rises. But it is also the nature of a given infection either to kill the host or to make him at least temporarily immune. So disease tends to use up the available human material: the wave sinks. But the immunity of individuals runs out, or the immunity of the group is diluted by susceptible newcomers, and so disease begins to spread again. This process is repeated over and over again, with various seasonal and other modifications, in those diseases which are native to a particular herd or have become acclimated in it. The curve representing their incidence rises and falls like a wave across a line of equilibrium theoretically drawn at the level where one new case occurs for each case that recovers or dies. Sometimes a combination of circumstances pushes the normal upswing of disease higher than usual, or an aggressive infection invades the herd from without; then there is an epidemic. Sometimes, when strong infection meets weak resistance all over the world, the epidemic becomes a pandemic. The epidemic is something relative, not absolute—something bigger and more explosive than the usual rising tide, something easier for the man in the street to grasp than for the scientist to define exactly.

Perhaps we must look to chance to explain why a rising wave of disease rises higher or spreads farther than usual. But the differences are so great, the tidal waves so striking, that the mind itches for something more specific. Do the factors tending to push the ordinary wave up come together in some new way? Or does some new factor enter the picture? When our forebears could not explain what happened in everyday terms they in-

---

* The Old English had a good word for it: *onflyge*, the on-flying. A general formula offered by an Italian statistician for the rate of increase of infected persons $x$ in time $t$ in a herd $n$ is

$$\frac{dx}{dt} = kx\,(n - x)$$

The trick is to keep the $n$ stationary and to define the constant $k$.

vented a cosmic or occult mechanism. Our intellectual climate robs us of that resource, but it drives us, too, along the road of more and more painstaking analysis of the factors at work. If we must bow to chance, we want to know exactly when and where and how, and we want solid ground under our feet when we do so. We shall not get all the unknowns out of our epidemic equation, but we want at least to get the $x$'s and $y$'s into some sort of comprehensible relation.

The way to begin is to set down in order the factors that normally shape disease prevalence. There must be first an infective agent, then a source or reservoir in which the agent is kept alive, then a vehicle by which it passes to new hosts, then a group of susceptible human beings so spaced that infection can spread from one to another. All these elements vary, and they may vary simultaneously. The causes of epidemics presumably lie within this set of variables or within their possible combinations. We must therefore retrace the steps already taken in the previous chapter, looking now at disease as a mass phenomenon rather than an individual misfortune.

### THE INFECTIVE AGENT

We have already seen that the organisms causing disease differ in virulence, that is, in the power to injure the host. Differences of this kind seem to play an important part in the way disease falls upon the people.

Two important diseases are at present far less deadly than they once were. Scarlet fever has passed through a series of changes. When Sydenham described it late in the seventeenth century he thought it negligible; late in the eighteenth century it was a killing disease; it grew milder in the first quarter of the nineteenth; then turned malignant again, so that in 1863, in England, it was killing more children than measles and diphtheria together; it then reversed itself once more and for the last two generations has been common but not dangerous. In the United States in 1938, according to the records, there were six cases of scarlet fever for every case of diphtheria, but they caused only half as many deaths as diphtheria did.

Smallpox has changed both in prevalence and in character. A generation like ours, vaccinated in its cradle or at school, has no fear of the disease, but in the seventeenth and eighteenth centuries nearly all our forefathers could expect to have it, many of them were pretty sure to be disfigured by it, and at times a quarter of those who had it died. Widespread vaccination has brought about the gross decline, but we must look farther for an explanation of the fact that when smallpox does occur today (and it is commoner than we realize) it is likely to be lenient and rarely kills. The behavior of both these diseases, one caused by a bacterium and one by a virus, has been altered by some obscure change, perhaps in the infective agent.

These changes affect chiefly the killing power of the microorganism. But the power to spread—more directly linked to epidemics—may also vary. One wonders if it did so on a grand scale when cholera burst out of India in 1817 to sweep over Europe and America. To be sure, the spread of cholera can be controlled by sanitary precautions, and we take credit to ourselves for having kept it pretty well bottled up in the East for several decades. But is the converse true? Were sanitary conditions suddenly worse, and travel suddenly greater, in 1817 than ever before? And if not, how can we be sure that some change in what Greenwood calls the "dispersiveness" of the microorganism did not take place both when cholera advanced and when it retreated?

Virulence and "infectivity" (or the facility with which the parasite spreads from host to host) do not necessarily go together; as Webster puts it, some strains of bacteria tend "to spread but not to kill," others "to kill but not to spread." When they do coincide, the strain may fairly be called "epidemic." Epidemic strains, then, may set the stage bacteriologically for such outbursts of disease as those described in earlier pages of this book. Less lethal strains which spread widely may set up a quite different sort of epidemic which leaves few dead and many immune.

So there are pneumonias, diphtherias, scarlet fevers, differing among themselves, presumably, in accordance with strain-differences in the micro-organisms that give rise to them. But when one variety of scarlet fever gives way to another, and the disease suddenly becomes lethal or universal or both, are we to suppose that one strain *a* has pushed a coexistent strain *b* out of the foreground, or that strain *b* has somehow changed into strain *a*? This question cannot yet be answered decisively. It is possible that bacteria differ among themselves at all times, and that now and then a virulent few seize an opportunity to grow and flourish, elbowing the less aggressive aside, just as the bullies do in any other concourse of God's creatures.

Years of tinkering with bacteria in the laboratory have shown that they do change. Some species go through curious alterations of size, shape, motility, and legginess. Many have "rough" and "smooth" phases. But, as Hadley says, "we still have little intimate knowledge of the private life of the bacterium." Some changes may be part of a normal biological pattern, others may occur at random. Nobody has set them in order, and indeed it is a question whether the tags by which some species have been distinguished from others have much meaning.

The life span of these micro-organisms is short, and if significant mutations occur and are perpetuated—as they might well be by natural selection—we might expect to see their gross effect in human disease if we watched it long enough, or in experimental epidemiology. In plenty of epidemics observers have persuaded themselves that some change in virulence was responsible for the course of events,* but it is not easy to demonstrate the change either in the field or in the epidemiological laboratory. Topley and Greenwood incline to the belief that given strains of bacteria may alter significantly in virulence; Webster, unable to find such changes taking place, holds that virulence is "a relatively stable property." There is more evidence for the loss of virulence as micro-organisms pass through resistant hosts than for the increase of either virulence or infectivity during the course of a given epidemic, but the facts at hand are scanty at best. Obscurity hangs over the world in which bacteria and the still more elusive viruses wax and wane, and sometimes consort with each other. The infective agent remains a stubborn $x$ in the epidemic equation.

## INFECTION AT HOME

We are on somewhat firmer ground when we look into the second factor in disease prevalence, the source or reservoir of infection, but here too complications are plentiful.

The chief source of infection for mankind, we know now, is mankind itself. Most of the communicable diseases from which men suffer are kept in circulation, like original sin, by the human race. If everyone with smallpox, measles, or syphilis should die tomorrow, or should be able to kill off entirely the parasites which infect him, letting none escape to other hosts, these diseases would presumably vanish forever. (We do not know what other ills might take their place, but the contingency is too remote to be disturbing on that account.)

* The British authorities who in 1920 reviewed the pandemic of influenza for the Ministry of Health suggested that the virulence of the plague bacillus at the time of the Black Death was enhanced by its rapid circulation among the beleaguered inhabitants of a Crimean town (from which infection is known to have spread to Italy and France), and that something roughly comparable to this may have happened to the causative agent of influenza in the great artificial aggregations of humanity which marked the first world war.

But some diseases would survive to trouble mankind even if every person obviously sick were eliminated from the human scene—not because the race would be reinfected from animal sources, but because the parasites lurk in convalescent or apparently well human bodies. Such are diphtheria, pneumonia, some varieties of meningitis; typhoid fever, cholera, dysentery; and malaria. Carriers play an essential part in maintaining the human reservoir of these infections, and carriers together with cases of illness too slight to be noticed fill in some of the most troublesome gaps in the theory of disease transmission. It was hard to believe unreservedly in contagion when A was sick while B, at his elbow, stayed well, but C, at B's elbow, fell sick of A's disease; men turned naturally enough to the air and stars to explain how infection fell upon both A and C. But when it was found that B, though apparently well, could borrow parasites from A and pass them on to C, the difficulty was smoothed out and no far-fetched hypothesis was needed. With existing techniques it is often possible to demonstrate the presence of diphtheria bacilli in B's throat or typhoid bacilli in his gall-bladder, and to trace their migration to C. But like God in Voltaire's epigram the carrier or missed case would have had to be invented if he had not existed, and now we postulate B—as in the spread of poliomyelitis—even before we prove him.

When we call B a "healthy carrier" we really mean that the bacteria he harbors—in his throat, for instance—do not trouble him in any observable way. They probably do react to some extent with his tissues. In considering the carriers of *Endamoeba histolytica* Craig stresses the point that the presence of the ameba in the intestinal wall, with or without symptoms of dysentery, is a pathological situation. It would be logical to think of infection as a continuous spectrum ranging from the carrier state at one extreme through various degrees of pathology to fatal involvement at the other. Disease in this connection would be merely a convenient term for those bands of the spectrum in which the disturbance of physiological function became apparent, and we should speak not of epidemics of diphtheria but of epidemics of infection with the diphtheria bacillus. An unusual prevalence of carriers would itself constitute an epidemic.

Like many logical procedures this might be irrelevant and would certainly be inconvenient, for it is harder to count carriers than to count the obviously sick, and without accurate counts epidemiology is crippled.* What we already know indicates that the picture would be radically changed by such a formula; infections with the meningococcus, the pneumococcus, and the diphtheria bacillus, for instance, are like icebergs, bulking much larger below the line of visibility than above it.†

However we define an epidemic, we must include in the human reservoir of infection not only the actively sick (who may shed organisms briefly as in measles or for many years as in tuberculosis), but also the slightly ill (who usually escape notice altogether), and the carriers (who, again, may be dangerous for a short time as in diphtheria or for a long time as in typhoid fever).

Of the diseases stored up in non-human reservoirs plague is the most interesting. In man plague is an accident; in rodents it is racial destiny. Dying rats were noticed in times of plague ages before their connection with the disease was established. In recent years rats and their fleas have been studied with lavish intensity: a British commission once examined and classified a

---

* In practice, moreover, one must take account of changes in the severity as well as the distribution of infection: an epidemic may be a shift in the infection-spectrum toward the band of frank disease, and such a shift may take place quite independently of changes in the prevalence of carriers.

† Routine observation of sample groups in Great Britain indicates that at any given time from 40 to 80 per cent of the population carry the "influenza bacillus," from 15 to 40 per cent the pneumococcus, from 6 to 25 per cent the meningococcus, and from 0 to 20 per cent the hemolytic streptococcus.

million rat fleas in India, and an English mathematician has plotted curves for brown-rat and black-rat epidemics separately. But while the rat is the common source of infection in cities and crowded agricultural countries it is probably not the ultimate reservoir. Plague lingers in focal spots: it is thought to persist century after century among the wild rodents that breed and burrow in the great central plateau of Asia where man himself may have originated. Today a number of gnawing beasts with Lewis Carroll names—susliks, tarbagans, bandicoots, gerbilles, hamsters, jerboas—as well as California ground-squirrels, are harboring plague in widely scattered regions. The level of infection in such reservoirs, and its potential danger to man, must rise and fall as rodent populations fluctuate, perhaps in response to climatic cycles, or as rodent herds wander across human pathways in search of food.

The rat is not the only hanger-on that has repaid human hospitality by sharing its diseases with man. Domestic animals—the goat, cow, and hog—maintain the reservoir of infection in undulant fever. Though the principal source of infection in tuberculosis is the human herd itself, the disease lingers in cows, and children may be infected by drinking their milk. Rabies comes to man chiefly from the dog.* Anthrax is a disease of many domestic animals; it passes occasionally to men who tend them or who handle their wool or hair in industry. Psittacosis is primarily the concern of parrots.

With the shrinkage of the wilderness the diseases which have their source in wild animals other than the plague-bearing rodents are relatively unimportant. But the sleeping-sickness of

---

* If rabies were as fatal to all animals as it seems to be to men and dogs, one might expect it to burn itself out and disappear. But it may have a base of operations in some more tolerant host-species: in Trinidad it has been traced to vampire bats which carry the virus for months at a time, and elsewhere skunks have been implicated. Moreover improved diagnostic methods have recently shown that even in dogs the disease may run an atypical course.

Africa may perhaps be traceable to such a reservoir: the parasites which cause it are so catholic in their tastes, living in wild animals, domesticated animals, and man alike, that it is hard to say where they are most at home. Jungle yellow fever, recently studied in South America, probably has an animal reservoir. Two diseases derived from wild life have made their debut in our own west: tularemia, found especially in ground-squirrels and jack-rabbits; and Rocky Mountain spotted fever, caused by a parasite which is carried by ticks from wild animals to domestic animals and man, but probably had its original home in the insect.

Such diseases result from a biological accident—the "straying of parasites," as Theobald Smith calls it, from an accustomed host to a new one. They complicate epidemiological theory by making it necessary to take account of two epidemic patterns, one in human beings superimposed on another in animals.* The factors which cause fluctuation in the animal reservoir are obscure. Those which raise or lower the level of a human reservoir are so closely linked with the sum of all the other epidemic variables that they can hardly be isolated.

INFECTION IN TRANSIT

Mass migration of parasites from the reservoir of infection to new hosts is necessary to make an epidemic. We know little about this factor in some kinds of disease—almost nothing (except in the most general terms) about the spread of infection from person to person in droplets, droplet residues, or dust. The respiratory infections and some others that presumably enter the

* The mechanisms of animal infection may not be too simple either. Shope has found reason to believe that the virus of swine influenza (which, we have seen, needs the co-partnership of the influenza bacillus to make the pig sick, but must have some place to stay when not making the pig sick) lives in a lungworm that lives in the pig's lungs after it has first lived in an earthworm that the pig eats. It sounds like the house that Jack built, only crazier.

body by way of the nose and throat run wild in the temperate zone. It is to be hoped that the air-centrifuge* and experimental techniques built around it will help clear up this fog-bound area of epidemiology.

Many infections in this group are commoner in winter than in summer, but it is hard to say whether this is because cold damp air directly favors their transmission, or makes the mucous membranes of the nose and throat less resistant, or merely drives people indoors to huddle together behind closed windows. Proximity must be an important factor in infection through the air as well as by direct contact, and one would expect respiratory infections to increase as the mean distance between one man and another decreases.

The transmission factor is more easily studied in diseases spread by way of the alimentary canal. Here epidemics burst out when infection scatters like spray from a garden hose, carrying one man's ill to many other men simultaneously. Until filtration or chemical disinfection of polluted water supplies became common, or cities found unpolluted sources of supply, there was nothing to break the impact of typhoid and cholera in communities where either disease once got a foothold. This condition lasted, in the United States, well into the present century. The excreta of a single patient, thrown on the frozen ground, once found their way in the spring thaws into the water supply of a small Pennsylvania city and led to 1,104 cases of typhoid fever and 114 deaths. Weather accounts for some variation in this factor: floods or waterlogged soil may carry pollution into the sources of supply, or drought may lead to the careless use of infected waters.

The typhoid bacillus does not usually multiply in water, but that is scant comfort when there is massive infection and the water is piped all through a community. In milk it can multiply,

* See page 84.

and not only typhoid fever but scarlet fever and septic sore throat have been spread by means of this health-giving beverage. On a smaller scale it can be transmitted in foods; more than one motherly neighbor has infected a tasty dish which has spread disease at a church picnic or wedding breakfast.

In malaria the transmission factor takes the center of the stage. Since there is no malaria without mosquitoes, and mosquitoes cannot breed without suitable water-havens, it would appear that once the entomological principles had been worked out one would know how and why malaria occurred. But years of study have proved only that no simple assumption fits the facts, and that the mass transmission of malaria is a complicated phenomenon.

Ross, who first saw the plasmodium in the mosquito, saw also the hazards of its travel from one man to another. A mosquito of a particular species, the *Anopheles*, must bite a human being whose blood contains parasites in a particular and intermittent phase of development. Escaping violent death, the mosquito must then live long enough in suitable conditions* for the plasmodia it carries to go through their sexual stage and for their progeny to move from its stomach to its salivary glands. Then it must bite a susceptible person. Ross amused himself by computing the chances that this chain of events would be completed in a village of a thousand inhabitants into which one stranger brought malaria. He thought the chances might be 4 to 1 against a mosquito's biting any human being, 4,000 to 1 against its biting the stranger, 12,000 to 1 against its then living long enough for the parasites to mature, and 48,000 to 1 against its then biting another person. So if less than 48,000 mosquitoes were present the village might escape infection.

* Humid air seems to favor the longevity and vigor of the mosquito and the plasmodium develops only when the mean temperature is 60° F. or higher.

Ross went on to demonstrate mathematically that there must be a critical point in the ratio of mosquitoes to men below which, other things being equal, the infection would die out, above which it would for the time being increase, and that a relatively small change in this ratio might produce striking changes in malaria incidence. In some circumstances an increase from 40 to 49 mosquitoes per person might raise the malaria prevalence from 5 to 100 persons per 1,000.

But even with all due allowance for these statistical factors the prevalence of malaria has not matched the prevalence of anophelines in Europe. There are more anophelines in some regions that are free of malaria than in others which suffer continuously, and the mosquitoes sometimes linger after the malaria disappears. These discrepancies have driven some theorists to think of malaria as a social disease, associated with poverty and disorder and disappearing with prosperity and stability. Yet sturdy and well-fed settlers put on malarious land have suffered cruelly.

A partial solution of the difficulty has been found in a more discriminating study of the malaria-bearing species. A Dutchman with a hobby called attention to the fact that the eggs laid by anophelines varied in pattern: some were dark, some light, some speckled. Other investigators studied the preferences of mosquitoes for one kind of shelter or another—for houses or stables. Still others applied detective-story techniques to the analysis of blood found in mosquito stomachs, and learned that some fed on man, others on animals. Gradually it became clear that, though they looked alike, anophelines differed not only in egg-patterns but in dietary preferences.* Some bit man and other animals indiscriminately, but others preferred horses, cows, or pigs, turning to man only when their favorite food was lacking, just as the

---

* Clinching evidence for the existence of such different strains was obtained by cross-breeding: the offspring, like mules, were usually sterile.

hungry guest must nibble at a sardine if his hostess has not provided beefsteak.

But horses, cows, and pigs do not have malaria, and mosquitoes that bite them do not spread malaria. So the vehicle of transmission was whittled down to those particular strains of *Anopheles* that like to go into houses and bite people, or will do so if other game is not available. Here was one clue to the disappearance of malaria in well-tilled regions. A settled agriculture means rotation of crops; rotation of crops means abundant fodder; abundant fodder means animal husbandry; and a full stable lures some kinds of mosquitoes from man. Conversely, the neglect of agriculture, or its dislocation in wartime, may remove the buffer between mosquitoes and man and so help to reestablish the disease.

So the pattern has been refined. But fundamentally the spread of malaria depends upon the presence of mosquitoes, and this in turn depends upon warmth and water, which vary with climatic and topographic changes. Man builds dams and roads and so turns running water stagnant, or drains marshes and reverses the process. Nature keeps altering the pattern of the weather. Man and nature together tinker with the variables that affect mosquitoes, and these react in turn on the spread of malaria.

Considerations of much the same sort apply to classic yellow fever. During the epidemic of 1878 *Harper's Weekly* published, with a full-page drawing, some verses which ran thus:

> This fragrant beauty seems the mask of Death;
> The whispering south wind is his poisoned breath;
> We weary for these warm bright days to end;
> The summer lingers at what fearful cost!
> O pitying God! in mercy to us send
> The white gift of Thy frost![2]

Almost the only hopeful thing about the century-long experience of the United States with yellow fever, before Walter

Reed confirmed Carlos Finlay's theory as to its transmission, was that cold weather put an end to its ravages. The *Harper's Weekly* poet was sound in his views, and today we can supply information which he lacked to justify them.

The common yellow fever mosquito, *Aedes aegypti* (stegomyia in the older texts), is at its best when the mercury stands above 80° F., begins to lose interest in life when it falls below 60°, goes into a coma before it sinks to 50°, and dies at the freezing point. Moreover the virus, though it stays with the mosquito till death, will not incubate or develop there when the temperature is much below 60°. *Aedes aegypti* is strongly affected by human habits; as we have already seen, it breeds in and about houses and other human establishments and dies out when small domestic water-surfaces are sealed or protected. It was man himself who courteously provided it with transportation and nursery facilities in sailing ships with open water-butts plying between Africa and the Americas, and so encouraged the passage of infection from shore to shore.*

In the transmission of plague some species of flea are more effective than others; one, for instance, gets very feeble when the bacilli block its stomach, while another returns to the attack as persistently as General Grant. And it appears that very hot dry weather is bad for fleas, not only reducing the average flea-population per rat, but limiting their range of travel, especially when they are infected. The bacillus in the flea on the rat in the rat-burrow, on the other hand, is as neatly sheltered from adverse climatic influences as the coffee in the thermos-bottle—or, for that matter, as the louse in the human shift.

In insect-borne diseases, then, the number of transmitting

* It took faster vehicles to bring a particularly vicious species of malaria-carrying mosquito from West Africa to Brazil in 1930, but aeroplanes or French destroyers seem to have done the trick, with disastrous consequences to Brazil. See page 187.

agents or vectors and their capacity to transmit infection may vary independently of other epidemic factors and so tend to alter the prevalence of infection.

INFECTION AND THE HERD

Shelley with his nosegay and the mosquito with a load of malaria might join in the question (the phrasing is Shelley's): "That I might there present it, oh to whom?" It takes two to make a communicable disease, one to give and one to take. In an epidemic, which is an affair of the herd,* there must be many takers for each giver. Those who can be takers we call susceptible, the non-takers, immune. A herd falls sick only when the susceptibles are numerous in proportion to the immunes. But the takers must also be within reach of the givers, and then (as they fall sick and become givers) of each other, and "within reach" means one thing for contact or air-borne infections, another for water-borne, and still another for insect-borne. The ratio of givers to takers, or more broadly the ratio of herd infection to herd resistance, makes a given disease sporadic, endemic, or epidemic. But in the herd, infection and resistance are complementary; one measures infection in terms of resistance and vice versa, and in spite of much ingenious theorizing it is still about as hard to give absolute values to either as it is to decide whether Tunney beat Dempsey because Tunney was the better fighter, or Dempsey, on that occasion, the worse. In most diseases, we can judge the virulence of the infective agent only in terms of its effect, and cannot easily count either susceptibles or immunes until infection has actually sorted them out.†

* Meaning all of us or smaller groups, according to circumstance.

† In diphtheria, and with slightly less precision in scarlet fever, it is possible by the Schick and Dick tests to discover and count persons with antibody protection. In some other diseases more laborious procedures, not convenient for general use, yield similar information.

The effect of a great disparity between herd infection and herd resistance is unmistakable. Medical history is too young to record the first contacts of mankind with the great plagues, but primitive peoples newly exposed to the civilized diseases have been ravaged in our own day. Measles killed about a quarter of the population of the Sandwich Islands in 1775, and was almost as devastating in one of the Fiji Islands a century later. It is said to have killed nearly half the Indian tribes along the Columbia River in 1829 and 1830, when the Oregon settlements were young. Lack of care for the sick may have raised the death rates, but the resistless spread of the disease among persons of all ages illustrates the principle that a generally susceptible herd is fair game for the invader.

Isolated islands tell a similar story. When measles was carried to the Faroe Islands in the North Sea in 1846, for the first time since 1781, about 6,000 of the 7,782 inhabitants caught it, none escaping except those ancients who had been infected in 1781 or earlier.* One Cuncliffe-Hyne, quoted by a correspondent of the *New England Journal of Medicine,* tells a grisly tale of St. Kilda. This is a tiny island in the Outer Hebrides, some hundred miles off the Scottish coast, accessible for less than half the year. In 1724 (the story goes) sheep-shearers who left St. Kilda to do their yearly task on a neighboring island were marooned there for months because in spite of their repeated signals no boat came to take them home. When a passing vessel did sight them and take them back they found St. Kilda entirely deserted, and came somehow to the conclusion that all their fellows had not only been killed by smallpox but had then been devoured by wild dogs! In this form the narrative must be apocryphal, but an eighteenth-century clergyman does record the fact that smallpox, brought to the island in 1724, killed all or all but one

* The Danish physician Panum studied this epidemic and his report is one of the classics of the epidemiologists.

of the adults who were then at home, leaving a number of orphans to be brought up by the few survivors who had been absent on a bird-catching expedition while the disease raged. St. Kilda puts in evidence too its traditional "boat-cough," a respiratory infection said to run through the entire community whenever a boat brought visitors to the island. The great Dr. Johnson pooh-poohed the tradition, as he would, but it is plausible enough in terms of modern knowledge, for immunity to colds and influenza is transitory and would soon be lost by such a group.

Why is measles, which can attack at all ages, ordinarily a children's disease, along with whooping cough, diphtheria, scarlet fever, chicken pox, and mumps? Because children, like these savages and islanders, lack immunity. In a sizeable human herd exposed to uninterrupted human intercourse most of those susceptible in infancy may expect to build up immunity—either by having the disease frankly or by receiving doses of infection too small to have visible effect—by the time they become adult. The only opportunity for the disease to spread widely is among children. So in the eighteenth century when smallpox was universal and no one was protected except by actually having it, this too was a children's disease. Any continuous and aggressive infection which makes its victims immune for life will tend to be concentrated among the newcomers in the human herd, while diseases like influenza and pneumonia, lacking this capacity, occur at all ages.

Children are immigrants into the human herd—immigrants whose susceptibility dilutes herd resistance and so helps to keep certain diseases in circulation.* Immigration is always a disturbing factor in the infection-resistance ratio. When it is studied on the manageable scale of a laboratory epidemic† the results are

* Various efforts have been made to show how the accumulation of susceptibles of tender years might lead periodically to the flare-up of measles, but this question of periodicity is too complicated for discussion here.

† See page 111.

curious and suggestive. When infection is introduced into a caged herd of mice not selected for innate resistance or susceptibility there is first a latent period during which the disease develops and spreads. Then the death rate begins to climb, reaches a peak, and slowly subsides. If the herd is left alone the epidemic comes to an end, but if it is replenished with fresh susceptible newcomers infection is lighted up again. The survivors of the first wave begin to die. The epidemic resumes its course. So long as immigration continues, the epidemic goes on, the death rate rising and falling as the new arrivals throw the ratio between resistance and susceptibility out of balance. If this goes on long enough, most of the animals alive on any given day will die eventually of the epidemic infection. As fagots are added to the fire, the back-log burns away.*

Herd resistance fluctuates then with the composition of the herd, continually altered by births, immigration, and deaths, and also with the degree and duration of the individual immunities which go to make it up. These in turn may fluctuate with the dosage of infection and the passage of time. In the herd the level of resistance will be continually rising and falling—rising especially when an epidemic makes many hosts freshly and strongly immune, falling as this immunity wears off. What Dudley calls an "epidemic of immunization" accompanies the epidemic of disease: its influence stretches away into the future like a man's

* This denouement seems not to be inevitable if innately resistant mice form part of the original herd and the additions to it. Nor can one assume that fate will hang so heavily over men at large as it does over mice in cages. The demonstrated effect of immigration in a mouse herd may none the less have some counterpart in human epidemics where most of the herd falls within average ranges of natural susceptibility and especially where association between its members is close and stable, as in a boarding school or other institution; the *Lancet* urged British army authorities in 1940 to keep the implications of this work in mind in regulating the admission of recruits to training camps.

shadow at sundown, but comes at last to an end, and that sooner for some diseases than for others.

This is at least what most epidemiologists believe today. If we knew more about the innate susceptibility or resistance of the laboratory animals whose checkered lives and catastrophic deaths we reason from, and if we had some way of finding out what varying resources human beings bring to their first contact with infection, it is possible that we should put less stress on considerations of this sort. We still have to reckon with the simple irreducible fact that people, like mice, are different and we do not know how or why they are different. Francis reminds us that almost three out of four Americans, for whatever reason, escaped influenza even in the pandemic year. Maori children Schick-tested in New Zealand showed considerably less susceptibility to diphtheria than half-bred or white children in the same district. We cannot rule out the presence in particular human stocks, perhaps even in particular human races, of a particular physiological complex that meets invasion with more, or less, than average success.

Yet it is hard to prove that such stocks exist because many other factors may be at work; we cannot count them, and it would be rash to trust to such a defense in the face of an active and belligerent germ. Specifically, it is difficult to measure differences in resistance due to race. When the aborigines of the American mainland or the Pacific islands take smallpox or measles very hard, one must ask what opportunities they have had to build up immunity. When the Negroes show high rates for pneumonia or tuberculosis one must rule out environmental differences and past history before one can point with assurance to a distinctively racial susceptibility. Natural selection should theoretically make a given herd increasingly resistant to a given infection, since the least resistant die out, but man lives so much longer and presumably changes so much more slowly than his parasites that it is easier to think of the shoe as being on the other foot, with the parasite doing most of the adapting. Perhaps a herd long infected with a parasite, like the West African Negro with yellow fever, may develop by natural selection a degree of tolerance which reduces the severity of the disease,* but that is about as far as we dare go without more evidence.

There can be no doubt that the bitter bread of poverty is seasoned with disease and early death. The "poore's plague" in London, the ravages of cholera among the "depraved" classes of New York, have already been mentioned. In Britain the economically independent have the advantage of unskilled workers in the general death rate and markedly so in the specific death rates for tuberculosis, pneumonia, and syphilis. The general death rate and the rates for pulmonary tuberculosis and pneumonia go up step by step as one goes down the economic scale.† The poor are at a disadvantage, moreover, in sickness as well as death. When the United States Public Health Service made its national health survey in the fall and winter of 1935–36 it found that pneumonia (in eastern cities) struck more than twice as often at people on relief as it did at people with family incomes of $2,000 or more, and that tuberculosis (in all the cities studied) caused almost four times as much disability in families with incomes below $1,000 (but not on relief) as in those with incomes of at least $3,000.

Here again, in spite of the obvious drift of the facts, we are

---

* In tuberculosis the advantage of long racial exposure seems to lie with the whites, and observers agree that its course in blacks whose contact with infection is relatively recent is unlike the typical chronic disease in white adults. Sometimes, as in Jamaica, it runs through whole families and is rapidly fatal. In South Africa, on the other hand, tuberculosis carried from the mines to the villages where natives live an easy outdoor life behaves much as it often does in a healthy white child, the infection being localized without serious damage.

† This is not so for influenza.

not sure just what causes the difference. It is too soon to correlate resistance specifically with nutrition, about which we are just
beginning to get detailed information. We can assume (to our
shame) that the poor are more likely than the well-to-do to die
for lack of suitable care when they fall sick; we can be sure that
they are likelier to fall sick when infection is transmitted by
vermin or faulty sanitation or facilitated by habitual huddling;
but actual net susceptibility is something we do not know how to
measure. As for inherited physiological inferiority, we know too
little about that to draw conclusions, and we are certainly not
justified in correlating it—in this reeling world—with economic
status.

Not only the number but the spacing of susceptibles is important. Suppose that only five per cent of the people of a given
town have neglected or refused to be vaccinated, and that the
five per cent are scattered at random. Then it is unlikely that the
peddler with a "breaking-out" on his face and hands will bring a
susceptible person to the door when he pushes the bell; the immunes will act as a buffer between the susceptibles and infection,
and there will be small chance of an epidemic. But if the five per
cent are concentrated on the wrong side of the tracks, and the
peddler works those streets thoroughly, there may be a fine crop
of new cases. In an English school it was found that the boarders, in continuous contact with each other, were immunized
against diphtheria by marginal infections much more rapidly
than the day scholars. In past years Schick tests have shown
that most city children of school age had immunity against diphtheria, while most rural children, for lack of contact with the
parasite, had none.*

Even if, for lack of acquired immunity, diseases once introduced into a country community spread as widely as in the city,
they stay longer in the city. In the village an epidemic may ex-

* But see page 293.

haust itself and all traces of infection may disappear. Smillie suggests that it takes at least a thousand people to keep a common cold in circulation. In the city, even at the trough of the epidemic wave there are people enough to carry infection along till the wave rises again. So, as Greenwood says, diphtheria, plague, and smallpox in England have tended "to leave the country and linger in the towns."

In the epidemic formula, in short, even if the dosage of infection remains constant, fluctuations in the number, ratio, and grouping of susceptibles and immunes will have a profound effect. To predict this effect, one would have to know how many susceptibles there are and where they are, and both facts are hard to come at. Inborn resistance may play a larger part here than we recognize, but so far as present knowledge goes the ratio between susceptibles and immunes is determined in the main by the past experience of the herd with the infection in question.

### SOME DETERMINANTS

So far we have tried to hold the principal factors in disease prevalence apart to see how they may vary independently. Now it is time to take a broader view.

First we must look into the mathematical possibilities of chance interaction among the basic variables. Take four pennies. Let each stand for one of the four factors in the perpetuation and spread of disease—the infectivity of the germ, the supply of infected persons or animals, the facility of transmission from person to person (or from animal to man), and the susceptibility of the exposed group. Let heads signify those values of the four factors that tend to accelerate the spread or intensify the force of infection, tails those values that have an opposite effect. Now toss the pennies. Occasionally four heads or four tails will turn up, more often some intermediate mixture. Altogether sixteen different combinations of heads and tails are possible.

We have already seen that each of the four major factors may be broken down into subsidiary variables. Thus the spread of malaria by mosquitoes may be influenced by warmth, humidity, the saltiness of standing water, the kind of vegetation that borders the streams, the number of mosquito-enemies present, the number of cows in the pastures, the number of screens in the houses, the prevailing rate of wages. If we knew all the underlying elements in our set of four variables (which we do not) and tossed a penny for each of them there would be a hailstorm of coppers and the mathematician would wear out his pencil figuring their possible combinations.

Obviously the way epidemics happen is not like the way pennies fall. One penny is as good as another, but the factors we are concerned with vary in importance in different diseases. One penny has no influence on the next in line, but some of the factors in disease prevalence are interlocking—for instance, immunity may increase with the spread of frank disease and the multiplication of carriers. The illustration is worth using, however, because it does suggest how much room there is within the range of chance variation for an amazing range of experience. Sometimes all the pennies fall heads up: a virulent organism is abundantly present and has favorable opportunities to infect a generally susceptible population, and the net result is a Black Death or an influenza pandemic. Perhaps we have no need to invoke a *deus ex machina* even for these extraordinary events. After all, people do sometimes get thirteen spades in a hand at bridge.

Yet we have not ruled out the possibility that the concomitant variation of the factors that produce disease has some pattern of its own, that the variables are to some degree lined up by a dominant principle. If we limit ourselves to saying with Greenwood that there is order in the phenomena of epidemics we shall find ourselves in good scientific company, but if we ask the epidemiologists to tell us what force it is that imposes such order they will quite properly refuse to guess.* There have been too many bad guesses in epidemiological history. Moreover the careful biologist today is disinclined to generalize beyond the point to which induction takes him; he has not been able to organize his principles into a deductive system.

In the present temper of the world the generalization which served human purposes ages ago, that God sends disease upon the people to punish them for their sins, is no longer useful. But another very old notion needs further examination. Does climate exert a dominant influence on disease?

~

Pestilence like rain falls on the just and on the unjust, and when men thought how common pestilence was at some times and how uncommon at others, they naturally connected its coming and going with the universality of the weather. Hippocrates did this quite simply, avoiding the pitfalls that lay in wait for those of his successors through the centuries who tried to explain this sort of correlation by a general theory. In recent years the rise and dominance of bacteriology have tended to shove aside the whole environmental approach to the study of disease.

The influence of climate on some diseases is beyond dispute. As we have seen in this chapter, certain parasites are dependent

---

* In some fields of knowledge the layman is justified in asking the scientist to furnish him with workable general ideas even if they are still tentative, for though science may be eternal man is mortal, and having little time in which to come to terms with his universe he needs a generally sound orientation more than he needs copper-riveted facts. But it is doubtful whether a master-theory of disease-incidence belongs in this class: in this field general ideas are still intellectual luxuries to be sought at the inquirer's risk.

upon weather both directly and indirectly through the fortunes of their insect hosts. The distribution of the insect carriers in some instances is definitely limited by temperature and humidity, and the same factors, operating on the food supply, must affect the size and distribution of animal reservoirs of infection. Climate and its emergencies have a definite influence on crowd formation and crowd movements, and perhaps on the means by which infection travels through a crowd. The evidence is not so clear as to seasonal and climatic variations in physiological resistance to infection, but it is strongly probable that they do occur.

How far one can say that some diseases are "tropical" and others not is a question that becomes harder to answer with every new link between continents and peoples. The part played in world history by some diseases that seem to have their proper home in the tropics is clear enough. If one thinks of the ice-ages, when killing cold came creeping down from the poles and then receded and crept down again and receded again—and reverses the pattern, one will have a very fair picture of the way in which yellow fever, malaria, cholera, and leprosy have surged out of the equatorial ocean to run up the shores of the temperate zone, leaving pools of infection high on land and gradually retreating again.

We think naturally of the diseases carried by flying insects as tropical, since broadly speaking they are endemic in countries where the climate favors such forms of life the year around, epidemic in countries where cold winters discourage them. All effortless life seems to flourish in the tropics and diseases caused by the higher parasites are common there, but human energy runs slow, and some diseases spread by casual sanitation also take on a tropical coloring.

Our own experience makes us think of the respiratory infections as belonging to cold and changeable weather—that is, to the temperate zone. "Catching cold" is a sorry pun, but it does reflect folk experience, and recent experiments suggest that colds are not easily transmitted when temperature and humidity remain constant. Three-quarters of the pneumonia deaths in Massachusetts fall between the beginning of December and the end of May. Among iron and steel workers the people who have the most pneumonia are those who work hard outdoors in all weather, or do tiring work in damp drafty places, or—like the blast-furnace men—run the risk of chilling by exposure first to excessive heat and then to ordinary temperatures.

One must walk warily here, however. The common cold cuts across all climatic barriers. Pandemic influenza visits every continent. Pneumonia takes heavier toll in some tropical cities than in any of the cold gray capitals of the North. More than half the cities with pneumonia death rates of over 350 per 100,000 (as reported to the League of Nations) lie between the Tropic of Cancer and the Tropic of Capricorn, and one, Guayaquil, is almost under the equator. Some are at high altitudes, some at sea level. What local changes of temperature may be at work we do not know, but certainly no gross generalizations as to climate seem to fit the facts.*

If one accepts the theory with which the name of Ellsworth Huntington is identified—that human beings function best in an optimum climate where temperature and humidity are moderate but change is frequent, and that differences in climate strongly influence civilization—both direct and indirect correlations between climate and disease become plausible. Men of this school have argued that excessive change—such as is common in the cyclone belts—is overstimulating and therefore destructive, and have sought to connect this factor with the incidence of a variety

* It may be significant that the hinterlands of some of these tropical cities with high death rates do not suffer so severely; perhaps human huddling—so conspicuous in some blistering tropical seaports—is the dominant factor in the spread of infection. Yet pneumonia was also found by Livingstone to be common in the heart of southern Africa.

of non-infectious disorders. One might also infer that long-range climatic changes must modify standards of living, the concentration of population, travel, and the like, and so have a bearing on the prevalence of infections.

The notion of biological cycles has fascinating possibilities, too. We see such cycles in our own backyards when we burn the tent-caterpillars—so many more in some years than others—off the apple trees. Masefield made a poem about the lemmings driven by fate to march into the western sea. The details are gratuitous —when the lemmings multiply excessively they are reduced by disease, not by mass suicide—but the fact of cyclical variation is sober truth. It is not implausible to connect such variations with climatic changes, and these in turn, perhaps, with the cycles of the sunspots. It is amusing to think of times and seasons at which all creation, from bacteria to man, may swagger and multiply, and others at which the life-force sags, men turn to philosophy, and the bacteria, having no philosophy, turn to dust. Things might not work just that way: a given variation might be positive here and negative there; the weather that suited one form of life might not suit another; the larger the animal, the more slowly its birth rate would change, so that some species must lag behind others. But as between bacteria and man significant changes in relationships seem possible. When disease has been quiescent—as it may be when the tide runs low among the attacking micro-organisms—herd immunity is presumably lowered, and a cyclical increase among the parasites or the creatures that carry them to man might then have marked effect.

Perhaps this ranges rather far from proven fact; the difficulty with our speculations about climate and disease is not that they are inherently impractical, for they might at least have predictive value, but that guessing tends to run too far ahead of knowledge. Such painstaking work as that which dries and dampens the environment of fleas in the laboratory, or maps familiar diseases county by county, is far from the philosophical ether in which some thinking about this subject has taken place: it may lead eventually to sound inductions which will strengthen our working knowledge of epidemic disease.

～

The effect of climate is complicated when men refuse to stay put. White men from the temperate zone go into the tropical zone for rubber or coffee or the devious concerns of empire; they bring black men from torrid lands into colder ones to dig gold or chop cotton or fight the white man's wars. To the great prehistoric drifts of population which may have been controlled by climatic changes history adds all sorts of cross-migrations motivated by the appetites of civilization. And when we have said all there is to say about animal reservoirs and swarming insects, it is still true that human disease is a function of human behavior, and particularly of crowd behavior.

There can be no epidemics unless men are close enough together for multiple infection to take place. The underlying mechanism in all epidemics is the juxtaposition of the infected and the uninfected. When the disease is present in one herd but not in another, there must be migration and intermingling before it can become established in the second. When it is once established, human intercourse tends to keep it in circulation, and alterations in the crowd-pattern which bring givers and takers of disease together in some fresh arrangement may raise it to epidemic levels.

So there have been school epidemics of mumps or chicken pox because little girls and boys moved from White Plains to Westport; town epidemics of typhoid fever because the Methodists liked church suppers; national epidemics of typhus because boys were called from the farms to the colors; regional epidemics of smallpox because white men went where red or black men lived;

world epidemics of plague because camel trains or sailing ships carried people on their lawful occasions from one herd to another.

Behind such events there is some change in the herd pattern, some going to and fro, some reshuffling of the givers and takers of disease. The simplest phenomenon of this sort is the movement of an infected individual or individuals into an uninfected but susceptible herd. The flight of refugees from plague-ridden cities was recognized centuries ago as a means of spreading pestilence and the futile rigors of quarantine were set up as a defense against it. Thanks to a Spanish chronicler, we know after four centuries the name of the Negro who, if report be true, first gave smallpox to the Indians of Mexico in 1520 and so paved the way for three and a half million deaths. In like fashion yellow fever came repeatedly from Havana to the American seaports in the last century; so the common cold still comes annually to Spitzbergen when the ice goes out and the ships from Norway come in.

Disease travels as men travel; as they travel faster infection does likewise. It took cholera six years to pass from India to Russia in the first quarter of the last century; today a traveler can span a continent while infection is still incubating within him. Public health men watch the air lanes like hawks, for if yellow fever should thus cross from Africa to India there might be fearful consequences, as Sidney Howard reminded us in his play Yellow Jack.

But infection need not be carried to the herd; the herd can come to the infection. That happened in Panama when de Lesseps tried to build the Canal without controlling mosquitoes, and lost a third of his white workers by yellow fever. It had happened before when Napoleon sent an army into Haiti, as Zinsser recalls, to suppress Toussaint l'Ouverture; of 25,000 troops, only 3,000 were left when the same disease had finished with them.

153

It may have happened in France during the first world war, when a little force of 11,000 Cape Boys and Kaffirs from South Africa lost more men from tuberculosis than 1,500,000 white British troops. It happened curiously in Manchuria in 1910, when the price of tarbagan skins rose so high that Chinese coolies pressed into the wilderness to hunt them. The native Mongols, following old tradition, avoided the sick animals and caught only the well ones, but the Chinese interlopers fell greedily on the stragglers and presently more than 50,000 persons were dead of pneumonic plague.

When the herd comes not only to infection but also to a strange environment disease may rise to fantastic heights. This happened during the early years of the present century when blacks from tropical parts of Africa were brought to work in the South African gold mines. Only natives who were hungry to start with could be hired; they made long fatiguing journeys; they exchanged village huts for vast compounds; they left torrid heat for the high cool Rand. They began to die of pneumonia even before they could be sent into the diggings, and at times in certain groups the disease killed them at the rate of approximately one man in twenty per year. In 1913 the government forbade further importation of laborers from the hotter regions north of 22° S. latitude. An army of a quarter-million natives still moved in and out of the mines each year, and though the selection of men not so terribly susceptible mitigated the danger, and protective inoculations from time to time apparently reduced the losses, pneumonia death rates remained two or three times as high as those for Negroes in the United States.

Pilgrimages and wars—involving mass movements, the commingling of herds, and crowding under abnormal circumstances—are traditionally breeders of disease. In India the periodical swarming of millions of Hindus about the sacred places and great fairs has repeatedly spread cholera, and the close association between festivals and epidemics is being broken only by vigorous public health effort. The pattern of war is exquisitely adjusted to the pattern of infection: the gathering of young men from every corner of the land, the herding together in camps and barracks, their exposure on active service to weather and fatigue and vermin, the scattering of prisoners behind the lines, and the reversal of the mass movements in demobilization, all encourage the spread of disease. The Franco-Prussian War of 1870–1871 provides a classic example. French troops picked up smallpox in civilian billets; the garrison of Paris and other bodies of troops suffered severely; French prisoners sent into German towns carried the disease with them, shared it with civilians, and touched off the greatest epidemic Germany had known in the nineteenth century. In the last war medical science held most diseases at bay on the western front, but in the east the ravages of typhus—described by Zinsser in *Rats, Lice, and History*—did full justice to military precedents. And one must not forget the pandemic of influenza. As for the present war, one can only wait to see what is revealed when the censorships are lifted. Forced and desperate migrations, superimposed on the wreckage of civil life, are a daring challenge to man's parasites.

The little epidemics of children's diseases, of the acute respiratory infections, and of some intestinal disorders that we face year in and year out feed on the restlessness of everyday crowds. In this country, at least, the isolation of the farmer and the self-sufficiency of the crossroads have both given way to motor travel. Mass migration has become a commonplace: almost any summer holiday, the *New York Times* points out, sees an exodus from New York twice as great as the exodus from Egypt that Moses led. City folk cannot earn a living without moving about and would be bored if they could; they fill subway trains with their sneezes, and—for relaxation—fill theaters with their coughs. In searching about for some explanation of the much-increased prevalence of influenza since 1890 the British Ministry of Health hit upon the growing tendency of workers to live in the suburbs and work in town and jam the trams and tubes in transit from one to the other—not as sole cause, of course, but as one factor that kept the whole epidemic mixture near the flash-point. In partially isolated groups like schools and institutions what Dudley calls the "rate of change of population" must have an influence on the mixture of givers and takers of disease; in the human herd at large what Stocks calls the "circulation factor"—the coming and going and intermingling—plays a similar part.*

Against a broader biological background, epidemics take their place as by-products of the universal struggle for existence. Each kind of living thing acts out its own destiny, but to seek sustenance, multiply, and die is the common lot of bacteria, mosquitoes, mice, and men. Few species are self-sufficient; man, for instance, lives by the death of plants and animals, and while some bacteria feed independently on soil and air, others, fantastically dependent, must be nourished by particular tissues of particular living hosts. (But even these parasites are less ruthless than man, for they kill what they feed on by mischance, not by habit.)

It is a law of life that organisms multiply up to the limits set for them by their environment and their competitors. The bacterium is no exception; like other living things, it is avid of space to grow in. When it happens to be carried to a new kind of host the results are unpredictable. It may be repulsed at once and completely. It may precipitate a brisk struggle within the host, with all the concomitants of acute disease. If it survives this struggle, and finds opportunity to travel readily from individual

* Though the evacuation of school children from London and other British cities in September 1939 resulted in widespread mingling of urban and rural herds, there was (at least in the first few months) no serious spread of childhood infections.

to individual within the new host-species, it may spread like wild-fire. Theobald Smith went too far, perhaps, when he suggested that "most epidemics or pandemics are probably due to strayed parasites," but the principle is one to be reckoned with. Plague illustrates the violence which may attend the casual invasion of the human species by a parasite which belongs to another host.*

Besides pressing against their environment, living things adapt to it. Dudley tells how a Canadian waterweed, when it first invaded England, spread so lushly that it choked up ponds and canals, but presently, reaching a state of equilibrium with its food supply and its competitors, became inconspicuous. The parasite adapts to its host by gradually abandoning those qualities which stir up trouble in favor of those which enable it to live unobtrusively and spread easily from one individual to another; this may be the price of survival. But man himself may delay such adjustments. Suppose Providence had moved the Indies and the Americas to the gates of fifteenth-century Spain; what an epidemic of plunder would have resulted! What man has done for his parasites is hardly less spectacular. By his migrations and his wars and his huddling in cities he offers them new worlds to conquer, gives them easy passage to the promised land, and so mitigates the rigors of their environment that they have less need to change their ways. We say that civilization conquers disease, and that is measurably true, but some of its mechanisms may also encourage disease by interfering with the natural cadences of adaptation.

The struggle for existence is a circus with more rings than Barnum and Bailey could have dreamed of. In each some species

* Though disease makes strange bedfellows, the chances that a given parasite will survive the transfer from one host to another are presumably better when the hosts are zoologically similar. If this is so, how fortunate it is (as Theobald Smith has pointed out) that men have surrounded themselves with cows and horses and dogs and cats—even with rats—rather than with apes and chimpanzees!

whirls its giddy way from birth to death. Where paths cross, trouble comes. The bacteria swarm, rats multiply, men travel. Caravans from Cathay traverse the Asian wastes where plague lies fallow; the world opens suddenly before the bacillus, and Europe is swept by death. The virus of yellow fever, already quiescent, perhaps, on the African littoral, is carried over the seas to America and riots through Indians and whites for a century. By accident or by fate, men and beasts and bacteria, as they serve the law of life, conspire to create epidemics.

### THE EPIDEMIC FORMULA?

What then is an epidemic? It is a tidal wave of disease. But it is also an incident in the adjustment of a parasite to an expanding environment, and, conversely, an incident in the mass immunization of a human herd against an inimical factor in *its* environment—a wholesale change of status with respect to a particular infection, with death as the transfer tax and herd immunity as a bonus.

Yet we have not found a formula for epidemics. Instead, we have found a host of variables—some independent, some interrelated, some proven, some guessed at, few well defined, and fewer measured. The parasite, it appears, may be either deadly or tame, a good traveler or a bad one, may associate feloniously with other parasites or work alone, may wander from an accustomed host to a strange one or come to terms with an old enemy. The animals harboring infection may migrate or stay put, may multiply incontinently or die off, may suffer epidemics of their own or reach a compromise with their parasites. The insects carrying infection may flourish or die as weather and the works of man dictate. Men may travel and carry infection with them, or stay at home with sagging resistance, but in one way or another they keep shifting the status quo.

So the modern epidemiologist, like the detective-story detective, is embarrassed by the number of clues he has uncovered. In this dilemma he may follow any of a number of courses. He may explain epidemics in terms of the particular variable he happens to know best—a fallacious procedure, but quite human, and one to which medical men are no more immune than others. So one finds virulence, or weather, or the vagaries of parasitism given the place of honor.

Or he may invent a concept for the critical factor in epidemicity, as Peters did in 1910 (a long time ago in medical research) when he defined "epidemic potential" in tortured phrases as "the head of power for epidemic spread, present at any particular stage of the epidemic, as gauged by the highness of the infectivity over the lowness of the insusceptibility of the population."[3] But this is a rather solemn way of marching around a circle back to one's starting point, for it is agreed, after all, that when disease gets the better of a crowd we call the result an epidemic.

Or he may try to bring the variables together into a pair of opposites, as Gill did in 1928 when he sought to explain "all epidemic manifestations" in terms of "loss of equilibrium between the dose of toxin [using this term broadly] and the degree of resistance, or, in short, between 'infection' and 'immunity.' "[4] Here again the central concepts are to some extent reciprocal, so that one runs the risk of elaborating the obvious in setting one against the other. But it is reasonable to suppose that effective dosage does vary independently of accumulated resistance in the herd, and the evidence, though scanty, points to a significant connection between depleted resistance and the rise of epidemics.

Or the epidemiologist may be disinclined to force the variables into any such pattern and may let them stand in naked simplicity as more or less clearly known elements in an equation of unknown form. Thus the British Ministry of Health remarks in its influenza report that "the epidemic is generated by the correlated action of several factors, $a$, $b$, $c$, $d$, $e$, etc." In such an array some factors affect the parasite, some the host, and some the environment common to both, and if the investigator plays no favorites among them this approach to the problem may be the most scientific of all. Moreover it is mathematically clear that in a given situation one factor or another may hold a key position. If $a$, for example, is consistently high then various slight changes in $b$, $c$, $d$, and $e$ may bring the sum or product of all the factors to the critical point at which an epidemic develops. The British epidemiologists offer the intermingling of crowds as such an $a$ factor in influenza. But if $a$, $b$, $c$, and $d$ are usually high a change in $e$ alone may serve to turn an endemic into an epidemic. Thus if many persons carrying a malignant strain of the plasmodium are scattered through a changing and susceptible population living in unscreened houses an increase of rainfall leading to a plethora of mosquitoes may set off an epidemic of malaria. One could not justly say that the crowding caused the influenza or the rains caused the malaria, but in each case a particular factor would have special importance.

This is not very conclusive or dramatic, but it is about as far as the evidence takes us. Breaking down the major problem into interlocking phases has led to more accurate information; the urge to put it together again has not been lost, but the time is not yet ripe. Epidemiologists are busy trying to learn *how* epidemics happen in terms of a finite series of variables—without indefinable or mystical interpolations—and to measure at least some of the variables. They cannot tell *why* epidemics happen and being scientists, not philosophers, they do not greatly care.

REFERENCES

1. Greenwood, Major. *Epidemics and crowd-diseases.* London: Williams and Norgate, Ltd.; New York: The Macmillan Company, 1935, p. 67.
2. Harper's Weekly, 22:837, October 19, 1878.

3. Peters, O. H. *Observations upon the natural history of epidemic diarrhea.* Journal of Hygiene, 10:602–777, December 1910.
4. Gill, C. A. *The genesis of epidemics and the natural history of disease.* London: Baillière, Tindall and Cox, 1928, p. 33.

## A NOTE ON SOURCES

This chapter owes much to British texts. Greenwood's, to which I have referred in an earlier chapter, is cited above: I have used it freely. No layman curious about this field should miss two brilliant papers by Dudley, *On the biological approach to the study of epidemiology,* and *The ecological outlook on epidemiology,* published in the Proceedings of the Royal Society of Medicine for November 1935 and November 1936 (29:1–14 and 30:57–70). The *Report on the pandemic of influenza 1918–1919,* by the British Ministry of Health (London: H. M. Stationery Office, 1920) is as interesting for its epidemiological point of view as for its factual content.

On plague in wild rodents Wu Lien-Teh is the authority. On mosquitoes and malaria I draw both on Ross' classic *The prevention of malaria* (New York: Dutton, 1910) and on Hackett's *Malaria in Europe* (London: Oxford University Press, 1937), an uncommonly readable book. René Sand has made the economic aspects of sickness his special field; Ellsworth Huntington and C. C. Mills have written on climate and disease. Cyclical variations are treated in a fascinating way in a paper by Elton on *Plague and the regulation of numbers in wild mammals* in the Journal of Hygiene for October 1925 (24:138–163). Since Hirsch there has been little inclusive discussion of geographical epidemiology: one wishes for more studies like McKinley's *Geography of disease* (Washington: George Washington University Press, 1935). Dr. W. Harvey Perkins and Dr. C. C. Dauer (then) of Tulane were helpful to me on this and many other subjects. For the geographical (and other) aspects of pneumonia I rest on *Pneumonia* (New York: The Commonwealth Fund, 1939) by my colleague Dr. Heffron.

# 6

## DEFENSES

To understand epidemics is one thing; to control them another. Logically, one would expect to know what causes a disease before finding out how to prevent or cure it. But logic—except in the form of hindsight—is a luxury that medicine cannot always afford. With a sick man before him the doctor must often take refuge in empiricism, which means doing something because—no matter how—it works. So quinine, borrowed from the savages, helped to assuage the chills and fever of Spanish adventurers more than two centuries before anyone had learned what caused the chills and fever, and vaccination, suggested by folk-lore, broke the grip of smallpox a century before the virus of the disease was found.

Yet the epidemiologist, opportunist though he is, cannot rely on happy accidents. While he hammers away at disease wherever he can land a blow, he seeks facts wherever he can find them, hoping that eventually logic will catch up with action. He is both scientist and trouble-shooter, and the two roles are complementary. Whatever contributes to the understanding of epidemics, as a problem in pure science, or to the control of epidemics, as a practical necessity, is good epidemiology. This chapter is about the practical side.

Control, as applied to epidemic disease, is a biggety word. If it were not for natural resistance to parasitic invasion and the

By GEORGE CLINTON, Governor of the State of New-York,
(L.S.) General and Commander in Chief of all the Militia, and
Admiral of the Navy of the Same :

# A PROCLAMATION.

WHEREAS by the Statute entitled "An Act to prevent bringing
" in and spreading of INFECTIOUS DISTEMPERS in this
" State," it is enacted " That all Vessels of whatever kind
" they may be having on board any Person or Persons infect-
" ed with the YELLOW FEVER or any other contagious Distemper,
" or coming from any places infected with such contagious Distemper
" shall not come into any of the Ports or Harbours of this State, or
" nearer the city of New-York than the Island commonly called Bed-
" low's Island:" And whereas it is represented to me that the City of
Philadelphia is now infected with a contagious Distemper ; where-
fore I DO by these presents strictly forbid and prohibit all Vessels
coming from Philadelphia aforesaid, and all other vessels coming
from any other place infected with any contagious Distemper, or
having on board any Person or Persons infected therewith from entering any of the Ports of this State, or to approach nearer to the City of
New-York than the said Island called Bedlows Island ; And I do further hereby direct all Vessels coming from Philadelphia aforesaid or o-
ther place infected with such contagious distemper tine opposite the said Island and below the point of Governors Island
until such Vessel shall be duly discharged ; And that no person
or Persons whomsoever, nor any Goods or Merchandize whatsoever
coming or imported in any such Vessel are to come or be brought on
shore or unloaded or put on board any vessel within this State, until the
Vessel so performing Quarantine shall be duly discharged as aforesaid, as every person offending in the premises will answer the same
at their peril. And I do also further enjoin and require the Branch
Pilots of this State and their deputies to be vigilant and attentive in
the performance of the duties required of them by the above recited
act conformably to the directions heretofore communicated to them.

GIVEN at the City of New-York under my Hand and the
Privy Seal this thirteenth day of September in the Seventeenth year of the Independence of the said State.

## GEO : CLINTON.

*Governor Clinton's proclamation of quarantine
at New York against shipping from Philadelphia in 1793: a classic defense against disease*

gradual adaptation of parasites to their hosts, we would have died out long before doctors and health officers made their appearance. The epidemiologist is working on nature's side, and if he need not be so modest as the physician who said that he amused the patient while God cured him, he can claim credit only for supporting his own species in a course which biological law prescribes.

To do this effectively he needs information of two sorts. He must understand the natural history, particularly the pattern of spread, of each disease with which he deals. Such information dictates his strategy: it suggests where and how he can interfere to hold the disease in check. And he must know day by day from what quarter danger threatens. This gives him his tactics.

Keeping tab on disease is something new in the world's history. Deaths have been recorded for several centuries, and a register of deaths by cause gives a crude retrospective picture of what has happened. But if something is to be done about disease before it kills, an earlier report is necessary. In this country cases of smallpox were recorded in colonial days, other diseases not till much later. Today reporting or "notification" as the English say is required by law for a long list of common and uncommon diseases.

The ultimate source of this information is the practicing physician, who is the first to see the sick man, and disease reporting rests on his intelligence and sense of responsibility. In the United States he telephones or writes his report to the local health officer, who relays the totals to the state health department, which telegraphs weekly summaries for the more important diseases* to the United States Public Health Service. Nor is this all. The nations exchange danger signals. One reads in the weekly bulle-

---

* Diphtheria, influenza, measles, meningococcus meningitis, poliomyelitis, scarlet fever, smallpox, typhoid and paratyphoid fevers, whooping cough.

tin of the Health Section of the League of Nations that within a fortnight of publication a white man has died at Tarkwa on the Gold Coast of what appeared to be yellow fever; that there is cholera at Ningpo; that Champaran and Muzaffarpur are newly infected with the plague; that there have been six cases of typhus in Jaffa and eight deaths from smallpox on the Blue Nile. Thanks to another League service centering at Singapore, the master of a ship plying the China Sea or the Indian Ocean can tune in his wireless any day and learn whether plague, cholera, smallpox, or some other rampant disease lies in wait for him at the port to which he is bound. It is easier to learn what perils lurk on the road to Mandalay than it was a century ago to gauge the danger of a trip from New York to Philadelphia.*

The laws and regulations regarding reporting take it for granted that sick people will be found. But this is not always true. Diseases which develop insidiously, like tuberculosis, may be unrecognized and unreported for a long time; diseases which carry social stigma, like syphilis, are neglected or concealed; diseases which take elusive forms, like poliomyelitis, are correspondingly hard to identify; obscure diseases like amebiasis, unless they are advertised by an epidemic, usually escape attention altogether. It took a long struggle to reach the point at which two new living cases were reported for each death from tuberculosis, and "case finding" remains an important defensive maneuver. With respect to syphilis, it is still an open question whether the epidemiologist will be allowed to do his work or not, and many years of public education will be needed before he can work effectively. The "missed case" of poliomyelitis or scarlet fever or typhoid fever—that is, an attack which disturbs the patient so little that it passes without notice—is a great convenience, as we have seen, in epidemiological theory, but it remains a thorn in the flesh in epidemiological practice.

* All this was true before the war: it may be true no longer.

Assuming, however, that we can find sources of infection, what can we do about them? Since infection travels from one living host to another, from the giver to the taker, we can

1. Make the giver non-infectious
2. Put a fence around the giver
3. Suppress the infective agent on its way between the giver and the taker
4. Put a fence around the taker, or
5. Make the taker more resistant

Most of the measures available to the epidemiologist fall under one or more of these heads. Illustrations come quickly to mind: we can cure a syphilitic, banish the leper to an island, destroy typhoid bacilli in drinking-water, shelter new-born babies in glass-walled nurseries, or vaccinate against smallpox. There may be several kinds of things to do about a single disease; in typhoid fever, for example, we can sometimes make carriers non-infectious; we can isolate the sick and disinfect their excreta; we can chlorinate water and pasteurize milk; and we can immunize those in danger of infection. Sometimes we must choose first one method and then another according to circumstance. Sometimes we do not know enough to do anything effectively.

### CURING OR KILLING THE GIVER

The sick man ceases to be dangerous to his fellows when he gets well or dies. So stated, this is cold comfort for the individual. Moreover the statement is not quite accurate. In some diseases the sick man ceases to shed micro-organisms long before he gets well; in others he may continue to shed them long after he has gotten well. The concern of the epidemiologist with the cure of the individual is therefore a variable quantity, looming large in diseases like tuberculosis and syphilis which make the giver dangerous for years, relatively slight in diseases like measles which spread chiefly before the characteristic symptoms appear. Strictly speaking we are concerned here with the cure of communicable disease only as it affects the movement of infection through the herd, but one can hardly avoid thinking of cure in more general terms.

It is the ineradicable human hunger for miracles that makes "cures" more impressive than the body's own resourcefulness. There could be nothing more wonderful than the way in which the inmost tissues mobilize to throw off the invader, but this goes on unseen and without our intervention, and it comforts us more to think of what the doctor does. What can he do? In some instances he can kill (or at least restrain) parasitic interlopers by the use of chemicals or heat.* In a few more he can loan the body protective substances borrowed from another body which has successfully resisted the same invader. In some instances he can cut infected tissue out of the body and so put a stop to the spread of infection to other tissue. But his fundamental service, and in many diseases his only one, is to give the body general support in its own efforts at self-defense—by helping it get rid of poisonous products, by the relief of weakening symptoms, by suitable nourishment, and by rest. Our common experience suggests that this general support has an emotional component: by *being* the doctor—the healer—he seems to be able to rally the patient's morale. How this works, and how much it is worth in dealing with infection, we do not know.

Consider drugs first. They are used with reserve by the good doctor, with enthusiasm by the poor doctor, and with rank credulity by the medically unwashed. It *is* wonderful that drugs should cure disease—rather too much so for the comfort of the scientific physician, who would rather know than wonder. Some of his most familiar drugs—quinine, ipecac—come to him straight from the savage. Modern chemistry refines these rude natural

* Fever therapy was briefly discussed on page 96.

products into their essential elements, creates substitutes in the laboratory, and goes on to build new compounds. But the process of discovery is a matter of shrewd guessing and dogged persistence rather than solid deduction from known principles. Paul Ehrlich, about the turn of the century, rationalized the problem by arguing that if one could find dye-stuffs which colored one cell and not another one could also find chemicals which would poison the parasite and not the host. But when he tried to find such chemicals he had to rely on trial and error, discarding 605 compounds before he hit on "606" or salvarsan, and testing many more before he was willing to commit himself to a cure for syphilis. Another investigator tried two thousand chemicals in the search for a specific against the pneumococcus, and got nothing more than mildly encouraging results with two of them.

Even the "great" drugs of medical history are still mysterious. Mercury, known for forty-five centuries, "has always been a storm center of therapeutics," according to Stokes, "praised as a panacea in one generation only to be relegated to obscurity in the next."[1] Quinine, to quote Hackett, "is a drug which physicians have used for three hundred years without coming to any consensus of opinion as to proper dosage, method of administration, length of treatment, pharmacological action, effective results, or prophylactic value, either individually or socially."[2] Old and new drugs alike must be handled empirically, for little is known about the way in which they work.

The disease in which chemical treatment most clearly serves the purpose of the epidemiologist is syphilis. Finding the infectious host and making him non-infectious by drug therapy is about all he can do to control the frail and brutal spirochete. From the time of the great European epidemic at the end of the fifteenth century to our own day, mercury was the doctor's main reliance in treating syphilis, though it poisoned the human body so readily that patients murmured "better the disease than the remedy." Recently other chemical agents have pushed mercury into the background—Ehrlich's salvarsan (called arsphenamine in the United States), and bismuth. None fulfills the old dream of a curative agent so powerful that a single dose would rid the body of infection; treatment is tedious and uncomfortable.* But these drugs do cure syphilis often enough to be a powerful weapon in restricting the spread of the disease.

Quinine is the classic remedy for malaria, but epidemiologists have reluctantly come to the conclusion that it cannot be trusted to exterminate the parasites. Nor do the modern synthetic substitutes, atebrin and plasmoquine, quite fill the bill. Plasmoquine, it is true, kills or inactivates the parasites when they are ripe to pass from the infected man into the mosquito, but it is dangerous in large doses and costly for widespread use. Modern treatment, juggling drugs and dosages to deal with different strains and stages of parasitism, can keep the individual from disabling disease; it has not solved the problem of breaking the endless chain of infection.

It was not until 1935 that a German pathologist reported that a dark red dye, belonging to a series long known for its penetrating qualities, would protect mice against death from virulent streptococci. This was startling news for two reasons: drugs had seemed to work much better against protozoa or spirochetes than against ordinary bacteria, and medicine had almost no defense against the streptococcus. English physicians tried the new drug, called prontosil,† on women suffering from puerperal fever, and

---

* Present methods of medication take at least eight to ten months. Under an alternative plan, still experimental, the patient is put to bed in hospital and the drug drips into his veins more or less continuously during his waking hours for five to seven days.

† Terminology, in the new pharmacology, is exact and ugly. Prontosil is the hydrochloride of 4-sulfamido-2′, 4′-diaminoazobenzene; prontosil soluble is the disodium salt of 2-(4′-sulfamido-phenylazo)-7-acetylamino-1-hydroxynaphthalene-3, 6-disulfonic acid. Compare this sort of thing with

reported their results almost jubilantly in the sober pages of the *Lancet*. Doctors everywhere began to test the new remedy and its active component, sulfanilamide, against maladies long thought to be hopeless or known to be stubbornly resistant to other treatment: for the first time in the history of the St. Louis Children's Hospital, for example, they saved the life of a child with a clear-cut streptococcus meningitis. They found that sulfanilamide seemed to work not only against the streptococcus but also against the meningococcus and gonococcus. Such results led to an outburst of experimentation with related compounds: one called sulfapyridine gave striking results in pneumonia.

No doubt these are life-saving drugs. Whether they will also check the spread of the diseases they cure remains to be seen. It happens that the streptococcus, the pneumococcus, and the meningococcus are all kept in circulation by slightly ill or symptom-free carriers rather than by the acutely ill, and are all capable of causing serious distress—even if they do not kill. It seems likely that the use of sulfanilamide and sulfapyridine against these three common parasites will still leave the epidemiologist plenty to do.

With gonococcal infections the case is different. These, like syphilis, must be checked, if at all, by cure of the infectious patient. Hitherto cure has been so difficult and uncertain that there has been no great incentive for the patient to make himself known to a doctor, and gonorrhea has smouldered everywhere without adequate recognition or treatment. Now that sulfanil-

one of Sydenham's formulae: "*Take of the conserve of* Roman *wormwood, of rosemary, and of* Venice *treacle, each one ounce; of the conserve of orange-peel, of candied angelica and nutmeg, each half an ounce; syrup of cloves, enough to make the whole into an electuary; of which let the quantity of a nutmeg be taken twice a day, drinking after each dose a small draught of* canary, *wherein* cowslip flowers *have been infused cold.*" Such a prescription need only be read to the patient: so lovely a cadence should be soothing even *in extremis.*

169

amide gives promise of quick and definite relief, this particular obstacle is removed. Unfortunately, however, it has been found that in some dosages sulfanilamide puts an end to symptoms without rooting out the gonococcus, turning the frankly sick into carriers. Here too the worth of the drug in preventing infection is still in the balance.

Trying to poison parasites without injuring the host is difficult business at best, often involving discomfort if not danger to the patient, and sometimes leading to curious results. By feeding himself small doses of poison—not quite enough to kill—Mithridates in Housman's poem worked up a degree of tolerance which made him indifferent when his friends "poured strychnine in his cup." Too conservative doses of lethal drugs, often repeated, may have the same effect on disease organisms: pneumococci have already been made resistant to sulfapyridine in experiments of this sort. Dudley makes the cheering observation that "it would appear possible to produce, by the mass treatment of a human herd, reservoirs of drug-resistant parasites from which the previously curable disease could be re-spread, but now in an incurable form."[3] Truly, as Colebrook and Kenny say (though in another connection), the appraisal of curative effect "is a matter of fine judgment, instructed by long experience."

Many workers have hoped that drug therapy could be freed from its dependence on mother wit and empiricism. A fresh effort to bring this about is based on an elegant deduction. All things turn to dust (the argument runs); if they did not, there would be no room for us in the litter of the past. The crucible of dissolution is the soil, its agents the micro-organisms. The soil then must hold living creatures fit for every kind of chemical reaction that the dissolution of once-living matter requires, and by proper search one should be able to find in it an agent for any specific task within this range of natural phenomena.

Ten years ago Avery and Dubos poured a solution of capsular

stuff from Type III pneumococci into mud chosen from a place where the soil was rich in carbohydrates and eventually coaxed out of the mud a bacterium capable of breaking down the carbohydrate capsule of the Type III pneumococcus and too fastidious to do the same chemical labor on any other type. A year or two ago Dubos turned again to the soil to find a micro-organism capable of destroying whole races of bacteria—all those that stain alike when the Gram technique* is used, including the pneumococci, the streptococci, the staphylococci, the diphtheria bacilli, and others. He watered a soil sample with a mixture of such bacteria, kept it under conditions favorable for bacterial growth, and waited; then by the usual methods combed out a species of bacillus, previously unknown, that mortally injured the Gram-positive bacteria. The killing substance which it released— not a protein but oddly related to the proteins†—blocked just one of the enzyme systems by which the bacteria functioned, the one responsible for oxidizing foodstuffs, but that was enough to kill them.

The purified lethal substance, gramicidin, is not yet either a preventive or a cure for the diseases caused by Gram-positive organisms. Five-thousandths of a milligram injected into the belly of a mouse protects the mouse against 10,000 fatal doses of Type I pneumococcus subsequently injected in the same way. But since it is insoluble it works only at the point of injection and will not spread through the blood-stream. Moreover it poisons dogs and is far from ready for experimental use on human beings. The clear possibility remains, however, that some form

* All bacteria can be divided into two groups: those that keep an aniline-iodine stain when washed in alcohol (Gram-positive) and those that lose it (Gram-negative). Various organisms attacking Gram-negative bacteria were subsequently found by similar methods at another laboratory.

† Its constituent parts, fewer than there would be in a proper protein molecule, were "unnatural amino acids," that is, mirror images of normal components of protein.

of this substance may be developed into an antibacterial weapon much more powerful than anything now available.

Whether this happens or not, the bacteriologist has a new tool for studying the peculiar vulnerability of the Gram-positive bacteria in their natural state, and a fresh incentive to work out the peculiarities of structure or appetite or chemical conditioning that make them Gram-positive. Armed with such knowledge, he may be able to put his hand on other weapons, safer or more convenient, with which to attack them. This is the road to rational as distinct from trial-and-error chemotherapy.

If the use of drugs to cure disease is still opportunistic, the use of serum is beautifully logical. It is an effort to make up a deficit in the sick man's own antibody production by borrowing antibodies from another animal.* These antibodies may be aimed directly at the invading organism, as in the case of pneumonia and meningococcus meningitis, or at the toxin which it produces, as in the case of diphtheria and tetanus. The horse is the animal usually chosen as the lender: it has a body large enough to yield generous quantities of blood, a smooth skin for the needle, and a tractable disposition. Since nature, like a careful engineer, operates with a considerable factor of safety, the horse repeatedly inoculated with the appropriate antigen makes more antibody than he needs; the excess can be recovered by bleeding and by refining the output. Horses grow old in such service, yielding up crop after crop of antibody, and even the timorous rabbit, sometimes used for the same purpose, can stand repeated bleedings through the heart wall, receiving in return an abundant ration and a degree of sanitary attention which must astonish him.

* Serum therapy must be distinguished from vaccine therapy. The former looks to the importation of ready-made antibodies. The latter looks to the increased production of antibodies by the sick body itself, on the hair-of-the-dog-that-bit-him principle. One injects organisms of the same kind as those causing the trouble and hopes that they will somehow stimulate the body to a sharper response. Vaccines are far more useful in prevention than in cure.

Now antibody is not something extraneous to the body which makes it; if it comes from a horse, it is horse stuff, if from a rabbit, rabbit stuff. The protein stuff of which one animal is made frequently causes disturbance when it is injected into a different kind of animal, and therefore serum treatment like chemotherapy has its own special drawbacks. The discomfort of serum sickness, and occasional graver risks, are the price we pay for borrowed protection.

Serum therapy is a dramatic effort to overcome infection which has a head start and which, unchecked, may lead to death. If used soon enough after infection has taken place, it works bedside miracles, but it does not stop the spread of infection through the crowd. Indeed, the serum used in diphtheria controls the poisonous products of the bacilli but does not suppress the bacilli themselves, so that the child whose life is saved may become a carrier and infect other children. Serum therapy is small help to the epidemiologist.

Surgery, too, is concerned chiefly with cure of the individual for his own sake. It is true that a great part of the tissue damage which the surgeon tries to mop up and control is due to infection, but the tissue he cuts away is more likely to be feeding poison into the patient's own system than to be scattering micro-organisms abroad. There are two interesting exceptions, however. In the persistent typhoid carrier the parasites often settle down in the gall-bladder, where they multiply freely and send their offspring out by way of the bowel to make fresh conquests. In a considerable percentage of cases removal of the gall-bladder rids the carrier of infection, and in some states public health funds are available to pay the costs of such a surgical coup as a means of preventing further distribution of the bacilli. But the operation is too serious to be lightly advised and may be unsafe in the later years of life, so that the health officer with a carrier to control must usually be satisfied with less drastic measures. In diphtheria the carrier state is usually transient, which is fortunate for the health officer, as the occasional convalescent who harbors the bacilli indefinitely is a baffling problem.* Sometimes the parasites colonize the tonsils and are concentrated there; in such cases tonsillectomy may serve the same purpose as removal of the gall-bladder in typhoid carriers. Otherwise there is little or nothing to be done.

Surgery is significant also as a means of inducing rest. The dog or cat on the hearth knows by instinct that rest is healing; Hippocrates knew it by observation; modern medicine is shot through with this principle. Rest in bed is the basic treatment of most diseases, but rest in the therapeutic sense means not merely husbanding energy in general, but relaxing the injured part of the body. The surgeon splints an infected leg; by-passes an irritated duodenum; collapses a diseased lung.

* An English health officer is engagingly frank about the difficulties of making the diphtheria carrier non-infectious: "We exclude the carrier, isolate him at home, taking care not to visit the home too often for fear of finding out that he is in intimate contact with his brothers and sisters. Occasionally, but rarely we take him to the Infectious Diseases Hospital. Daily or twice daily (oftener in hospital), according to our energy, we spray his throat and nose with the various nostra which energetic firms manufacturing disinfectants, chemical and bacterial, press upon us, in the hope that we will kill the K.L.B. [virulent diphtheria bacillus] before we destroy the mucous linings of the nose and throat. We do not take swabs to find the presence of carriers amongst the contacts of carriers, for that would mean a conflict between an aesthetically satisfying scheme of prevention, and an impossible scheme. Should our 'hope-springs-eternal-in-the-human-breast' scheme fail to produce a negative swab, we do a virulence test, praying vigorously that it will be negative. It is, however, often positive. Then we gouge out the tonsils, ventilate the antra with drainage holes, slit the nasal septum, and generally hand over the child to the ear, nose and throat surgeon. Eventually, sometimes sooner, sometimes later, the child becomes negative, we wipe our brows and return the child to school. We have far too much intelligence to search vigorously for contacts, for we know very well what we shall find—far more carriers than we can deal with."—Paul, Hugh, M.D., D.P.H., Present practice in regard to quarantine and disinfection, *Public Health*, 7:203–206, April 1938.

Here we touch a point of vital interest to the epidemiologist. In tuberculosis it is the open lesion—the lung ulcer—that sheds micro-organisms into the sputum and so releases them for circulation among the crowd. This process may go on for years, subjecting the sick man's family to heavy risk. To bring it to an end, the lesions must be healed. No drug or serum accomplishes this, and the doctor can do little more than see to it that the body has complete rest and the nourishment it needs to work out its own salvation. Recently the physician has learned how to encourage the healing process by enforcing rest still more specifically on the infected lung itself. The method most used is to puncture the chest wall and admit air to the space between it and the lung, cushioning that lung against expansion when the chest is lifted, and reducing the inrush and outflow of breath that normally keep lung tissue busy. This gives the tissue a holiday in which the body's healing mechanisms may work upon it with a minimum of interruption. If the damage caused by the bacillus has not gone too far, such a respite may permit the centers of infection to be walled off, so that the sick man ceases to shed micro-organisms and may be able to go back to a relatively normal life without danger to his associates.

So much for cure as a means of making the giver non-infectious. Death has the same effect: if the giver dies, his parasites ordinarily die with him. In civil life we cannot bring ourselves to kill each other for the safety of the herd (except in the case of that obscure malady crime) but we can exterminate lower animals which threaten us by shedding micro-organisms to which we are vulnerable.

The ways and means vary, of course, with the value of the animal. It has taken twenty years of education and legislation, sweetened by bounties for slaughtered animals, to bring the United States to the point where it is virtually free of bovine tuberculosis. More than 200,000,000 tests have been made, and approximately 4,000,000 infected animals have been sacrificed.* A similar campaign is on foot against *Brucella* infections, which make cattle abort and may cause undulant fever in human beings, but this infection spreads rapidly and lingers stubbornly and will be with us for a long time.

When the infectious animal is not property but a pest the health officer turns to massacre, killing the innocent with the guilty. In plague-ridden districts the slaughter of rats becomes a routine protection. In 1935—not a very bad plague year—the public health commissioner reported the killing in India and Burma of exactly 5,350,003 rats.† Rats, to be sure, do not stay massacred: the race is hardy, prolific, and peripatetic. They must be kept at a distance by rat-proofing of buildings and ships, and stopped at ports of entry by a species of quarantine, but these

---

* Yankee ingenuity was quick to grasp the possibilities of this situation. Early in the campaign certain cattle dealers in the Connecticut valley bought up condemned cattle by the carload, plugged them with old tuberculin which masked their infection temporarily, and scattered them artistically about dairy farms. When the effects of the tuberculin had worn off, they asked to have their herds tested. Of course the infected cows were once more condemned and the second bounty found its way into the speculator's pocket. Better technique in the tuberculin test has put an end to this fraud.

† A well-organized campaign in Guayaquil, Ecuador, in 1929 and 1930 led to the death of some 172,000 rats and helped to end twenty years of plague. It is interesting as an illustration of the careful investigation which parallels mass slaughter. Twenty-five thousand rats caught in traps were examined for evidences of infection, and two workers took 29,000 fleas from 5,000 rats for identification of their species and sex. At first the trapped rats were drowned and then searched for fleas. The difficulties of this procedure are reported with beautiful candor: "Live fleas were frequently found on the dead wet rats, and some of them eluded the searcher, not only entailing the loss of the fleas, but also subjecting the workers to the possibility of being the hosts of plague-carrying fleas. It required much time properly to search a wet rat for fleas, and after three or four hours the searcher becomes tired and careless." Later rats and fleas were killed together by poison gas and the fleas safely combed out. *Public Health Reports*, 45:2077–2115, 2880–2887, September 5 and November 21, 1930.

precautions lead us beyond the scope of our first category—curing or killing the host as a means of checking the spread of infection.

## ISOLATING THE GIVER

And the leper in whom the plague is, his clothes shall be rent, and the hair of his head shall go loose, and he shall cover his upper lip, and shall cry, Unclean, unclean. All the days wherein the plague is in him he shall be unclean; he is unclean; he shall dwell alone; without the camp shall his dwelling be.[4]

There is a great gulf between the tragic cadences of Hebrew law and the lenient regulations of modern household quarantine, but the principle involved is the same—a persistent and, on the whole, futile hope that the community can keep its skirts clear of infection by casting out or shutting up the sick. On an earlier page this defensive maneuver was called putting a fence around the giver: the expression was figurative, but as recently as 1935 a wooden fence was actually built, under official direction, around a house in New Orleans where a case of diphtheria was thought to be threatening a school next door. The tradition dies hard.

Leprosy is preeminently the disease which men have tried to control in this way. In medieval Europe, when leprosy was widespread, one found lazar-houses* everywhere—two thousand of

* Named for Lazarus, the beggar "full of sores" who lay at the rich man's gate in the New Testament parable. But the easy-going medieval mind, in fine confusion, also made the Lazarus who was the friend of Jesus the patron saint of lepers. This association, Creighton says, did much for the "prestige" of leprosy; it "brought all persons full of sores within a nimbus of sanctity"; they were "Christ's poor." It was therefore a virtuous act to care for them. At the same time, though there was little clear thinking about contagion, the lepers "were, to say the least, undesirable companions." The word leprosy, in medieval as in biblical times, was apparently used for many skin conditions and probably also for syphilis. It would be a mistake to think of the lazar-houses as pest-houses pure and simple; they seem to have been intended, in large part, for the ailing poor in general.

177

them in France alone. Today, knowing not much more than Moses did about the way leprosy spreads, we still rely chiefly on segregation to control it, though we soften the sentence of exile with meliorating devices like parole. Old associations would make us shrink from a leper if we saw one, but in fact the disease is not easily spread from one person to another except in long-continued intimate contacts, and even then its communicability seems to vary with the geographical setting, so that a leper on Fifth Avenue might be quite harmless and one on Canal Street, New Orleans, or in the tropics generally, a source of real danger.* We can hardly suppose that segregation alone made leprosy leave Europe free—or nearly so—in the fourteenth and fifteenth centuries, and have no assurance that segregation is diminishing its prevalence today.

Both leprosy and tuberculosis are transmitted at close quarters by people who are infectious for a long time, and of the two, at least in the temperate zone, tuberculosis is the more dangerous. But while the fear of "catching" leprosy may have led to the leprosarium, it was not a like fear of tuberculosis that led to the sanatorium. That was established as a place for treatment before tuberculosis was generally recognized as a highly communicable disease.

The pest-house was the more direct descendant of the lazar-house. At times of special danger pest-houses for explosive diseases—smallpox, yellow fever, cholera—were thought to be civic necessities. They gave rise to bitter controversy: learned investigators proved to their own satisfaction that smallpox spread from them—presumably by air, though in some cases even against the wind—but the evidence did not stand critical examination. In the nineteenth century in England fever hospitals were expected to put an end to scarlet fever and diphtheria. They did not do so.

* A sprightly account of thirty lepers going about their business in New York will be found in—of all places—*The New Yorker* for March 12, 1938.

Turning the Englishman's castle into a pest-house when any-one in the house was so unlucky as to catch the plague was standard procedure in the great London epidemics: sick and well were shut up together and if Defoe is to be believed cruel hardships resulted. The blue or red cross on the door barred the inmates from nearly all human contact. Nowadays household quarantine has been whittled down to a set of mild and often flexible restrictions (sometimes signalized by a printed sign tacked up beside the door) designed not so much to segregate the patient himself as to control the community contacts of other members of his family, who may be in the incipient or carrier stages of infection. It is important, of course, to separate the patient from susceptible persons; this too is a flexible procedure, ranging from fairly rigorous isolation in smallpox to tying a yellow band around the arm of a child with whooping cough and turning him loose to play by himself in his own backyard. Isolation may be as important for the sick person as for those still well: fewer children die of measles when care is taken to keep them separate from other children or adults who might share pneumococci or streptococci with them and so make their last state worse than their first.

The less we know about a disease, the more likely we are to push the sick person away with a vague gesture of fear; witness the clamor, when a case of poliomyelitis is reported, for all sorts of restrictions which in point of fact may be quite useless. The more we know, the more we sharpen our definition of isolation. So the really significant change which has taken place in the past generation is that isolation has become selective: instead of incarcerating the patient, we put only those barriers around him which are called for by the way his disease spreads. Thus if he has malaria we put him behind screens where no mosquito can tap his infected blood. If he has typhoid fever, we disinfect his excreta. If he has tuberculosis, we burn his sputum. If he has trachoma, we insist on his using his own towel to wipe his face and hands. If he has any of the diseases spread by personal discharges, we see to it that those who wait on him sterilize their hands and change their clothing before mingling with others.

The weight of experience has indicated that children with acute infections can be cared for side by side in the hospital with reasonable safety if some slight barrier is put between one bed and another and if the nurse and doctor disinfect themselves meticulously every time they pass the barrier. Still puzzling cross-infections sometimes occur, and what is now known of airborne infection throws some doubt on the adequacy of this technique. A curtain of ultraviolet light* may be a desirable addition to the barrier. On such a basis of selective isolation the pesthouse, so far as it survives at all, has moved into the hospital.

Isolation, theoretically attractive, and now more skilfully applied than it used to be, still fails as a community safeguard because one cannot find, much less shut away, enough of the people who are actually capable of giving infection to others. The obviously sick may be few beside the inconspicuously sick or the apparently healthy carriers. Carriers are not only hard to find but hard to discourage. A child carrying virulent diphtheria bacilli, found in suspicious proximity to a known case, may be kept out of school. A typhoid carrier can be forbidden to handle food for others; this bears hard on some who live by the practice of cookery—like the late Typhoid Mary, of dismal fame—but most carriers in such a situation prefer losing their jobs to losing their gall-bladders and the restriction is certainly a reasonable one. Some desultory efforts have been made to keep carriers of the dysentery-producing ameba out of like occupations. Little has been done in other carrier-borne diseases. The epidemiologist isolates the giver so far as he can, but he must have other strings to his bow.

* To be considered more fully on page 185.

## CUTTING COMMUNICATIONS

Isolation is designed to keep the man known to be sick from communicating his sickness to someone else. In certain types of disease the epidemiologist can cut communications on a broader scale: without knowing who is sick, or where, he can interpose a barrier between givers-if-any and takers-if-any. Moreover he can keep this barrier up all the time; he need not wait till sickness strikes: he can forestall it.

Cutting communications is possible when the micro-organisms in question spend an appreciable amount of time in transit from one human host to another. It has been most successful as a defense against micro-organisms that travel in water, travel and multiply in milk, or spend part of their life cycle in an insect host.

The bacteria that survive a Rhine-journey down the water-courses from one man's intestine to another's gullet—those, in particular, that cause typhoid fever, bacillary dysentery, and cholera—are vulnerable at any point of their extra-corporeal travel, but most accessible when they pass through the artificial channels of a city water supply. Here they can be strained out of the water by filtration or killed in it by chemical treatment, usually with chlorine.* This is all but universal practice today in civilized urban and semi-urban communities.

It was not so yesterday, however. The ancient Romans, drawing clean water from the hills by gravity, did better in this respect than our immediate forefathers. The cities of the nineteenth century, with steam pumps at their disposal, often took the water nearest at hand, though it came from the same river into which they dumped their sewage. There was an easy-going assumption that running streams purified themselves, but nature

* The cysts of *Endamoeba histolytica*, the cause of amebic dysentery, are not harmed by chlorination that destroys bacteria.

will not hurry even for the Board of Aldermen, and the task that London or Hamburg or Pittsburgh laid on her was impossible. The water of one American city was described thus:

> The appearance and quality of the public water supply were such that the poor used it for soup, the middle-class dyed their clothes in it, and the very rich used it for top-dressing their lawns. Those who drank it, filtered it through a ladder, disinfected it with chloride of lime, then lifted out the dangerous germs which survived and killed them with a club in the backyard.[5]

The great urban cholera and typhoid epidemics of the nineteenth century were a logical consequence of practices that no well-bred house-cat would countenance.

England and Germany led the way in water purification, but Hamburg had more than eight thousand deaths from cholera transmitted in raw river water as late as 1892. It was not until the turn of the century that American cities generally began to filter their supplies, with dramatic results. In Pittsburgh, one of the worst offenders, the average annual death rate from typhoid fever toppled from 132 to 19 per 100,000 when filtration was inaugurated. The running fight for pure water in the cities was largely over before the first world war, and typhoid fever, though still common enough in rural regions with a low standard of living, has never since been a dominant threat to American health.*

In milk—that "vital and vexing" food, as Bigelow called it— many bacteria can travel and some can multiply. Some come from the cow herself, some from the people who handle the milk. Here too parasites in transit are vulnerable.

* It is worth repeating that it is not filth, but a particular infective organism in the water that breeds disease. Typhoid bacilli are present in water only when they have come from a carrier or case of typhoid fever. Usually one cannot find them there by bacteriological tests, so one hunts instead for *B. coli*, a generally harmless parasite of the human intestine. If one finds *B. coli* there is sewage in the water, and where sewage goes typhoid bacilli can go too.

Antibacterial defenses in the milk-vat, like those in the public reservoir, are still new. All through the nineties the pediatricians and public health men were fighting the battle for clean milk— that is, milk free of the dung and associated filth which ladies and gentlemen (not yet extinct) had been drinking for years without question. Not till the next decade did the public and the milkmen become convinced that milk must be not only physically clean but free of disease-producing bacteria, and that pasteurization was desirable and feasible. Indeed some milk dealers learned their lesson before their customers and pasteurized their milk secretly. But by 1936, it is estimated, 83 per cent of the milk sold in cities of more than 10,000 was pasteurized.

The beauty of pasteurization is that it gives blanket protection against the accidents that may upset the most careful routines of milk production. Tuberculous cows have been largely weeded out of American dairy herds, and cows with *Brucella* infections, still numerous, are gradually being disposed of in like fashion. Known carriers of typhoid bacilli can be kept out of dairies. Utensils can be sterilized. Milk can be promptly covered and cooled. But diphtheria bacilli or hemolytic streptococci from the sore throat of an otherwise healthy milker may be coughed into the milk, or planted in it by a careless thumb, or rubbed into the cow's udder, which, once infected, sheds myriads of organisms into the milk-pail. The streptococcus sometimes sets off an epidemic of septic sore throat, the most explosive of all milk-borne infections. In 1928 this seized upon one out of every four people in Lee, Massachusetts, and killed one out of every hundred. Pasteurization coupled with scrupulous care of milk after it is pasteurized is the only effective defense against such perils.*

* The connection between raw milk and epidemics is clearest in the diseases mentioned. Increase in pasteurization has also been associated with a marked decrease of infant deaths from "summer diarrhea," but a number of other factors, including better pediatric practice, are probably at work here.

Thanks to chlorination of water and pasteurization of milk we no longer expect to have typhoid fever or cholera and few of us encounter septic sore throat. But against "flu," colds, and pneumonia, and other infections carried on the air we breathe, our defenses are feeble indeed. We can sometimes cure pneumonia; we cannot do even that for colds or influenza, but can only wait to get well. Isolation is futile, for the micro-organisms are ubiquitous. Can we cut communications through the air?

This is what the forefathers were trying to do when they lit bonfires in the street, or smoked cigars, or sniffed at camphor to save themselves from plague or yellow fever.* This is what

---

* Personal fumigation went to great lengths, if one is to believe the verses circulated by Hartford newsboys on New Year's Day, 1793, and now preserved in the collection of the New York Historical Society:

> And lo! where, o'er the eastern shores,
> BOSTONIA lifts her haughty towers,
> What motly scenes salute our eyes!
> There each succeeding day still brings
> A mixture strange of various things,
> Small-pox, Physicians, State-intriguers,
> John Hancock's speeches, flags, and negroes.
> There, where volcano-like, on high
> Thick clouds of vapor blot the sky,
> Goes on the purifying work,
> Where men are smoked in place of pork;
> Lest dire infection should expand
> Her fatal venom o'er the land;
> For smoke, 'tis said, in certain cases,
> As well as bacon, *cures* diseases.
> Besides, how delicate, and neat!
> What luxury in such a treat!
> How grateful to the *gentle* throng,
> Whose nerves more tenderly are strung,
> To stand and sweat an hour or two,
> 'Till fumigated thro' and thro'!

Someone, apparently in a contemporary hand, has written in the margin: "They really did smoak the passangers in the Stage to prevent the spread of small pox."

184

Lister was trying to do when he sprayed carbolic acid about an open wound in the operating room.* After his day doctors and public health men lost interest in air-borne infection and even, as we have seen, denied its importance. This was just as well, for they had tremendous jobs to do in cleaning up water and milk supplies, babies' bottles, mosquito hatcheries, and the like. Now that these grosser problems are less troublesome, new techniques have made it profitable to think seriously again about infection through the air.

One can kill many kinds of disease-producing organisms in the air by irradiation with ultraviolet light. The most effective waves for this purpose, rather shorter than those used for artificial "sun-tanning," are thrown off by a mercury vapor arc light housed in quartz or special glass. Where the pale bluish light is strongest, the bacteria die almost instantaneously; where it is weaker the lethal effect is slower. A lamp or lamps of sufficient strength, strategically placed, can throw a defensive curtain of light between babies in a nursery or patients in a hospital ward, or presumably, keep the air of an operating room or schoolroom reasonably free of infective organisms. Experiments now under way should soon indicate whether sterilizing the air in this way materially reduces cross-infection. The cutting of communications through the air is just beginning; its technique and strategy must be worked out; its importance remains to be demonstrated.

Checking the insect-borne diseases calls for different strategy. Parasites travel in water, milk, or air, but need not do so if other vehicles, such as food or fingers, are available. The parasites that cause yellow fever or malaria, on the other hand, are wholly dependent on the mosquito for the transfer from host to host

---

* Lister's practice was a logical application of what Pasteur had learned, and though it was presently abandoned as an unnecessary refinement it was sound in principle. While asepsis in the operating room is mostly a matter of sterile field, instruments, and materials, there is some residual danger by way of the air to which surgeons are again giving attention.

which makes their survival possible.* Instead of attacking the parasites directly, we try, by destroying their means of travel, to leave them stranded in the blood-stream of their diminishing victims.

The name of Gorgas is firmly linked with the thesis that the way to exterminate yellow fever is to exterminate the mosquito that carries it. It was Gorgas, after Reed showed the way, who made this thesis work in Havana and later at Panama. In Havana he and his men searched gutters and puddles; screened and oiled cisterns and water barrels; card-catalogued every pot and pitcher; persuaded casual Cuban housewives to empty little jugs every day; and so, for practical purposes, rid the town of *Aedes aegypti*. Meanwhile they put yellow fever patients behind screens as soon as they were found, and held ships at quarantine to prevent the importation of fresh infection. The results were amazing: in 1896 there had been 1,282 deaths from yellow fever; in 1900 there were 310, in 1901 eighteen, in 1902 none. Gorgas had abruptly ended a century and a half of yellow fever in Havana.† In Panama, when bureaucratic stupidity permitted, he did likewise, and so made it possible to dig the canal.

Rio de Janeiro, New Orleans, Vera Cruz demonstrated in turn the worth of Gorgas' methods. In 1916 a commission organized by the Rockefeller Foundation and headed by Gorgas reported that yellow fever could be wiped out from the American continent. By 1925 the continental total of reported cases had fallen to three. Yellow fever in the cities was controlled by controlling the mosquitoes that carried it. When water supplies went underground and the cisterns and buckets in which the

---

* There may be some other insect vector in jungle yellow fever. By design (in fever therapy) or by accident (as in transfusions) malaria can also be transmitted directly from person to person in human blood.

† It was only fair that an American should do Havana this service: American troops (then colonials) may have carried the infection to Havana in 1762.

*Aedes aegypti* bred disappeared, much of the danger from yellow fever automatically and permanently vanished.

Malaria is different. The dominant vector of yellow fever hugs human houses; cannot fly far; dies out in cold winters, leaving only uninfected eggs. A score or more of different kinds of *Anopheles* carry malaria; all breed in the open, some in standing water, some in running streams, some in fresh, some in salty water, some in sun, some in shade; some species can fly two, three, even eight miles; some can hibernate. What works against one may fail against another. American officers in the Philippines, trained to mistrust marshes, encamped their troops in the hills—which turned out to be the worst possible place, since the local malaria-carrying mosquitoes bred in upland streams. On a Malay seacoast clearing the jungle kept mosquitoes away, for they loved the shade; ten miles inland, clearing the jungle made mosquitoes multiply, for there they loved the sun. Jig-saw Europe is harassed by various marauding species, the principal offender, *maculipennis*, being a regular big bad wolf among his kind—large, impudent, strong-winged, and winter-seasoned. The United States is more fortunate: except on the western coast the epidemiologist can safely ignore all species but one, *quadrimaculatus*,* which is dangerous chiefly within a mile of its breeding place. An invader from Africa, *A. gambiae*, has been making alarming gains in Brazil since its appearance in 1930. This species carries malaria so efficiently and is so hard to control (breeding quickly in casual fresh-water pools) that, in the words of an observer on the firing-line, "this invasion . . . threatens the Americas with a catastrophe in comparison with which ordinary pestilence, conflagration and even war are but small and temporary calamities."[6]

---

* That is, four-spotted, named for the pattern on the wings. Except as a person with ankles, the epidemiologist is not concerned with the many species that do not spread disease.

Whatever the species, the best way to get the mosquito out of a given malaria situation is to make it impossible for the females to lay their eggs anywhere within flight range of the place to be protected. Breeding places can be eliminated by drying them up —this has been done at points in the Pontine Marshes in Italy, where malaria is being driven from a stronghold of centuries— or by changing their character so as to make them distasteful to mosquitoes. Thus a great lagoon which used to make life miserable in Durazzo was rid of appalling numbers of mosquitoes by letting in enough sea-water to discourage both fresh and brackish water breeders. Our own *quadrimaculatus* is thwarted by ditching which makes standing water run freely.

Failing this, there are various ways of killing larvae or wigglers. One can simply poison them, usually by dusting Paris green on the water by hand, from a boat, or even from an aeroplane—a bold gesture found practical in the mosquito control service of the Tennessee Valley Authority. Or one can simultaneously suffocate and poison them by oiling the waters. Or one can import enemies to eat them up. An insignificant minnow, voracious and hardy, which is native to the Florida Everglades and goes by the name of *gambusia*, has become a citizen of the world because it eats wigglers so greedily.

The subtlest way of killing wigglers in impounded water is tinkering with the water-level. Without vegetation or the floating debris of vegetation, the wiggler lacks both food and shelter. The vegetable matter attracts and harbors the minute creatures on which he feeds, and smoothes out the little waves which might drown him. If wavelets and fish can break and nuzzle, respectively, against a clean bank, his doom is sealed. Alternately raising and lowering the water helps to make this possible. When the water slides up the shore it carries debris with it and drives land plants back; when it slides down again it leaves the debris —and some larvae—behind. If this cycle can be completed at least once in every ten-day wiggler lifetime, few mosquitoes will come to maturity.

We pass rapidly by the control problems which other insects create. Fly control is largely a function of general sanitation, and has ceased to be important in motorized cities. Plague fleas, and the rat fleas which occasionally spread endemic typhus in the United States, can hardly be dealt with apart from their hosts. There are adequate motives, other than epidemiological, for the extermination of bedbugs, which in fact seem to be guiltless as carriers of disease. Lice present a serious problem because of their association with epidemic typhus, but it would be a rash commentator who tried to add anything to Zinsser's account of that subject. The technique of delousing has been standardized, and "the mortality of lice" in the first world war, Zinsser says, "must have been the greatest in the history of the world." The fate of lice and men in eastern Europe, however, is yet to be revealed.

### ISOLATING THE TAKER

Locking the doors against disease is a forlorn hope, as Poe knew nearly a century ago when he wrote *The Masque of the Red Death*. One can, however, get behind certain fences that offer some protection when disease is abroad.

The skin itself, we have seen, is a barrier of sorts against the entrance of parasites. One can reinforce this barrier. Wearing shoes, for example, is a good way to shut out the hookworm, which usually enters the body from contaminated soil through the skin of the naked foot.* Wearing rubber gloves protects the

* While the larger parasites have not been considered in this book, the Odyssey of the hookworm is too good to leave out. It enters the foot, gets into the lymph channels, wriggles its way clear up to the thoracic duct, finds itself in the vein that feeds the heart, is pumped out with the blood into the lungs, gets stuck in the capillaries there, breaks through into the air passages, climbs the windpipe to the throat, is swallowed, goes down the gullet, and comes to rest in the intestines! And after all this it makes the host lazy!

hunter or the housewife as the rabbit with tularemia comes out
of the trap or goes into the pot; the same habit helps to safeguard the workman who handles hides, hair, or wool that may
not be free of anthrax. The doctor who treats syphilis in the
clinic wears gloves rather more to protect himself than to protect the patient. Certain mechanical contraceptives provide some
degree of isolation in sexual contact, and so add something to
the defenses against syphilis or gonorrhea. The doctor may
spray tannic acid over burned flesh to form a film that keeps out
wandering bacteria, and external dressings on wounds generally
have, in part, a similar function.

Masking the nose is less effective: the gauze that many people
wore during the influenza epidemic seems not only to have had
little effect in barring out the virus, but may actually have made
matters worse by interfering with normal function and so with
physiological resistance. A chemical spray to create a barrier at
the nerve endings in the nose has been used experimentally as a
protection against poliomyelitis, but the evidence for its usefulness is by no means clear.

Physical protection may sometimes be effective at a little
greater distance from the body. The trench which Congo natives
dig around their village to keep out the rats which carry plague,
and the rat-guards placed over the hawsers when ships lie in
port, are safeguards of this order, together with the more familiar screen that keeps out mosquitoes. The classic form of protection against flying pests is the bed-net, a fallible and uncomfortable device to which Europeans clung—both at home and in
the tropics—long after the Yankee had turned to the window-
screen as a more serviceable alternative. The protection of susceptibles by screening is rather more useful against malaria than
against yellow fever, for the *Anopheles* breeds outdoors and
comes indoors at night to bite, while the *Aedes* may breed indoors and bites by day. Unhappily screening is commoner in

non-malarious regions where it is merely a convenience than in fever-ridden communities where it is urgently needed. The Italians, realists where malaria is concerned, have made screening compulsory in the Campagna, and teach their children at school how to mend the screens.

There are two obstacles to general screening in malarious regions: the initial cost (which can be met by united effort: one Tennessee county screened 84 per cent of its rural homes in four years), and the difficulty of upkeep. The shiftless tenant farmer who just naturally kicks his way out of a screen door is a discouraging person to deal with, but health workers do not hesitate to build sanitary privies for him in spite of similar discouragements, and as Hackett says "All experiments prove that imperfect screening, no matter how bad, keeps out more anophelines than no screening at all."

Shutting susceptibles up to ward off all and sundry infections is not often feasible. The Dionnes, to be sure, have survived the hazards to which the circumstances of their birth exposed them, and that is a medical triumph, but they have not escaped the sniffles and their doctor thought it best to remove their infected tonsils. It is good practice to keep new-born babies in hospital behind glass through which their proud and slightly superfluous papas may peer harmlessly, and even in the relatively uncontrolled environment of the home the sterilization of nursing bottles and the like sets up a sort of deadline against the approach of intestinal parasites.

Anxious parents often feel, when measles or whooping cough or poliomyelitis is abroad, that their children would be safer in the bosom of the family than at school. Though the health officer may bow to public opinion and close the schools, he usually has little faith in such a step. If families live far apart, as in farming country, and children meet only at school, some good may be done if the school is closed promptly enough. If the community is well seeded with infection and children play freely with their neighbors little is to be gained by keeping them at home—or sending them to the movies. It is usually better not to try to segregate the susceptibles, but to examine children as they come to school and segregate those who seem to be infected. More ambitious interference with the ordinary movements of crowds—such as the closing of churches and theatres in the influenza pandemic of 1918—has been found ineffective.

Quarantine at seaports and airports is an effort to put a fence around an entire nation. It had its beginning in the attempt of the Italian merchant cities in the fourteenth and fifteenth centuries to keep plague at bay; travelers were detained for forty days (hence the word *quarantine*) to make sure they were harmless before they were admitted. Panic has sometimes sharpened its edge: travelers have been threatened indiscriminately with hanging or shooting,* and cautious Englishmen have burned ships from plague ports. Early attempts to keep yellow fever and cholera out of the United States came to nothing because no one knew enough about the way either disease was transmitted to apply quarantine intelligently. Quarantine always fails when carriers and mild cases slip through; it works only when infection can be recognized in marginal as well as frank forms. When cholera threatened New York again in 1911 federal quarantine accomplished its purpose: carriers and cases were screened out accurately by examining the stools of thousands of passengers and seamen, and the entry of the disease was blocked.

Quarantine is useful only when the infection to be shut out is exotic. There is no point in trying to exclude a disease already well domesticated, for then even healthy newcomers (as has been shown with mice in the laboratory) fan the epidemic flame. At best this sort of barrier may be a vexatious interference with trade and travel, and the tendency has been to make

* See pages 9 and 13.

it less and less onerous, more and more selective—a sieve or filter, as Rosenau says, and not a dam.*

Air travel, by jazzing the tempo of cross-migrations in the human herd, has laid fresh burdens on quarantine. In many parts of the world it is now possible for a man to board a plane with unsuspected infection in his blood, jump a continent or an ocean, and land in an uninfected country, ready to spread disease, before anyone knows he is sick. It may take six days for yellow fever to develop: Howard Hughes flew around the globe in less than four. Commercial airlines link Africa, where yellow fever lingers, and India, where it is still unknown. The steps taken to guard against this particular hazard will be considered in Chapter 8. A health worker in Central America suggests that the modern highway, inviting the peon as well as the plutocrat to go traveling, may come to be a more dangerous channel of infection than the airlane: it is harder to watch the roads than the airports.

Quarantine is a gallant effort, against considerable odds, to limit the prevalence of some diseases geographically. It cannot eradicate a disease from the human herd, and conservative authorities like Topley and Wilson believe that "under the conditions of modern transit, there seems little possibility of preventing the introduction into any one part of the inhabited world of any infective parasite which is prevalent in another."[7]

## REINFORCING THE TAKER'S RESISTANCE

Within limits we can guard ourselves against the attack of disease by sea and land, by water and perhaps by air. Here and there we can shut away the giver of infection or put a fence

* Federal quarantine in the United States applies to cholera, yellow fever, typhus, plague, smallpox, leprosy, and anthrax. Smallpox is by no means exotic, but quarantine is desirable to exclude more virulent strains than those prevalent here.

around the susceptibles. But like the robots in Čapek's *R.U.R.*, the parasites still come marching over the barriers in endless hordes. Our last defense is within the body itself, in the bloodstream and the tissues, which learned to deal with invaders to the best of their ability long before science arose, and will go on doing so even though man, in his present madness, succeeds in destroying all that he has learned. It is by finding ways to reinforce the body's resistance that epidemiologists have done some of their finest work.

The basic bargain which communicable disease offers is this: be sick and get over it, if you can, and you stand less chance of being sick in that particular way again. Only certain goods are offered on these terms; one cannot buy lasting immunity from pneumonia, or influenza, or colds in this fashion, but one can be pretty sure of value received in yellow fever, smallpox, measles. So men have tried in various ways to beat the devil around the stump, to cheat death by trafficking with infection.

Smallpox hung over our forefathers like death and taxes. Early in the eighteenth century, English physicians learned from the Greeks to inculcate smallpox deliberately, by pricking or rubbing infectious matter from a pustule into the skin, in the hope of giving the patient a mild attack which would protect him from the disease in its more vicious forms.* The technique ran the gamut from a Dutchman's delicate plan of rubbing a thread carrying infectious matter through a blister on the arm to an Englishman's heroic slashes in one arm and the opposite leg. Unfortunately it was hard to tell just what the result would be; it was generally thought that light infections resulted, but some inoculated persons died and others passed on the disease in natural form to their companions. There is little or no valid statistical evidence that the process diminished the prevalence

---

* Some Scots had a like habit of infecting children "by rubbing them with a kindly pock."

of the disease; many of those inoculated must have been already immune or highly resistant.

Reasoning of much the same sort bobbed up again, rather later than it should have done, when Walter Reed's work on yellow fever first took convincing form in Havana. It seemed a hopeless task to eradicate mosquitoes, and since most of the experimental infections in Reed's work had been mild, it occurred to Gorgas (as it had to Finlay) that if a well person deliberately let himself be bitten by a mosquito infected by a mild case he too might have a light case and become immune. A few volunteers liked the idea, but several of them died and the experiment was quickly brought to an end.

Short of actually exposing a person to disease, it is still possible to be less vigilant at one time than another. Measles, as universal today as smallpox used to be, is dangerous to young children and potentially dangerous to adults, but causes children of school age little trouble unless complications occur. The obvious strategy is to keep young children from having it at all, and to guard against complications in older children, but not to protect older children entirely lest they grow to maturity without immunity. Antibodies against the virus are contained in the human placenta, in the blood of persons newly recovered from the disease, and to some extent in the blood of the average adult. Administered to a child known to have been exposed to measles,* they temporarily stiffen his resistance. If given early after exposure they tend to prevent measles entirely—until the next time; if given later, but before the disease shows itself frankly, they tend to modify it so that illness is reduced and complications are rare. Yet this "modified measles" makes the child immune; the patient buys immunity at a bargain.

---

* The practical limitations of a procedure which depends upon knowing just when a child has definitely been exposed to measles are obvious. See, in this connection, page 291.

Some diseases can be definitely prevented. Freedom from smallpox has become as common as the fear of it used to be. For this we have to thank the cow, in which smallpox is replaced by a mild local infection traditionally called cowpox and now renamed vaccinia. It would be superfluous to recall Jenner and his work; the essential point in vaccination is that the human host deliberately submits himself to a mild disease which leaves him immune against a more threatening one. Vaccination induces an attack of cowpox, and experience leaves no reasonable doubt that it protects against smallpox. From 1933 to 1937 the thirteen American states with compulsory vaccination laws had a yearly average of 0.57 reported cases of smallpox per 100,000 population, while twenty-two states in which vaccination was left entirely to personal initiative had 14.1 cases per 100,000. Those who prefer smallpox to vaccinia are, of course, vociferous, but they are a vanishing tribe.

Smallpox vaccination is a rather special kind of immunization. We pass on to the more general formula, which is as elegant as anything in medicine. The parasite, we know, brings certain chemical stimuli called antigens to bear upon the cells and body fluids. These in turn react in a defensive way, and once having done so, are more or less conditioned to repeat the process if the same antigens turn up again. The problem then is to find antigens, not in themselves harmful under the circumstances in which they are given, to set the protective machinery in motion.

Most bacteria are of variable virulence: when young or well nourished, for instance, they are more dangerous than when old or starved. Pasteur stumbled on the principle of immunization by noticing that old cultures of certain bacteria did not make chickens sick. The power of the parasite to exert antigenic influence may outlast its power to cause disease, or even its life, for the stuff of which bacteria are made sometimes continues to stimulate bodily responses after the bacteria are dead. One can then make parasites into vaccines* useful for preventive purposes by weakening them or killing them, the favorite lethal agents being heat and chemicals.

In its simplest aspect, then, active immunization consists of giving the body dead bacteria to practice on so that it forms habits of resistance which subsequently check the invasion of living bacteria of the same sort. Immunization with living bacteria, even when they have been artificially weakened, is playing with fire. Cattle and sheep are still vaccinated against anthrax in this fashion, but only in districts where anthrax is already common. The use of B.C.G.—a vaccine made of living tubercle bacilli—to protect babies against tuberculosis has been a subject of sharp controversy.

In the United States the most familiar example of the use of killed bacteria to prevent disease is inoculation against typhoid fever—a sorry practice at best, because it is a confession of failure in the decencies of sanitation. If something like two and a half billion bacilli which have been first carefully nurtured and then cooked to death are injected under the skin, the body acquires some degree of resistance to typhoid bacilli for the next year or two. It is hard to say just how much this resistance is worth, and experience shows that a mass attack will break it down. But gross figures—not too satisfactory to the careful statistician—suggest that the widespread use of this procedure in the first world war probably helped to keep the incidence of typhoid in the Allied forces at a remarkably low level.†

* *Vacca*, the cow, has nothing to do with most vaccines; the word carries over from vaccination against smallpox.

† In most parts of the country there is now more reason to seek protection against whooping cough than against typhoid fever. Vaccination against this disease is briefly discussed on page 291. I sidestep the vexed question of bacterial vaccination against the common cold, but commend readers interested in this procedure to two papers by Diehl, Baker, and Cowan in the *Journal of the American Medical Association* for September 24, 1938 (111:1168–1173) and August 24, 1940 (115:593–594). In a carefully controlled

In the Orient, where plague and cholera are still to be feared, vaccines have been used against both diseases for many years. The Japanese report good results in the prevention of cholera, the public health authorities of India in the prevention of plague. Both vaccines are made of heat-killed bacteria, and neither gives protection for longer than a few months or a year.

The formula runs afoul of difficulties when one tries to apply it to the pneumococcus. Here antigens vary from type to type within the species; each type has its individual chemical characteristics; protection against one may be valueless against another. So the doctor, if he lacks the gift of prophecy, must fill his gun with buckshot, guess which types are most likely to turn up, and try to hit all of them at once. After disappointing experience with shifting targets in South Africa, where vaccination against pneumonia was being tried for the sake of the highly susceptible blacks in the mines, the health authorities made up an omnibus vaccine containing eight different types of pneumococcus, two of streptococcus, and four other species of bacteria often associated with lung infections. Favorable results were claimed for it. In this country a much neater vaccine consisting of chemical fractions of pneumococci of Types I and II (which cause half our lobar pneumonia) has been tried out on large groups of men in the Civilian Conservation Corps. Again the gross results suggest that such inoculation gives some protection, but how specific this protection is and how long it lasts are still uncertain. It is not yet clear that vaccination against pneumonia either with whole micro-organisms or with antigens derived from them will be a practicable public health measure.

study of cold vaccines in the student health service of the University of Minnesota they found that the most one could claim for the vaccines was a 25 per cent reduction in the incidence of colds—or about one-half cold per person per year in the group studied. However, some students who had been "vaccinated" with plain salt and water were so happy about the results that they wanted to repeat the treatment another year!

All the vaccines mentioned thus far are intended to keep bacteria from getting a foothold in the body. Protection of a different order can be had against diphtheria. Although we know no way to attack the bacilli directly, we can educate the body to neutralize their toxin and so to strip them of their greatest threat. The trick is turned by the injection either of toxin in its natural state accompanied by enough antitoxin (borrowed from a horse) to check its poisonous effect, or of toxin denatured by chemical treatment (and then called toxoid).

Diphtheria immunization bristles with paradoxes. English workers offer evidence that at least in some circumstances a person immune to diphtheria toxin not only may carry virulent diphtheria bacilli in his nose or throat but is more likely to do so than a person picked at random from the crowd. If then the health officer immunizes only school children (who are easier to get at than their younger brothers and sisters) he may actually increase the chance that they will carry virulent bacilli home to the susceptibles in the nursery. This possibility seems to be supported by some instances in which, when perhaps a third of the children of a given community have been immunized, the incidence of diphtheria has gone up instead of down. The moral seems to be that if the health officer begins this job he must see it through. Even though there is no good reason, theoretically, why antitoxic immunity should lead to freedom from bacterial infection, some American and Canadian experience suggests that in a community which has been well salted with artificial immunity not only the number of cases but the number of carriers falls to low levels.

Immunizing against the viruses naturally poses new technical problems. It is hard to say when a virus is dead, especially as we are not sure that it was ever alive. Even if one substitutes the more cautious word "inactivated" for "dead," it is doubtful whether a virus in that condition is capable of giving the host a really good supply of resistance.* But granted that the best immunity against virus diseases is got by actually having the disease, that immunizing power is greater in active than in inactive viruses, and that active viruses are dangerous things to handle, it may still be possible to bargain for immunity without too great a risk. In fact viruses are so adaptable to various hosts and various tissues that such dickering holds some promise of success.

Nature has solved the problem very neatly in the case of smallpox by providing a convenient source of naturally attenuated virus, and man has improved on nature by transplanting virus from the calf to the hen's egg. When we come to the recent story of yellow fever we shall find a virus attenuated by long cultivation in other than human tissues playing an important role. Recent experiments indicate that the viruses of rabies, influenza, and measles may possibly become less dangerous to other hosts as they adapt themselves to growth in the cells of the chick embryo. It is not always true, however, that a virus is weakened by passage through an animal not its accustomed host. Some investigators hoped that poliomyelitis virus recovered from artificially infected monkeys might be a safe immunizing agent for man, but present evidence indicates that no living vaccine can safely be used against this disease and that non-living vaccine is without much effect.

If a virus enters the body by some other route than the usual one the body *may* be able to deal with it in such a way as to set up immunity. This method has been tried in inoculating monkeys against the parrot disease, psittacosis; the monkeys die if the virus is put into the trachea, but merely make antibodies if it is put into a vein or muscle. Sometimes one can cushion the effect of an active virus injected for immunizing purposes by giving the host at the same time serum containing borrowed antibodies.

* Andrewes, however, found an influenza virus which he called "as dead as a doornail" almost as good an antigen as living virus.

This method has been used with apparent success in animal diseases such as cattle plague and dog distemper.

Even if the resistance set up by an inactive virus be slight and temporary, it may serve as the entering wedge for a more rigorous course of immunizing injections. This is the principle on which Pasteur based his method of protection against rabies. The virus contained in the spinal cord of a rabbit was weakened by drying. Inert material was first injected and then little by little the virulence of the injections was stepped up until the antibody response was sufficient to deal with a natural infection. This at least was the original theory; later workers have modified the process in detail and recent experiments have emphasized its limitations when used after exposure to rabies. But it has also been found that if the virus is progressively weakened by treatment with chemicals or ultraviolet light, it will protect experimental animals against later infection.

The production of virus vaccines without contamination and in quantity is a pretty problem in itself. Living tissue cut in fine pieces and kept alive in a nourishing solution in a laboratory flask —a refined environment which somehow suggests Gilbert's "most particularly pure young man"—sometimes forms a better milieu for their cultivation than the gross animal body. More and more use is being made of the chick embryo as a cheap, convenient, and well-guarded forcing-bed for the growth of viruses. Vaccines to protect men against yellow fever, horses against equine encephalomyelitis,* and fowls against certain diseases of their own are now being produced in this way. Some of these must be artificially inactivated before they are safe for use.

How do we know whether active immunization does what it is meant to do? It is possible to recognize and, in relative terms, to measure antibodies in the blood, but one cannot guarantee that they will be adequate to check an actual invasion. What we want

* See page 298.

to know is whether immunization really prevents disease when the host is attacked in force. In the laboratory one can inoculate a series of animals, give them a measured quantity of infective material in such a way that they cannot escape exposure, and see how many of them fall sick. Comparable information about human beings is harder to get. Experimentation is often dangerous and, in small series of cases, inconclusive. Lump-sum figures drawn from the comparative experience of large immunized and unimmunized groups usually fail to answer two essential questions: how many people in each group were actually exposed to the disease, and how long were they in danger? One can arrange sickness and death rates in a before-and-after immunization sequence, but that may not mean much. Epidemic diseases are always in unstable equilibrium, rising and falling like waves even if nobody does anything about them, and what we take to be a triumph or a failure of preventive medicine may be only a ground swell in the natural history of the disease. While most of our public policies with regard to immunization are justified by the weight of evidence, few are supported by rigorous mathematical proof.

We cannot breed human beings like mice for resistance to disease. Nor have we any evidence that we can make them immune by feeding them better food, putting them in better houses, cutting their work below the range of extreme fatigue, or paying them better wages. But by such environmental measures we may be able to fit them to wrestle more sturdily with infection, and we may slow down the rate at which infection runs through the crowd. As standards of living rise the mean distance between one person and another tends to increase: the family huddled in a peasant hut or a city tenement can hardly avoid sharing its parasites indiscriminately, and there are many reasons beyond the desire for creative expression that justify Virginia Woolf's plea for "a room of one's own." Freedom from vermin and shelter from flies and mosquitoes are demanded as a matter of course when housing reaches a modest level of comfort. Sanitary "conveniences" are epidemiological necessities, but they are often least in evidence where they are most needed as defenses against disease. Intelligence may be the basis of self-protection, but it needs to be reinforced by things and services that cost money. Where poverty and ignorance together block the way, the epidemiologist may be reduced to largely futile gestures.

"There are evils," the British Ministry of Health once remarked, "the removal of which is not within the province of epidemiologists to discuss. We can but note them and remark that no technical device of the sanitarian, no resource of the laboratory, can have any effect in the reduction of death and sickness from epidemic or even endemic disease at all commensurate with the consequences which must follow a *universal* improvement of the standard and conditions of life."[8]

## REFERENCES

1. Stokes, J. H. *Modern clinical syphilology*. Philadelphia: W. B. Saunders Company, 1926, p. 136.
2. Hackett, L. W. *Malaria in Europe: an ecological study*. London: Oxford University Press, 1937, p. 177.
3. Dudley, Sheldon F. *On the biological approach to the study of epidemiology*. Proceedings of the Royal Society of Medicine, 29:1–14, November 1935.
4. Leviticus, xiii:45–46.
5. Porter, Charles. *Then and now*. Medical Officer, 31:25–28, January 19, 1924.
6. Barber, M. A. *The present status of* Anopheles gambiae *in Brazil*. American Journal of Tropical Medicine, 20:249–267, March 1940.
7. Topley, W. W. C., and Wilson, G. S. *The principles of bacteriology and immunity*. 2d ed. Baltimore: William Wood and Company, 1937, p. 986.
8. Great Britain. Ministry of Health. *Report on the pandemic of influenza 1918–1919*. London: H. M. Stationery Office, 1920, p. 191–193.

## A NOTE ON SOURCES

This chapter is based chiefly on the standard texts already mentioned in connection with earlier chapters, supplemented by the current journals. I have drawn also on Smillie's *Public health administration in the United States* (New York: Macmillan, 1936); on Prescott and Horwood's edition of Sedgwick's *Principles of sanitary science and public health* (New York: Macmillan, 1935); on articles by Park and Winslow in Volume 12 of the *Practitioners Library of Medicine and Surgery* (New York: Appleton-Century, 1937); and on the anniversary volume of the American Public Health Association, *A half-century of public health* (published by the Association, 1921).

The journals are bursting with chemotherapy; a paper by Dale in Physiological Reviews for July 1923 (3:359–393) gives a good background for the newer developments. The Lederle Laboratories were good enough to show me the commercial production of serum. Creighton is fascinating on leprosy and smallpox. On such problems as isolation Chapin's *Sources and modes of infection,* previously cited, is a classic, though his views of air-borne infection probably need revision. On insect-borne diseases I have used Gorgas' own account of *Sanitation in Panama* (New York: Appleton, 1915) and the biography by Mrs. Gorgas and Hendrick (New York: Doubleday, Page, 1924), as well as articles and the often-cited book on malaria by Hackett.

For unpublished details and general orientation I am grateful to Dr. Frank G. Boudreau, late of the Health Section of the League of Nations and now of the Milbank Fund; to Dr. René J. Dubos of the Rockefeller Institute; to W. F. Wells of the University of Pennsylvania; to Dr. Ralph W. Muckenfuss of the New York City Department of Health; and to Dr. Donald T. Fraser of the University of Toronto.

FROM PUBLIC HEALTH BULLETIN 65, MAY 1914, BY COURTESY OF THE UNITED STATES PUBLIC HEALTH SERVICE

G marks the spot where typhoid bacilli entered the water supply of Rockville, Maryland, in the winter of 1913–1914 and spread typhoid fever through the little town. Lumsden of the Public Health Service worked out the story: a sick visitor at house A infected the privy B which drained into the "spring branch" D which at F ran into the "secret ditch" which passed near enough to the pumping station G for foul water to seep at times into an imperfectly protected well

# 7

## DETECTIVE WORK

WITH the exception of the *very* high-minded who never read detective stories, everyone knows how to find a murderer. You reconstruct the circumstances of the crime, noting with passionate care every deviation from the normal. In the group involved, you begin by suspecting everybody, and eliminate suspects one by one as they fail to measure up to your yardstick of opportunity plus motive. While this process is going on, some unusual combination of circumstances leads you to the murderer.

Finding the source of an epidemic is something like that. It is rarely so neat as the detective story, but neither is the everyday practice of criminology. One must study the circumstances meticulously, separate the unusual from the usual factors, and close in on the way people were infected by ruling out all the other ways in which they might have been.

The detective has two datum-points against which to check his suspicions: opportunity and motive. Motive is of no help to the epidemiologist. The motive of the principal protagonist never changes: the parasite is always striving to propagate its kind. The human accessories may show either carelessness or cupidity or both, but not deliberate intent. Even in war we have not yet reverted to that stage of brutality at which epidemics are wilfully created (though if anyone finds out how to prevent their backfiring we shall probably come to it). So it does the investigator no good to look for evidences of guilt. As Mustard puts it: "The focus [of infection] has no guilty conscience, manifests no suggestive emotions under grilling, exhibits no suspicious action under surveillance; and none of the sources—water or milk or oysters, for instance—changes in color or in taste in any way that might not be associated with complete innocence."[1]

Unraveling the plot of an epidemic may take either of two forms. The disease may be one not yet explained, and the normal chain of causation may have to be worked out. Discovering the parasite and its mode of travel under such conditions calls for amazing ingenuity, and many good stories of that sort have been told in other books. Here we are concerned with a more limited problem: finding the way in which a known parasite with known habits has gotten into circulation in a specific group of people.

This group may be small or large, but the story is often clearest when the cases are few. In fact a polished piece of field investigation, leading to a conclusive finding, is rarely possible when the population is still saturated with disease. There are too many clues. When a once-prevalent infection has begun to yield ground, as typhoid fever has done, and cases are spaced far enough apart to be studied with some precision, the time has come for intensive sleuthing. Field epidemiology in this limited sense is part of the mopping-up process when a disease is already in retreat.

Confronted with an epidemic of such character and proportions that it might have spread from a single focus, the epidemiologists hunt for that focus. The obvious place to look for clues is in the area where the experience of one sick person overlaps that of another and differs from the experience of people who did not fall sick. If such a common factor is found, the next step is to discover how it was or might have been related to a demonstrable source of infection. Clearly some diseases are much easier to study in this way than others: if the only relevant common factor in the experience of a group of malaria patients is that they were all bitten by mosquitoes the epidemiologist has little to work on. Even in such a discouraging situation, however, he can sometimes travel a long way.

There was, for instance, an outbreak of malaria in the neighborhood of a small stream in rural Georgia. A farmer had been cutting timber and letting the slash rot in the water; his neighbors were convinced that the rotting wood was breeding disease. The county health officer hunted for male mosquitoes along this stream, and found none—a good sign that *Anopheles* were not breeding there, for the male, suffering perhaps from a mother-fixation, never gets far from the cradle. But when he mapped all the cases of malaria he could find, they spread themselves over a circle with a radius of about a mile and a half—a longish but quite possible flight range for *Anopheles*. At the center of this circle the health officer found a little pond thick with mosquito larvae. It had been built, for his own pleasure, by an old fisherman whose joints creaked too badly to take him farther afield. He had no malaria, nor did his family, and he protested bitterly when the neighbors came and cut his dam. But the neighbors were right: one of his tenants, a Negro recently come from a malarious district, was housed within easy reach of the pond, and there was every reason to believe that the combination of convenient breeding place and infected blood had touched off the little epidemic.

It is not often possible to work out a malaria episode so clearly. Nor is it usually profitable to attempt close-range sleuthing in outbreaks of air-borne disease. Tuberculosis has its own epidemiology, of which more later, but this involves so generous a time-factor that we need not consider it here alongside the diseases that flare up quickly. When people are shut away in institutions, such as asylums, their environment is relatively static and one can sometimes trace the effect of factors which would pass unnoticed in the world outside. Smillie has reported institutional outbreaks of specific types of pneumonia which seemed to be associated with the movement of carriers from one ward to another. But generally speaking so much depends on our own fluctuating resistance, so many strangers breathe our air, and so many strangers and friends alike carry parasites of the sorts which may infect us, that it would be futile to try to find out from which of them we catch a cold, a pneumonia, a meningitis.

The happy hunting-ground of the epidemiological detective is among the diseases which infect the intestines and spread by way of the intestinal discharges. Water, milk, and foodstuffs can carry the parasites, and each of these vehicles can be followed from one human contact to another, often with satisfying accuracy. The chain is long enough to get well tangled at times, short enough to form an indisputable link between host and host. The two questions posed by any epidemic are clearly separated: which of the several possible vehicles is actually carrying the parasites, and where did they come from in the first place? The good epidemiologist is not happy till he has answered both questions and drawn a line under the sum of his findings. But often he can do what most needs to be done after answering the first: if water is spreading typhoid, for instance, it can be boiled or chlorinated at once, checking the epidemic before the infection is traced to its source.

Perhaps the early work on water-borne cholera and typhoid fever gives the lie to the statement that refined sleuthing becomes possible only when disease begins to thin out. Snow's study of cholera in London set the pace for the investigation of public water supplies and did so brilliantly. It took sound deduction to establish beyond cavil the fact that polluted water supplies were responsible for the great city epidemics in the United

States in the nineties and early years of the twentieth century. But, operating on such a scale, the epidemiologist had to be satisfied with proving the existence and the effect of contamination: he could hardly expect to trace it back to specific human sources. It is this finishing touch which makes the stories of smaller epidemics more interesting.

The epidemiology of typhoid fever, of cholera and the dysenteries is a refined technique applied to a thoroughly unrefined subject. Though the facts may lead the investigator a merry chase, the trail is the trail of human feces. The stories which follow have been chosen to show the epidemiological detective at work; not all of them deal with typhoid fever, but the sensitive reader had best skip at once to the next chapter.

### THE CASE OF THE METHODIST LADIES

The Methodist ladies of Hanford, California, had a bright idea. There was going to be a fair in town, and everybody would drive in from the farms and there would be a big crowd and where would they all eat? If the ladies got together and cooked up a real good meal they could take the Sunday school chairs out of the basement and set tables down there and there might be a hundred people who would give half a dollar apiece for a home-cooked dinner and that would just about finish paying for the new carpet.

The sun is bright in the San Joaquin Valley and even in March the days are good and warm. There would have to be iced tea and salad, but you couldn't expect folks to do without a good hearty dish to start with. What about chicken pie and mashed potatoes? Mrs. Pingree had an awfully good receipt for Spanish sauce and she might make up a batch of spaghetti with it. Then there's always somebody who likes baked beans, and of course pie for dessert. It would hardly be any more work to serve supper too, and they could have ice-cream at night so as to make it a little different.

So the feast was spread and the people came. Of course it was a job to keep the dishes washed up especially before the water got hot and all that gravy and spaghetti to scrape off the plates and who'd have thought the Jamesons and the Browns would have come in as early as eleven o'clock but of course they did have a long ride home and probably they wanted to get away sooner than most. They were all done and out of the hall by twenty past. It was too bad Mrs. Pingree didn't bring the spaghetti a little sooner but anyway it was hot at the top and people seemed to like it. The chicken pie was the big hit, though; most everybody had some of that.

This was on Tuesday. On Friday word went round that Mrs. Clarke, who had been at the dinner and helped wash dishes, was sick. On Saturday four more people fell ill. By Monday night the town was full of sick people; the little hospital was crowded; the doctors were fagged out. The symptoms pointed strongly to typhoid fever. Hanford had never seen anything like it. The town water came from deep wells, a good part of the town was sewered, and typhoid had been unknown for a long time. Besides, this was California. The people who got sick were certainly people who had been at the dinner or supper, but who ever heard of typhoid developing in three or four days? Usually one counts back at least a fortnight from the time a patient takes to his bed to find the probable time of infection. It must have been the dinner and it couldn't have been the dinner. So the board of health called in the state health department to solve the riddle.

The sick list kept growing: by the time the state investigation was fully under way almost eighty cases had turned up, and when the epidemic had run its course the total stood at ninety-three. One hundred and fifty people had dined or supped at the church; almost three out of every five had sickened. Eight cases among people who had not been present were puzzling only so long as it took to find out that they too had eaten food brought from the church: the neighbors were kind enough to take a basket in to one family where the housewife was just back from the hospital, and two mothers took food home for their children. The youngest patient in town was a sixteen-months-old baby who had been "cute" over a mouthful or two of Methodist food; the oldest was sixty-five.

When it was clear that the disease was typhoid fever and had come from the dinner and supper, the first job was to hunt for the particular kind of food that had been so heavily infected as to cause the trouble. By counting noses (with or without statistical ritual) it is often possible to trace a food-borne epidemic to a single dish which most of the sick have eaten, and then, by looking carefully into the antecedents of that dish, to discover the source of infection.

Suspect No. 1 was the chicken pie: nearly everybody, sick and well, had eaten it, and there was gravy-on-the-side in which germs might lurk. But the chicken pie proved to be triplets: three different lots had been made by three different cooks, and all three lots had been sampled by the people now sick. It stretched probability too far to suppose that these three sources could have become infectious all at the same time. Mashed potatoes went with the chicken pie for those who wanted them, but many did not, and the milk in them was traced to a safe source. The spaghetti was almost as popular as the chicken pie, but several patients were sure they had eaten none of it. Green salads are often of questionable repute, but this one was made with home-grown lettuce watered from the city mains and fertilized with manure from the home barn: the people who grew it had not been sick before, and caught typhoid fever now—good evidence that they had not been infectious previously. Ice-cream was served only at night, and most of the sick people were found among the noonday diners. The baked beans, the pies, the cheese, the bread and butter, and so forth, reached too few people to account for the wide spread of infection. The clues all seemed to run out.

But the food must have been contaminated somehow: could the bacteria have traveled from hand to plate to food to mouth? Was someone scattering them as she helped in the kitchen? One hardly expects complete sterilization when flustered females wash piles of dishes in odds and ends of pans with odds and ends of water, but it would be hard to plant enough bacteria on any given dish to account for the massive dosage that seemed to be at work here. When people come down with typhoid in three or four days some extraordinary concentration of parasites—a regular mass migration—must be looked for. Moreover there were cases among those first hurried families who ate and left by 11:20, and that cut the time pretty fine for kitchen contamination.

At all events the bacteria came from a human source, and the next step was obviously to look into the health status of everyone who had a hand either in preparing or in serving the meals. There were twenty such people. They fell into two groups: eleven had already caught typhoid fever; nine had not. None of the eleven could have been carriers, for carriers do not infect themselves. If they really fell ill after the dinner, their alibis were good: they could not have brought infection to the dinner. But Mrs. Clarke—who was sick on the third day—perhaps she was already infected before the party began? Typhoid may begin insidiously, and "walking cases" have often spread infection. If this was the case, her blood should show evidence of infection at an early stage of the disease. But this did not happen for full fifteen days, and she was accordingly ruled out. Another early case, a lone man whose wife browbeat him into helping in the kitchen, did remember that he had had suggestive symptoms before the day of the dinner, but investigation showed that these had been due to other causes.

This left nine people who had been definitely in the picture and who did not contract typhoid. One of these women did not reach the hall until noon, which eliminated her, since the first cases had been infected before that time; another had done nothing but make a pie and a cake and peel some potatoes, and these articles of food had already been ruled out. Seven suspects were left. All had been busy and helpful at the dinner. If there was a carrier among them, laboratory examination of urine or feces should reveal the infection, although even here there was a chance that the investigators would draw a blank, since carriers often excrete bacilli at irregular intervals. Specimens from all seven were packed in ice and shipped off to the state laboratory. This was several hundred miles away, air mail was still unknown, and it would take some time to get the reports back. Meanwhile, the investigators kept on asking questions.

Two of the seven suspects, it was found, were old typhoid cases. The close relatives of such cases—if they were carriers— ought either to have had typhoid themselves or to have developed immunity by a succession of small infections. So when new cases turned up in both families, that ruled them out. Another woman was married to a man who had had typhoid many years before, and had a daughter who had also had the disease, but she kept a boarding-house and had not infected her boarders: that made it unlikely that she was a carrier. Several others gave histories which were not very enlightening, and only one told a story which seemed to contain a helpful clue.

This was Mrs. Pingree, a widow who had formerly supported herself and her family by taking in boarders. Seven or eight years before the church supper, two of these boarders had developed typhoid within a week of each other, and the doctor could never quite explain how they got it. Some years after that

213

two more cases developed among Mrs. Pingree's boarders, and these, too, were hard to account for. The investigators found two of these old cases living in Hanford, and both insisted that they had eaten regularly at Mrs. Pingree's table several weeks before they fell ill. Here was a story of familiar pattern: a disjointed series of occasional cases among the associates of a person involved in the handling of food. Mrs. Pingree, so far as she knew, had never had typhoid fever, though she remembered that her daughter had suffered from it thirty-five years before. But when the reports came back from the laboratory the case broke: she was a carrier, and the only one among the seven suspects.

Now Mrs. Pingree was the lady with the toothsome recipe for Spanish spaghetti, and since she had made all of it, whereas several people contributed chicken pies, her contribution came nearest to being a statistically satisfactory source of the widespread infection. But it seemed very odd, indeed, that the kind of dish which burns the tongue even after it is spooned out on the plate could have been the vehicle of such massive infection. Cooked bacteria are dead bacteria, and dead bacteria do not cause disease. It is true that Mrs. Pingree had also waited on table, had cut the bread, and had busied herself about the kitchen, but she did not reach the church until ten o'clock on the morning of the dinner, and that left little time for bacteria which she might have spread on this food or on the dishes to multiply to so great an extent. The spaghetti, moreover, had been baked at the hall after she brought it in, which ought to have sterilized it.

Nevertheless, here was the stubborn fact, and the investigators began to dig into the history of that dish of spaghetti as thoroughly as the amateur detective looks into the history of the blonde who bought a pistol at the pawn shop the day before the murder. Mrs. Pingree had cooked and washed the spaghetti in town water, made the sauce, and set them aside separately on the day before the dinner. At ten o'clock on the fateful Tuesday she had mixed the sauce and the spaghetti in a big dishpan, sprinkled the top generously with cheese, and brought it to the church, where it was promptly put into the oven of the gas stove and cooked as long as time allowed, although Mrs. Pingree's neighbors felt that longer cooking would have been a little nicer. Some of it was eaten before 11:20. It looked very much as though the spaghetti, cooked or uncooked, had caused the mischief. By the end of the day, when all the dishes had been sloshed about, the bacteria might well have been scattered over everything in sight, and that would account for the fact that some guests who did not eat the spaghetti picked up the infection nevertheless.

At about this point the investigators packed up and went home. They had found the carrier, the epidemic was subsiding, and there was work to be done at the state laboratory. But they had not yet written Q.E.D. to their demonstration. The director of the laboratory, with Mrs. Pingree's recipe in his pocket, called in his wife. Between them they concocted in their own kitchen a mess of sauce and spaghetti identical with Mrs. Pingree's dish. Some of the sauce was put aside, sterilized, and then inoculated with a minute dose—one ten-thousandth of a cubic centimeter—of a culture made from Mrs. Pingree's own bacilli. This was put into the incubator and after twelve hours the bacilli had multiplied 2,940,000 per cent. Evidently the sauce afforded congenial pasturage. Meanwhile, the rest of the sauce, with the spaghetti, had also been inoculated with typhoid bacilli and cooked in the family oven at a proper baking temperature. After fifteen minutes the temperature midway between the top and the bottom of the pan was only one degree above that of the room, and it became clear that it was impossible to get the spaghetti hot enough in the gas oven to kill the bacteria. So the investigator carried the dish over to his laboratory and put it in a hot-air sterilizer. Half an hour of cooking at something over 320° F. turned the top a luscious golden brown and when the door was opened an appetizing smell filled the room. The dish looked hot and would have passed in any well-regulated kitchen as nicely done. But in the middle of the dish the thermometer still showed the temperature of a cool summer day and the bacilli were still alive close under the golden crust. Vowing that he would cook that spaghetti to a finish, the doctor put it back into the oven and baked it until the surface was beginning to burn and the edges were sizzling. Even then temperatures at the middle and bottom of the mass fell far short of the minimum point for pasteurization. Within an inch of the top, it is true, the mass was nearly sterile, but if one pushed down two and a half inches the typhoid bacilli were still flourishing.

The answer was clear. Within the limits of edibility one cannot sterilize a mess of baked spaghetti. Mrs. Pingree had unwittingly planted in fertile soil the seeds of a disease she did not know she had. A lush growth of bacteria was sprouting in the bowl of sauce that stood waiting through a warm March day and night. The gentle warmth of the gas oven may have speeded the process; certainly it did not check it. When the tables were set, a bumper crop was ready for harvest; by the end of the day the harvest was in.

Perhaps the Methodist ladies' idea wasn't such a good one after all.

### THE CASE OF THE WADING BOYS

It is pleasant to live in Blackwood *if* you live on the right side of the railroad tracks. On the wrong side the Massachusetts terrain, so lovely when unspoiled, has not been bettered by civilization. Little ugly frame houses straggle along irregular streets, which, though they bear dignified names, have come to have a rather bad reputation. Behind the houses on one long winding street there runs what is left of the Siasconset River. Like most rivers which have become too familiar with manufacturing towns, it has a bedraggled look. The water is sometimes odorous because of tannery wastes, and sooner or later it gets most of the sewage produced along its banks. These backyard rivers which fringe small cities may have lost their charm for the fastidious adult, but to a small boy running water is running water, salamanders live under slimy stones, pebbles splash as loudly in murky as in clear pools, and the youngsters who lived along the river bragged about it even to those schoolmates who came from politer environments.

In May 1930 a nurse from the Blackwood schools turned up at the offices of the state health department with some bottles of water which she wanted analyzed. There were, she said, two cases of typhoid in one of the public schools. The water was from a brook in which the children had paddled.

In Massachusetts three cases of typhoid are an epidemic, two that suggest a common source are a challenge, and even one is a matter for earnest inquiry. So investigation began quickly. The boys were Michael Ferrara and Timothy O'Shea, six and eight years of age respectively, neighbors and schoolmates. Where did they get typhoid?

Perhaps the milk they drank at home was infected? Both families took milk from the same dealer, but the supply was pasteurized and was then being used by nearly half the families in the city. If it were a source of disease it would be logical to find many other cases, but there were none. Had a sick person infected them directly? The boys had not been away from home; no one else in the family and none of the neighbors was sick. The water supply? Both families drank city water, which had left all the rest of the town unscathed. But both youngsters, on being questioned, told of splashing around in the Siasconset. Here was one common element not likely to have affected many

217

other people. The water was undoubtedly very dirty, and colon bacilli were found in it.

Neither Mike nor Tim was very sick, but the disease did not stop with them. Before it had run its course, six small boys and one four-year-old girl, sister of one of the boys, became ill. All of the families concerned lived within half a mile of each other. Five of the seven children had waded in the brook. Two of them, falling ill later than the others, had apparently caught the infection from members of their own family.

Obviously the brook required attention. The water contained raw sewage. One of the boys had not only splashed in it, but had drunk it. It took no great amount of engineering skill to discover that at times of heavy rain, fresh sewage from the mains could flow directly into the brook, and naturally just at these times of high water it became most inviting to small-boy explorers. Cesspools, not too tightly built, bordered the gully. Some families had the habit of deliberately using the seepage from them to fertilize their thrifty backyard vegetable gardens.

The layman would have been satisfied by this evidence. The sequence of sewage–brook–boys seems complete. But the health department was not wholly convinced. Sewage in water is not uncommon, and unless it contains the specific bacilli of typhoid it cannot cause that disease.* There was no proof that the water was responsible.

So other clues were patiently looked into. Most of the youngsters in the neighborhood were in the habit of buying goodies from a store kept by a vast motherly Greek woman named Somkopoulos, who fell under suspicion when it was learned that she had once had typhoid. But there was no record of illness among her black-eyed daughters, who usually tended shop and handed out the ice-cream cones, and it was hard to see why little boys— no fonder than little girls of ice-cream—were so much likelier

* See the footnote on page 182.

218

to fall sick. This clue played out completely when a series of stool examinations showed that Mrs. Somkopoulos was not shedding typhoid organisms.

Another check was made on the milk supply, without result. A youngster was found who had had typhoid two years earlier and was just getting around once more to meet his old friends, but he too produced negative specimens. Sewer connections which might pollute the brook were looked into, but no evidence of overflow could be found. The cesspools remained, but there was no record of typhoid in the houses which they served. The epidemic was classified (with reservations) as water-borne, and the health department kept an anxious eye on the situation.

So 1930 passed into 1931 and as summer came on the small boys began again to fall sick with typhoid. Before the year was over five youngsters from four to ten years of age had been infected. Four of them lived in the same neighborhood, and one, though a resident of the "better" side of town, was connected with the wrong side of the tracks through frequent visits with his mother. The last to take sick was the son and heir of one Giovanni Pepito. Pepito said he himself had been indisposed some time before. Laboratory examination of his stools showed that he was discharging typhoid bacilli. He was kept under observation all through the next year, and in due course, the specimens remaining positive, was classified as a typhoid carrier. Pepito was quite willing to sign an agreement offered by the health department which pledged him to wash his hands after every visit to the toilet, never to work in any kitchen or restaurant, and to keep his family immunized. Here was a present source of infection. Still, except for the one case of his own youngster, there was no indicated connection between this carrier and the numerous small boys.

In 1932 there were no cases of typhoid reported in Blackwood. In 1933 one six-year-old boy from the same neighborhood fell sick. In 1934 there were two, a ten-year-old and a twelve-year-old. In questioning these boys, the dogged investigators found the going easier than before: at six or seven the fear of a spanking is a vivid deterrent to confidences; at ten or twelve one can, within limits, be reasoned with. One of the youngsters, talking a little more freely than his predecessors, let fall the interesting information that all the boys in the neighborhood who played around the school yard thought it a rather smart trick to drink out of an old pipe which stuck out of the ground where the bank ran down to the dirty little stream, and which occasionally had water in it. With the town engineer's help it was discovered that the pipe in question was a drain for seepage, built directly beneath a sewer. The pipe had originally gone into the river, but where it was exposed the boys of an earlier generation had found it easy to break. The curious fact was that this pipe ran directly beneath the sewer line which served the street where Mr. Pepito lived. This was significant. No matter how careful Mr. Pepito was to keep his hands clean, no matter how faithfully he fulfilled the carrier agreement, he could not help discharging typhoid organisms into this sewer, and the seepage therefrom was providing the favorite drinking water of the small boys in the neighborhood!

Was the recent illness of Mr. Pepito irrelevant, and had he been shedding typhoid organisms before 1931 when they were discovered? He had moved to the house in 1928 or 1929. The youngsters began to fall sick in 1930. It is too late to answer the question definitely, but the pipe was closed up; the boys at the playground found other places to quench their thirst; and typhoid ceased along the Siasconset.

### THE CASE OF THE LADYLIKE OYSTERS

The competent health officer knows about how much typhoid fever to expect in his clientele at any given season of the year.

In the winter of 1924–25, first in New York and then in Chicago and Washington, cases began to multiply far more rapidly than usual, and between the middle of November and the middle of January these three cities had full-sized epidemics and ten others* had at least three times as much typhoid as they should have had. When the trouble was past, it was estimated the normal toll of the disease had been increased by some 1,500 cases and 150 deaths.

In every epidemic, Lumsden says, there is a peculiar fact, and that peculiar fact, skilfully used, holds the key to the plot. The peculiar fact about this epidemic was that it flourished most conspicuously among women of the right class and age for putting on a pretty frock and going out to dine at a smart restaurant. Early in the investigation it occurred to at least one of the epidemiologists concerned that such women like small oysters and have far more opportunity, especially in large cities, to gratify this taste than the rank and file of children, housewives, and burghers generally. As everyone knows, raw oysters can carry typhoid bacilli.

Few epidemics have been more thoroughly studied. In the three cities chiefly affected, not only the local health department but the United States Public Health Service, for reasons which will presently appear, made intensive investigations, and each time the facts grouped themselves in the same curious pattern.

Take Chicago first. In December and the first three weeks of January, when past experience would have led the health officer to expect some 33 cases of the disease, typhoid fever struck at 129 people in the city and 34 in its more comfortable suburbs. When these cases were spotted on the map, they grouped themselves along the Gold Coast on the North Side and, a little less elegantly, around Jackson Park on the South Side. In the com-

* Buffalo, Cincinnati, Grand Rapids, Jersey City, Memphis, Pittsburgh, Providence, Rochester, Scranton, and Yonkers.

fortable wards the incidence was two and a half times as high as in those where the well-to-do and the poor were mixed, and nine times as great as in the poverty wards. Almost twice as many women as men between twenty and thirty-four years of age fell sick; in the middle-aged group fewer women than men were ill. Children suffered hardly at all. Not a single case was reported among Negroes. Over thirty per cent of the sick who were studied were reported as not gainfully employed, but personal investigation made it clear that these idlers were from the upper and not the lower end of the economic scale. One out of every five sick persons came from the professional group; one out of every ten was a stenographer or woman clerk.

Try to find out where and what a hundred city-dwellers have eaten in the past month and you will have some idea of the difficulty which the investigator faces in running down the causes of such an epidemic. When he rings the doorbell, he will find some of his cases dead, some in delirium. Some will have left town to get well; many more will have forgotten the essential facts. The investigators in this case were lucky, however, in that the period during which the infection might have been acquired included three holidays—Election Day, Armistice Day, and Thanksgiving—all worth celebrating with a good dinner, and all likely to stand out in the gourmet's memory.

So, methodically, the schedules were filled out. Hunch or no hunch, every possible source of infection—within reason—had to be looked into before even a promising explanation was accepted as final. The federal investigators got complete histories from ninety cases in Chicago and its suburbs. These people were sufficiently scattered so that their drinking water came from three separate intakes in Chicago and one in Evanston, and careful checking of the well-controlled city supply indicated that there had been no lapse in the usual protective measures. If water had been responsible for the infection, moreover, there was no reason for the preponderance of cases among the well-to-do. Less than half the persons studied were in the habit of drinking milk as a beverage, and as the domestic supplies were pasteurized and came from twenty-two different sources, there was little help there. Practically every maker of ice-cream who supplied the local market would have been implicated if this had been the cause of the trouble. Even the consumption of cheese was tabulated; solid conservative taste was revealed, for the users of American cream cheese outnumbered all those who toyed with Roquefort, Camembert, and Swiss, but less than half of the sick who were studied had eaten cheese at all.

Every person in the group, however, had eaten a meal in a public eating-place at least once during the period when infection might have been brewing, and every one of Chicago's smarter eating-places had served a meal to some typhoid victim during this period. Were there carriers in the kitchen or at the dishwashing machines? It strained the imagination to the breaking-point to suppose that they had simultaneously shed organisms in scores of cabarets and hotels and restaurants all over Chicago.

The poisonous stuff must have come from something eaten, and presumably from something eaten raw. It is a poor meal that does not include lettuce or celery or both; most of the sick had eaten them, and it was not easy to be sure that these wholesome vegetables, traveling naked and unprotected from soil to table, had not carried bacilli. But again the law of probability was invoked. Unless most of the celery or lettuce had come from a small number of infected areas, or had been handled by a small group of infected persons, it was unthinkable that so wide a spread of disease could be traced to this source.

It takes patient sleuthing to follow the trail of a head of lettuce in a great city. If it comes to the table wan and wilted, it can truthfully say with Snow White, "You don't know what I've been through." From grower to middleman to speculator to market it is bandied back and forth—in the leaf or on paper—so many times that the record is dizzying. Taking as a sample four restaurants where a number of sick people had eaten, the investigators learned that lettuce sold in the city came from so many points in California, Idaho, Illinois, and Michigan that only a pandemic in the hinterlands could have explained simultaneous infection of the lot. Celery, too, reached these four restaurants from eleven different points in Michigan, three in Illinois, and one in New York, and there was little overlapping between one supply and another. All kinds of things might have happened to any part of it, but the chance that the same kind of thing had happened to all of it was remote. Moreover, when the investigators rang doorbells in other neighborhoods, some as well off as those from which the sick people came, others less prosperous, they found that three out of four of all the people interviewed also ate raw celery and lettuce. If Chicago's supply had been infected during this period, why had not these people, too, furnished their share of the sick?

Oysters are different. Of 887 persons interviewed in these "other neighborhoods," only twenty-five were accustomed to eat oysters on the half-shell. But of the ninety typhoid patients who gave a complete account of themselves, seventy-six remembered eating raw oysters on the half-shell, either in Chicago or elsewhere, during the period in which the disease might have developed. Seventy-three of them recalled that they had eaten bluepoints. The bluepoint may or may not be a biological entity, but every waiter knows that when a customer orders bluepoints he wants small oysters. And small oysters are ladylike: the American male may smack his lips over Chincoteagues and Lynnhavens, but his consort (who of course does not smack her lips at all) has something of the same reticence that the bishop displayed when he admitted that his first oyster made him feel as though he had swallowed a baby; she likes her shellfish to be of discreet proportions. Of course, by the same token, clams are even more ladylike than oysters. But only one of the ninety sick persons remembered eating raw clams in the Chicago district.

Here and there, an individual story underscored the probability that small oysters were the cause of the trouble. There was, for example, the student at Northwestern who had eaten dormitory meals as long as she could stand them and on the first of November, with her married sister from out of town, came to Chicago for a party. At luncheon both women ate tomato soup, rolls and butter—not very likely, in the situation, to have been infected; at dinner they were agreed only in ordering bluepoints and coffee. But after the girl had gone back to college and her sister had gone home, both fell ill and both developed typhoid. Two couples who motored to Joliet for dinner ordered bluepoints all around, but when the waiter came he said, "Sorry, sir, there are only three portions left." The disappointed man escaped disease; two of the oyster eaters had typhoid.

There is, however, nothing intrinsically evil about a bluepoint. Millions are eaten with complete safety and there was no more reason to suppose that all the bluepoints in Chicago had suddenly become infected than to make the same charge against all the lettuce. Unless it could be shown that the suspected oysters came from some particular source where infection might have occurred, the case was still wide open. The next job was to trace them back to salt water.

This was relatively easy in Chicago, so far out of the oyster belt that the business was handled almost entirely by five wholesalers, who helped the investigators by turning over their records and shipping bills. Out of five million oysters shipped into Chicago in four months, a million and a half came from a single producer, which may be called Bivalve, Inc. The investigators estimated that less than one in fifty of the population of Chicago could have eaten oysters from Bivalve, Inc., during the period of the epidemic. But when the oysters actually eaten by the sick people who were studied were traced back to their source, it was found that four out of five of these people had eaten at restaurants where oysters from Bivalve, Inc., had been served. The 1.4 per cent of the people in Chicago who might have been exposed to infection from this source accounted for 82.5 per cent of the cases studied. Normal experience would lead the health officer to ascribe at least a quarter of the cases to non-epidemic factors. The evidence was strong, therefore, that the epidemic wave rose high because the oysters supplied by Bivalve, Inc., spread infection.

Meanwhile, similar work was afoot in Washington and New York. In Washington, as in Chicago, most of the sick lived in a comfortable quarter of the city; many of the homes were dotted along Sixteenth Street and Connecticut Avenue; women from twenty to thirty-four years of age suffered more heavily than men of the same age, though the disparity was not so marked as in Chicago. Of the thirty-six persons for whom records were secured, three-quarters had eaten raw oysters, some of them repeatedly, and though the oysters shipped by Bivalve, Inc., amounted to less than five per cent of Washington's supply, eighty-six per cent of the oyster-typhoid group had eaten at places where these oysters were available and might therefore have been exposed to them.

In New York, naturally, the epidemic took larger proportions. The cases reported reached a total of 913. In Manhattan 117 women and only 76 men in the group from twenty to thirty-four years old were sick. The federal investigators studied 263 cases, mostly inveterate lunchers-out or diners-out. One hundred and seventy-six of them had eaten oysters on the half-shell and fifty-nine had eaten them only once in the month, falling sick, on an average, twenty-two days later. Not all those who ate oysters, of course, could remember where and when they had done so, and the federal investigators hunting for the restaurants implicated had as much trouble finding some as many another visitor to New York has had in trying to locate that nice little place in the fifties that Cousin John likes so much. Ninety-six restaurants where the sick had eaten yielded information as to the origin of their oyster supply. From this point, the investigation became as complicated as an income tax blank. The oysters under investigation had been handled by eighteen different wholesalers who bought in every conceivable combination from six different producers, some of whom also shipped directly to hotels and restaurants. It took tables, charts, slide-rules, and endless patience to unravel the facts. But a reasonably complete story was worked out for 96 sick persons. Eighty-nine of them might have eaten oysters supplied by Bivalve, Inc. Two had eaten only such oysters, and three had eaten only oysters supplied by another company whose dock was alongside that of Bivalve, Inc., and which sometimes traded oysters with that concern. Taken in conjunction with the findings from Chicago and Washington, and similar findings on a smaller scale from seven of the ten cities mentioned earlier as having a marked excess of cases, this was enough to pin responsibility for the epidemic on a particular dealer.

This was of some importance. There had been so much typhoid that when oysters were first implicated the bottom dropped out of the market. On December 9 the health commissioner of Chicago had warned his public not to eat raw oysters; on December 17 the health commissioner of New York had embargoed oysters originating anywhere in Lower New York Bay. From a quarter to three-quarters of the normal trade of other oyster-producing areas vanished; men were out of work; even the innocent haddock and his kind were under suspicion. As late as January 15, the Illinois State Department of Health ruled that no oysters could be sold in the state unless the purchaser promised in writing not to eat them raw. Obviously something had to be done to save a legitimate industry and quiet public fear, and this the United States Public Health Service did.

While it was a useful service to lift the burden which had rested on the industry as a whole, the investigators would like to have traced the infection in the oysters sold by Bivalve, Inc., to a definite source. In this they were disappointed, and the climax of the story is a little blunted by the impossibility of showing just how these oysters came to grief. Bivalve, Inc., had a good reputation among health officials who knew its methods. Its growing beds were well off shore, presumably in clean water. It is true that the dredging boats which worked over the oyster beds had no provision for the disposal of excreta, and pollution there was possible, but no connection with a focus of infection could be found. This hazard was removed by mid-December.

It is also true that in October and November there had been outbreaks of typhoid fever in the town where the dredgers docked and from which the oysters were shipped. Fishermen tied up their boats and loiterers strolled along the shore where oysters waiting shipment were stored in shallow water. What "walking cases" or temporary carriers may have been abroad during the time when the oysters were contaminated no one will ever know.

Fifteen hundred people learned to their cost, however, that the elaborate system by which their appetites were titillated might become a means of broadcasting infection. Some of them inherited the ills of strangers a thousand miles away. It's a complicated world, and only endless vigilance on the part of people we never see makes it tolerably safe to live in.

### THE CASE OF THE ELDERLY VILLAGERS

I started to call this story The Case of the Homeless Horse, but, whatever the conventions of the detective yarn, which always begins with a corpse, one cannot be flippant about the diseases in which death waits just around the corner. There *was* a homeless horse in the story—a horse and some pigs, and, because Hiram Bentley, who owned them, had no place of his own to keep them in, he bargained with old Mr. Enderby, who agreed to stable the horse and provide a pen for the pigs if Hiram would do the milking.

Mr. Enderby, now nearing his eighty-sixth year, kept one cow and was too old to milk her himself. For sixty of the seventy years he had lived in Fairfield he had been the town butcher, but now he had retired and lived comfortably in one of the white houses with blue shutters that made passing drivers from the city envious. A widow of sixty years kept house for him, and a son-in-law completed the family. The other children and grandchildren, one in Fairfield, the rest scattered over the state, came in for a visit now and then, but most of Mr. Enderby's neighbors were old people like himself. Dr. Phillips, who had carried his worn black bag around Fairfield for a mere quarter-century, was still thought of as being rather a newcomer, and he in turn didn't speak to a younger competitor who had spent a couple of decades in the village.

When Mrs. Cooper, at eighty-seven, took to her bed in March with headache and a bad sore throat, her daughter had the same difficulty hardly a week later, and her middle-aged boarder fell sick in the same way the next day, Dr. Phillips knew that something was wrong. These were not ordinary sore throats; people were good and sick, with headache, nausea, fever, and prostration, and they stayed sick several days.

On the last Monday in March he was called to Mr. Enderby's house and found still another bad sore throat. The old man had been taken sick on Sunday and by Monday morning he was very uncomfortable. That night Annie Putnam, a married daughter, came down from Manchester to see how her father was getting on. He got on badly, developed pneumonia, and died early in the afternoon on Tuesday. On that same day his housekeeper and his son-in-law both had sore throats, and the next day Mrs. Putnam, who was staying over for the funeral, had a like complaint. Her older brother, who still lived in Fairfield, had felt signs of a cold the day before his father died and was presently sick with pneumonia.

Dr. Phillips knew that Mr. Enderby kept a cow—one knows everything about one's neighbors in Fairfield—and that there was always fresh milk on the table. He knew too that there was milk enough so that some of Mr. Enderby's neighbors bought a bottle or two regularly and that sometimes what was left over found its way into other households. He called in the state department of health to find out whether there was some connection between this milk and the dozen or more sore throats which by this time had turned up among Mr. Enderby's neighbors and relatives.

The reason was not far to seek. Scrapings from a number of the sore throats showed the hemolytic streptococcus, a treacherous organism at best and one which now and then shows a particularly virulent form, spreading quickly in milk and striking hard at its victims. When the investigators hunted up the milker, he was sure that nothing was wrong with the cow, but they all went out together to look at her and found that the right fore quarter of the udder was caked and scabby. When this was pointed out to Hiram, he admitted that he had noticed something odd about the udder and the milk. The milk had been "a little brown," but he didn't think much of anything was the matter and had just rubbed a little camphorated oil into the udder in the hope of softening it to make milking easier.

When the milk from the diseased quarter was put aside to permit any bacteria which it contained to grow, there were clear signs of hemolytic streptococcus, and when scrapings were taken from the milker's throat the same parasite turned up in great numbers. The indications were that Hiram, with a sore throat that had not bothered him, was shedding organisms which his hands carried to the cow's udder, that these had set up a local inflammation in a single teat, that organisms drawn down with the milk from this quarter—which was mixed in the pail with milk from the healthy quarters—spread rapidly in the milk, that all the housekeeper's care in straining and bottling the milk had no effect on this invisible contamination, and that the milk had then imperiled all those who drank it.*

There is not much suspense in this story, and beside such disasters as the septic sore throat epidemic in Lee† the outbreak does not bulk very large. But it is fascinating to watch the rings spreading from a pebble even in a tiny pool. There was Mr. Enderby's own household of three: all three drank the milk, all three became sick, and one died. One of Mr. Enderby's sons, with his wife, had visited Mr. Enderby on Sunday. They took a bottle of milk home with them that night; both were sick by Tuesday. There was Annie Putnam, who came with her boy to be with her father in his illness: she was ill when she went home after the funeral, called a doctor three days later, died four days after that. The boy, who drank no milk, escaped. Another of Mr. Enderby's sons brought his wife and his five daughters to the funeral: two of the family used the milk—one a girl just turned seventeen who refused whipped cream (which had been

---

* When not one cow but hundreds or thousands are concerned in a given milk supply, discovery of the source of infection is naturally more difficult. In such cases the hunt proceeds by a process of elimination. First pooled samples of milk are studied farm by farm, then pooled samples from four cows at a time, then samples from individual cows, until the contaminated milk is traced to one or more animals. It may even be necessary to take samples from each quarter of the udder before an internal lesion is located.

† See page 183.

bought elsewhere) and took plain milk because she was determined not to trifle with her figure; she too fell sick. There was also J. K., another Enderby, who went through pneumonia but lived. His wife, who seems to have caught his infection a little later, was the only secondary case in the group.

Jennie Rogers, upstanding and independent at seventy-five, who lived close by and took milk from Mr. Enderby, fell sick the day before he did, and would not hear of going to bed. She kept going as long as she could in spite of an angry ear, but gave in on the seventh day and went into the hospital, where she died within three hours. Among the other neighbors who used the milk regularly, Mrs. Cooper's household of three produced three cases. There were three Johnsons, and all of them fell ill. Sometimes a neighbor came by and brought a bottle or pitcher to be filled, and occasionally one of the regular milk dealers in town took a bottle or two when his own supply was short. This group of users produced a case or two, and the last case of all befell the soda-jerker at the drugstore, where three or four quarts of Mr. Enderby's milk had been used when the regular supply ran short. Some of this milk went into milk-shakes for passing motorists; three were identified and followed up, but they seem to have escaped infection. The boy behind the counter served himself only too well. The epidemic stopped when the board of health condemned the cow, which was presently slaughtered, and forbade Hiram to milk any other cows until his throat was well.

Not counting the itinerants, ten families in Fairfield and three in neighboring towns had been exposed in some degree to the infected milk. In twelve of these thirteen families there was at least one case of infection; in six families everyone was sick. Of twenty-three persons who were known to have used the milk raw, nineteen were infected directly and one indirectly. The fifteen throats from which cultures were taken all showed the characteristic organism. A little trouble goes a long way when the hemolytic streptococcus is at the bottom of it.

Pasteurized milk spreads no sore throat.

## THE CASE OF THE SLEEPY LOBSTERS

They don't often have typhoid fever in Pompton, a city of something over a hundred thousand in Massachusetts, and when nine cases turned up in July 1929, along with another in West-brook to the north, one in Durham to the south, and four in Aspetuck, a few miles away, the state health authorities swung promptly into action.

The peculiar fact in this instance was that the disease seemed to be attacking well-to-do adults in family groups. Only two children were affected, and their parents were also sick; more-over, this family (in Durham) was related to one of the sick men in Westbrook.

In such a picture it is easy to exonerate the water supply, for all the towns had public water and there was no reason why it should have been so selective in its action. When the usual ques-tions were asked about the milk supply, it developed that every family affected bought milk from a different dealer. There was no question in most of the cases of contact with a person ill of typhoid, and if the trouble was traceable to food, as seemed probable, the investigators suspected that some delicacy might be involved. Otherwise, one would have expected to find cases in as many poor as well-to-do families.

The first house visited was one in which the patient had died. This was Mrs. Marian Perkins, a motherly widow who lived alone and helped to pay the grocery bills by serving meals to a Mr. Phillips. She had taken sick on July 5. Her fever went high; she was harassed by chills and the distressing symptoms which accompany typhoid, and died suddenly a week later. Her doctor was not quite sure what the trouble was and ascribed her death in his official report to "congestion of the lungs with dilatation of the heart" of unknown origin. Later, however, he was convinced that she must have had typhoid fever. Her boarder fell ill on the same day as she, and two days earlier, it developed, her married daughter, who often came with her husband to eat with her mother, had also taken sick. The son-in-law had had typhoid fever as a child, and had been immunized as a soldier in the first world war. While he had some pain, he escaped fever and no trace of the typhoid parasite could be found in his stool specimens.

Timothy Ryan was sanitary inspector for the same town. Shortly before falling ill he had been inspecting dairies in Vermont, and had found some of them bad enough to shut off their milk supply. But he knew of no typhoid fever in the area he had visited and had probably not been infected there. When the investigators questioned him about what he and his family had eaten, he mentioned the fact that they had had lobster on one day late in June and that it had tasted spoiled. The investigator pricked up his ears, but after all this was the sort of clue that the author usually lets fall at about page 50 of a detective story just to throw the careless reader off the track. Spoiled food by itself does not give people typhoid. Nobody had ever known the bacilli to be carried by a boiled lobster—a horny-shelled creature with meat so carefully protected that it takes a skilful hand to get it out, and one which always goes through boiling water before it reaches the dinner-table. Mr. Ryan remembered the occasion because he had bought the lobsters on his birthday and they had formed the *pièce de résistance* of the birthday dinner. There was a special sale of lobsters that day, in fact, which he had noticed as he walked down to the office. He had mentioned the sale to his chief, the health commissioner, who was equally fond of lobster and asked Mr. Ryan to buy one for him. The health officer's wife, as it happened, was also among the patients.

Checking back, the epidemiologist discovered that Mr. Phillips—a wholesale grocer who naturally did the marketing for Mrs. Perkins—had also bought boiled lobsters from the same market on the same day as Mr. Ryan. This was either an odd coincidence or, however improbable it seemed, an important lead.

Peter Simpson, who lived in Westbrook, was a fond grandfather. There were only adults left in his own family, but a son, who lived in Durham, usually came in with his wife and two children to take supper with the old people on Sunday evening. Sometimes, however, the grandparents visited their son, and on one such occasion about two weeks before these occurrences boiled lobster had been served as a special treat. It was made into a salad which the adults enjoyed heartily, and small portions were put on the children's plates to see what they would do about it. On July 3 or thereabouts the son's wife took sick; on the fifth or the sixth the son fell ill, three days later the grandfather. A little later one of the children—though not definitely sick—seemed more tired than usual and had a slight afternoon temperature. Both children later gave indication by blood tests of typhoid infection. Their mother died. It turned out that the lobsters had been bought from the same store at which the other patients had traded.

Mrs. Fisher, another patient, was a part-time telephone operator at another branch of the market where the lobsters had been sold. She usually lunched alone at home and remembered buying boiled lobster on some day in June, not at her own place of work but at the store already named by so many others.

In an out-of-the-way part of Aspetuck, fifteen miles from Pompton, lived Mrs. Vitale. Her husband usually bought the family supplies in Boston, but once in a while he traded in Pompton on his way home and one day, finding lobsters cheap there, he brought one home with him. Only his wife suffered from his shrewd marketing. Two other cases in Pompton could not be connected in any way with the lobsters, but, after all, a certain amount of typhoid does occur even in well-kept Massachusetts, and it is rarely possible to show that every individual sick at a given time in a given city has been infected from a single source.

Out of these fifteen cases, then, at least a dozen and possibly thirteen could be connected definitely with boiled lobster bought at a given store, and in six of them the purchasers remembered clearly that the date of purchase was June 27. In every family but one, the housewife who prepared the food fell ill, and this one woman had had typhoid fever before.

When the trail of the lobsters was picked up at the market, the story became still more interesting. A carload of lobsters had been bought for a small chain of stores. The wholesaler who provided them reported that on their way by rail they had been delayed because of a hotbox and when they reached him they were obviously in poor condition. The buyer said they looked weak and "sleepy." It was decided, therefore, to boil them up at once instead of sending them out alive, as usual. The chain stores got them at a bargain and promptly advertised them for sale, but someone soon noticed that even after emergency treatment they seemed a little spoiled, and they were promptly recalled. Two of the four stores in the chain sent back all their lobsters, but a hundred had already been sold in each of the two other stores, at one of which the typhoid patients had bought them. No infection was reported from the sales at the other store, so that a hundred hastily purchased lobsters had been responsible for the thirteen cases. It was the only bargain sale of the season.

How could boiled lobsters become infected? Nine employees at the store might have handled them. However, when stool and urine specimens from these nine persons were examined, not a single one showed typhoid infection. One had had typhoid fever twenty years before but had been steadily on the job at the store ever since, had negative specimens, and so far as the record went had never infected any other person before the outbreak. At the wholesale dealers, the man whose job it was to boil lobsters regularly had had typhoid fever eight years before—such people turn up with amazing frequency in any thorough investigation—but though his blood test was positive, stool and urine examinations gave no indication that he was a carrier. Moreover, he had not handled this particular lot of lobsters, which were boiled by two temporary workers who had been laid off before the trouble was discovered.

Just as the investigation seemed to have come to a dead end, someone remembered that another man had worked for a time in the lobster room of the wholesale warehouse. He had fallen sick and had been paid off on June 14—twelve days before the suspected lobsters came in—and after leaving he had gone to the hospital to die. At autopsy his body showed the ravages of typhoid fever.

How could this unhappy stranger have infected lobsters which reached his place of work long after he had left it? The answer can hardly be worked out in detail, and perhaps it is just as well not to ask. In the room where empty lobster barrels were kept and in which both boiled and live lobsters were stored a thick coating of slime afforded a congenial medium for the preservation of bacteria. The barrels were "washed out with a hose when they smelled bad," the investigators were told. The sick man, working about this room, had been known to vomit frequently. What other liberties he may have taken in his misery must be left to the imagination.

Suppose lobsters fresh from the boiling pot were dumped into a slimy barrel in which bacteria had been unwittingly planted. At the bottom or sides of the barrel some would be covered with slime. Not all would run this risk—and not all the lobsters that were sold made people sick. But those which were contaminated were handled by housewives who pulled and twisted the claws and cracked the shells and picked out the meat bit by bit and then arranged it neatly on the salad plates. It is not hard to believe that some infectious stuff was transferred in the process from shell to meat. One cannot prove that the thing happened in just this way, but the two who died and the eleven others who were sick were victims in some such fashion of a chain of circumstances which Conan Doyle himself could hardly have invented.

## THE CASE OF THE PLUMBER'S PATCHWORK

You can hardly write a proper detective story without introducing, at an early stage, a neat and plausible hypothesis which seems to fit the facts nicely but unfortunately leaves the way open for a fresh murder or two and so collapses with a bang.

Meeting in Indianapolis in October 1933, the American Public Health Association—a sort of Crime Club for epidemiologists (among other things)—heard such an explanation of a troublesome outbreak of amebic dysentery in a Chicago hotel. One day in August two cases of this uncommon disease had been reported from two different hotels. This was as many as Chicago usually produced in a whole month, and the Board of Health, sensitized by a similar outbreak in another hotel in 1926, got busy at once. Both patients, it appeared, had eaten at the Coliseum Hotel,* and other guests there were sick. The Board took a room and bath at this hotel—though rooms and baths were at a premium in Chicago's World's Fair year—and began rushing hotel employees to stool and promptly searching the feces under the microscope for the parasite that causes the disease. By the first of September, thirty-one cases and eleven carriers had been found

* I follow the discreet practice of the official reports, which politely disguise the names of the hotels affected, though a government document locates them plainly on a map of Chicago and leaves no doubt as to their identity.

among employees and guests. These included "five cooks, one sauce maker, one cold meat man, one baker, two butchers, five dish-washers, two counter girls, one waffle girl, seven waiters and one pantry boy." Lurking in the background, indeed, was a baker who had been found infected six years before, and was supposedly cured, but had somehow got back on the infectious list. The hypothesis was that foodhandlers who were excreting parasites were bringing dirty hands to their tasks, and so stirring infection into the hollandaise and spreading it on the canapes and planting it on the dessert spoons.

This was the respectable way of explaining the spread of amebic infection in temperate climates, and most of the physicians who had written about the disease had maintained that it did not or could not burst out in epidemic form, since it did not leap from the acutely sick to the well, as most explosive diseases do, but spread slowly from carriers.* One parasitologist had played Cassandra on this theme, warning American public health workers in 1932 that infection was widespread and might cause trouble, but he too felt that "under conditions prevailing in a modern town or city or in a properly sanitated military camp or post, an epidemic of amebic dysentery is practically impossible." [2]

---

* The *Endamoeba histolytica* has two life-stages. The naked cell oozes its way into the wall of the large bowel and may cause ugly ulcers, often shaped like a buttonhole, which produce acute and painful diarrhea and may lead ultimately to death. The ameba in this stage is vulnerable and cannot survive passage through the digestive tract of a new host. But if bodily resistance is good, and the parasite gets only a limited foothold, individual amebae turn into hard balls or cysts and cut loose, passing out of the intestine. The carrier may shed cysts for a long time without any obvious symptoms of infection, and it has been estimated that from five to ten per cent of the whole population may be carriers in this fashion. The cyst is tough enough to resist the chlorine in drinking water which kills typhoid bacilli and other bacteria. When it is swallowed, however, the shell is digested and the ameba is free to divide neatly into eight daughter-cells and repeat the process of colonization in the bowel of the new host. Cyst production, which transmits infection, is thus a function of the carrier state rather than the acute illness.

Something very like an epidemic was occurring in a city so modern that it was at that very moment celebrating a Century of Progress, but it did not at once occur to the local epidemiologists to hunt for a new explanation.

There was more to come, however. The evening papers in Indianapolis carried a brief summary of the report on the Chicago cases. This was interesting reading for one Indianapolitan who had two people sick of amebic dysentery in his own family after a visit to Chicago. He lost no time in hunting up the principal author of the paper and telling him about them. This led to further questions, and it came out that at least eight cases leading back to Chicago were at that minute known to Indianapolis doctors. This was news to the Chicago health workers, and when they got home they promptly reported it to their chief. Meanwhile, they learned, new cases had been developing at the Coliseum, and it began to be clear that something much bigger than anyone had suspected was afoot.

As a matter of fact specialists in tropical diseases in various cities had for some time been seeing patients who had fallen sick with amebic dysentery under curious conditions. Ordinarily the victim feels uncomfortable for a long time before he has to call a doctor, but these patients had been suddenly seized on the road or in a train, or as they came home from a holiday trip; they had severe attacks; and as the doctors questioned them it turned out that a good many of them had been to Chicago.

With the Indianapolis situation in mind, the Chicago health workers began to wonder seriously how many visitors had caught this unfamiliar disease and what was happening to them. So they took an unprecedented step: they began to comb the country for cases. They mailed questionnaires at first to the out-of-town guests who had been registered at the Coliseum in June, July, and August, and later to thousands of other visitors. The questions ran thus:

1. Were you courteously received and treated by all officials with whom you came in contact while in Chicago and at A Century of Progress Exposition?
2. Have you any suggestions for better future control that will add to the comfort and convenience of visitors, should the Century of Progress Exposition be continued in 1934?
3. Did your observations show that food and dish washing were handled in a sanitary way?
4. Did you or any of your family develop any sickness while in Chicago or after you returned home?
5. If any illness did develop, please state below the exact nature of your sickness and date of first symptoms.

This was a masterpiece of tact. Few who received it had any inkling of its purpose, and as the inquiry was broadened—over 100,000 questionnaires were mailed eventually—the replies were just as likely to stress the outrage of charging ten cents for a visit to the public toilets at the Fair as they were to report significant symptoms.

Yet as the early returns straggled in there was plenty of evidence that amebic dysentery was not uncommon among people who had stayed at the Coliseum during the summer. Within a few weeks, indeed, this evidence was so strong that a public warning was broadcast, and then a great mass of information began to pour in. Whenever suspicious symptoms were reported, the Board of Health hurried back an answer—using the telegraph and long-distance telephone for quick results—urging the correspondent to get immediate medical care if he had not done so, asking for the name of his physician, and then warning the physician not to forget the possibility of amebic infection.

This advice was received in various ways. Some doctors were grateful, others annoyed. One lady conspicuous in the nightclubs of the nation, for example, had been taken sick on a trip through the far West. Her doctors, when reached by telephone, told the Chicago Board of Health in effect to mind its own busi-

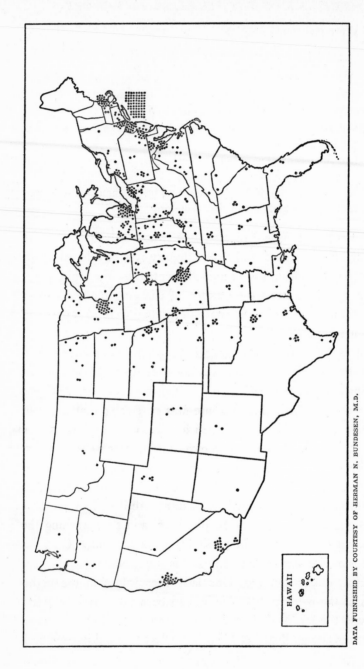

*The epidemic by questionnaire: cases of amebic dysentery reported to the Chicago Board of Health as originating in Chicago during the Century of Progress Exposition*

ness, operated for appendicitis, and lost their patient. Only under threat of police action when the body was brought through Chicago was it possible to secure an autopsy, and that confirmed the suspicion that the lady had actually died of amebic dysentery.

When the evidence was all in, months later,* 1,409 cases had been found, and there was reason to believe that the actual total was considerably larger. These cases were reported from four hundred different cities and from all but five states. Nearly three-fourths, 1,050 in all, had occurred among guests or employees of the Coliseum and the neighboring Athenaeum Hotel. Of the ninety-eight persons who died, seventy had apparently contracted the disease at these hotels.

As a check, questionnaires were sent also to registered out-of-town guests of four other large downtown hotels, and it soon became apparent that the source of trouble, whatever it was, was sharply localized. Indeed if one stayed a month or more at either the Coliseum or the Athenaeum in the summer or early fall of 1933 one's chances of getting amebic dysentery seemed to be something like 14,000 times greater than if one just went to Chicago to see the Fair. Even brief contact with these two hotels might be dangerous: one of the questionnaires came back from a New York woman who had spent a single day and night at the Coliseum with her sister from California. She herself was on a sickbed; her sister was already dead.

While this epidemic by questionnaire was being pieced out of the records, the health department continued to make stool examinations at the two hotels. As fast as employees were found to be infected they were taken out of the kitchens and pantries for treatment. But this means of control got nowhere. Instead of diminishing, the number of carriers increased. Cooks, waiters,

* Compilations were made as of June 30, 1934, but the epidemic period was considered to run from June 1 to December 31, 1933. Only scattering cases originated after that date.

and bell-boys who had been free of infection when the first study was made had mysteriously acquired it in the interim. If this was a food-borne epidemic, it was not running true to form. But how could it be anything else? Flies? There were no flies in the elegant dining-rooms and bedrooms of these hotels. Water? Chicago water was carefully sterilized, constantly tested, and there was not enough dysentery in the city at large to throw suspicion on this common factor.

Yet the food-borne infection theory did not work as a premise for control, and stubborn facts kept turning up to challenge it. As the story was put together by matching case reports and the registration books of the hotels, waves of infection were revealed. For example, it was highly unhealthy to stay at the Coliseum in the week before the Fourth of July, but during the rest of July one was relatively safe. There were higher peaks in the latter part of August and early October. For several days during these peak periods the rate of infection ran as high as three, four, or possibly five per cent of the registered guests. This did not seem to fit with the theory that carriers were continuously transmitting infection.

A specialist on tropical diseases drafted into service to study the outbreak made an experiment which threw more doubt on the food—infection theory. From the groups most likely to be infected—immigrants from hot countries—he chose a number of the dirtiest kitchen workers he could find, took scrapings from their fingernails, cultured them, and found little evidence that amebic cysts were lurking there.

Still more conclusive was the fact that approximately a third of the guests and employees who fell ill at the Athenaeum had apparently not eaten meals in either hotel. In the Athenaeum, employees who worked above the second floor, wherever they ate, were much likelier to become infected than those working on the first two.

Late in November, therefore, the investigation took a new turn. The upper floors of the Athenaeum had one thing in common with the Coliseum: they shared the same "house water" system. Was something polluting the drinking water inside the hotels?

Now a modern hotel, as Arnold Bennett and Vicki Baum have told us, is a very complex institution. The Coliseum and the Athenaeum were old and honorable hostelries; the Coliseum in particular, with its plush-and-marble lobby, was a landmark for discriminating travelers. The Athenaeum was more than forty years old; the Coliseum had been completed, by easy stages, more than a quarter of a century before the Fair. Behind the opulent surfaces of each was a wilderness of service quarters, a labyrinth of pipes. The plumbing, originally designed for modest nineteenth-century needs, had grown like Topsy as the hotels pushed upward. To explore it was like uncovering a buried city. The operating force had inherited a system they had no hand in planning; at some points it was literally true that no one knew whether a given pipe carried water or sewage.

So a competent engineering staff was put to work to study the plumbing. At times fifty or a hundred persons were busy at some part of the task. Bit by bit the system was mapped and tested. Danger points soon came to light, though it was not until after New Year's Day that the chief engineer of the hotel confided to the investigators that on July 2, in the midst of an early morning downpour which loaded the sewers to the breaking point, a house drain under the basement floor had burst and flooded the ice-storage room, the laundry, bakery, pantries, iceboxes, and other parts of the basement, though the main kitchen escaped. This was sensational news. The trouble had been quickly corrected, and disinfectants scattered liberally, but the kitchen staff still remembered how hard it had been to serve breakfast that morning, and it is unlikely that the exacting guests had gone without their ice-water. Still, infection had been at work all through the summer, and no single accident could account for its persistence.

The guest-room plumbing was put through a series of tests which later made dramatic and unpleasant reading in the newspapers. The long vertical stacks running through tiers of bathrooms proved treacherous. A red dye was placed in forty toilet tanks and when these at a signal were simultaneously flushed, the water in the bathroom faucets began to run red, indicating that when the plumbing was used intensively, dangerous siphonage could occur. But even in a hotel as overcrowded as Chicago hotels were in the summer of 1933, it was hardly likely that the conditions of this experiment would often be reproduced.

There were more serious conditions, however. At two o'clock one morning the sanitary engineer had stumbled on something really significant. He found a cross connection between pipes hung on the basement ceiling where sewage could pass through a leaking or partly open valve into the drinking-water supply which served the whole of the Coliseum and the greater part of the Athenaeum. The cross connection had been installed some twenty years before—long after the original plumbing had been approved by the city inspector—to permit an excess of water used in the cooling system to be discharged into the sewers instead of overflowing a collecting tank. It was so designed, however, that when one of the pumps which circulated water through the cooling system was shut down for repairs or otherwise, hydraulic pressure in the sewer would force sewage back into the water tank whenever the valve was not absolutely tight. When the engineers and the epidemiologists compared notes, it was seen that infection had risen sharply at just those times when one of the pumps was out of service. If the plumber and the public health man had got together earlier, such a hazard could not have existed. But so long as this condition continued it was easy to see how infection could have been spread repeatedly through the Coliseum and the upper floors of the Athenaeum.

Nor was this all. In February another dangerous leak was discovered. In a dark corner in a basement room a branch sewer was found directly over the tank in which refrigerated water for drinking was stored. Some time in the dim past a plumber had occasion to unscrew a plug in the clean-out section of this branch sewer. The plug stuck, and before he could move it he had to drill a hole through the cap. When the job was finished, instead of threading a smaller metal plug into this hole, he took out his jackknife and roughly whittled a wooden plug, hammered it in, picked up his tools and returned to the bosom of his family. But wet wood rots. And as the years passed and the overloaded sewers did their work, the plug went the way of all wet wood. When found, it could be picked out with the tips of the fingers; it was pitted, stained with sludge, and frankly leaky. The sewer was so designed that under ordinary conditions water would not reach the plug. But it drained twenty bathrooms in quarters which were in heavy demand during the Fair, and it discharged into a storm sewer. On the evening of June 29 there was a heavy shower just at the time when footsore visitors were repairing to their rooms after a day of sightseeing. Under such conditions it was inevitable that the water should back up in the sewer and that the leakage, which might be measured in drops under ordinary conditions, should swell to a stream of several cubic centimeters per second. From the plug the water dripped on to a pump; from the pump it could run to the top of the tank, seep around a loosely fitted cover, and so carry the sewage from twenty crowded rooms directly into the cool water from which guests throughout the hotels were slaking their thirst. Small wonder that the Coliseum at the end of June was an unhealthy place to be.

More or less continuously during the summer, and especially

when the sewers were overloaded or a pump was out of service, the hotels, already infected, were drinking their own sewage.

It took over a quarter of a million dollars and more than a mile of new pipe to modernize the plumbing of these hotels. But the job was done, and though they played host to another great surge of visitors in 1934, there was no return of the first year's disaster. One might search far before finding a safer place to stay, from this particular point of view, than the Coliseum or Athenaeum today.

Here was the perfect technological epidemic. For an epidemic, there must be a susceptible herd. Technological achievements beckoned eight and a half million people to Chicago, and modern transportation brought them there. One hundred and sixty thousand persons had contact with the Coliseum or the Athenaeum in seven months. There must be a vehicle for the transmission of disease. Two hotels, through technological flaws, had become effective machines for feeding one man's poison to another. They produced an epidemic which medical opinion held to be impossible, and civic pride unthinkable. The city failed its guests because at one vital point the century of progress had been a century of patchwork, obsolescent equipment giving way piece by piece to new facilities which never quite caught up with the demands progress might lay upon them.

Technology, again, created the epidemic as a social fact. The sick men scattered over a continent; the mails, the telephone, and the telegraph pieced them together, revealed the shape and magnitude of the disaster, demonstrated the need of control. Technology, in the end, uncovered the flaw, explained the fact, applied the control, and ended the hazard.

A hotel is no better than its plumbing.

## REFERENCES

1. Mustard, Harry S. *Rural health practice.* New York: The Commonwealth Fund, 1936, p. 440.

2. Craig, Charles F., quoted in *Epidemic amebic dysentery; the Chicago outbreak of 1933.* National Institute of Health Bulletin No. 166, March 1936, p. 3.

## A NOTE ON SOURCES

All the personal names and some of the place names used in this chapter are fictitious.

Most, but not all, of the investigations here summarized have been reported in print, as follows:

The Methodist Ladies: Sawyer, Wilbur A. *Ninety-three persons infected by a typhoid carrier at a public dinner.* Journal of the American Medical Association, 63:1537–1542, October 31, 1914.

The Ladylike Oysters: Lumsden, L. L., Haseltine, H. E., Leake, J. P., and Veldee, M. V. *A typhoid fever epidemic caused by oyster-borne infection (1924–1925).* Supplement No. 50 to Public Health Reports, Washington, 1925. *Also*, Bundesen, H. N. *Typhoid epidemic in Chicago apparently due to oysters.* Journal of the American Medical Association, 84:641–650, February 28, 1925.

The Sleepy Lobsters: Anderson, G. W., and Scamman, C. L. *Typhoid fever apparently spread by boiled lobster.* Journal of Preventive Medicine, 4:405–410, September 1930.

The Plumber's Patchwork: *Epidemic amebic dysentery: the Chicago outbreak of 1933.* National Institute of Health Bulletin No. 166, March 1936.

*Also*, Tonney, F. O., Hoeft, G. L., and Spector, B. K. *The threat of amebiasis in the food handler.* Journal of the American Medical Association, 101:1638–1639, November 18, 1933.

*Also*, Bundesen, H. N., Tonney, F. O., and Rawlings, I. D. *The outbreak of amebiasis in Chicago during 1933.* Journal of the American Medical Association, 102:367–369, February 3, 1934.

*Also*, Bundesen, H. N. *The Chicago epidemic of amoebic dysentery in 1933.* Public Health Reports, 49:1266–1272, October 26, 1934.

For unpublished material and supplementary details I am indebted to Dr. Wilson G. Smillie of Cornell; Dr. L. L. Lumsden of the United States Public Health Service; Dr. Wilbur A. Sawyer of the Rockefeller Foundation; Dr. Gaylord W. Anderson, lately of the Massachusetts State Health Department; and the late Dr. F. W. O'Connor of Columbia.

# 8

## UNFINISHED BUSINESS

WE HAVE heard a good deal about the triumphs of preventive medicine and can be justly proud of them. Most of us, instead of dying incontinently of communicable disease, may now expect to live to run the gantlet of diseases which seem not to be communicable. White men who curb their *Wanderlust* are in no great danger from such grisly enemies as plague and cholera; the grosser manifestations of smallpox, yellow fever, typhus, and typhoid fever are now inconceivable in civilized countries at peace. We have a practicable method of checking at least one of the acute communicable diseases of childhood. We have some notion of how to defend ourselves against infection even though we do not always succeed in doing so. These accomplishments are familiar and I shall not say much more about them than I have already said in earlier chapters.

We are still a long way, however, from putting an end to pestilence. Go far enough—and in some instances not so very far—from New York or Paris and it is still possible to watch cholera, plague, yellow fever, malaria, smallpox, or typhus at work. Tuberculosis and syphilis are next-door neighbors, pneumonia and influenza our familiar companions. Neither white nor yellow nor brown men do curb their *Wanderlust* entirely, nor has war been abandoned as an instrument of national policy and bacterial exchange. Every advance in the speed of transportation makes it harder to isolate any nation. There is always India —with a fifth of the world's leprosy, nearly three-quarters of the world's reported plague, nine-tenths of the world's reported cholera, and more than nine-tenths of the world's reported deaths from smallpox—to be considered, and the unfinished business of the epidemiologist in Java or Kurdistan or the valley of the Orinoco may one day concern us deeply. Even in the United States, for all the spectacular changes that have taken place, every fifth death can be reasonably attributed to parasitic invasion (if we include the viruses among the parasites) and if we knew more about the remote causes of many chronic disorders of the heart and kidneys the ratio would undoubtedly be higher.*

There is indeed no finished business in epidemiology. Some diseases seem to be beaten and then turn up in new and baffling forms, as yellow fever did. Some could probably be rooted out of the temperate zone if the public health men, who know what to do, could persuade the public to let them do it—as in smallpox†— or to foot the bill—as in malaria. Some others no one does much of anything about because no one knows what to do—influenza and poliomyelitis, for instance. Whether or not there are actually

* Even the most trustful reader must realize that such figures are crude and vulnerable estimates. The statement made here and related computations throughout this chapter are based on the United States Census classification of deaths by cause for the five years 1933–1937. I have counted as infectious not only the group which is labeled infectious and parasitic, but also acute rheumatic fever, *tabes dorsalis* and general paralysis of the insane (both attributable to syphilis), all meningitis, diseases of the ear and mastoid process, acute endocarditis, bronchitis, all the pneumonias, pleurisy, diseases of the pharynx and tonsils, diarrhea and enteritis, acute nephritis, puerperal septicemia, and osteomyelitis. For the year 1938 the ratio of infectious deaths to all deaths was slightly under one in five.

† The United States, though a poor second to India, leads all the other countries of the world in reported cases of smallpox and instead of decreasing, the disease is actually more prevalent than it was ten years ago.

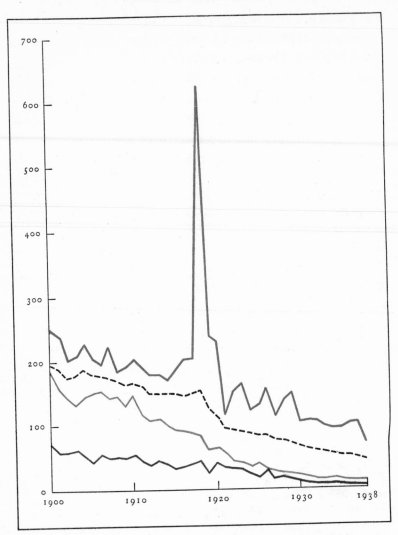

II. *Death rates for influenza, pneumonia, and bronchitis* ——— ;
*all forms of tuberculosis* – – – ; *typhoid and paratyphoid fevers,
dysentery, cholera nostras, diarrhea and enteritis* ——— ; *and diphtheria, measles, scarlet fever, and whooping cough* ——— . (*Deaths
per 100,000 population, registration states of 1900*)

new diseases, there are certainly some, like encephalitis, that seem freshly threatening. And underneath all that is done in the name of communicable disease control are the tides of epidemicity, rising, falling, and not infrequently mocking the overconfident.

It is hard to measure net changes in the burden of disease, harder still to explain them intelligently. By limiting the question to a single country with good statistical habits, say the United States, forgetting the merely sick, and counting only those dead of a given disease, one can get facts of a sort. But death rates by cause are based on individual death reports, and these may reflect anything from skilful diagnosis to sheer guesswork. Diagnostic fashions change and experts keep tinkering with the classifications of disease. National rates in this country go back only about a generation and so reveal no long-time trends, and have just begun to be truly national: only ten states* were in the registration area in 1900 and the last of the forty-eight came into the picture in 1933. One has only to let the inner eye rest first on New Hampshire and then on New Mexico to realize how some rates may have been skewed by these geographical changes. Many state and city rates have more history behind them and are geographically consistent, but these like the national rates may be distorted by changes in the age-composition of the population. Thanks to a declining birth and immigration rate and a lengthening of the average life, middle-aged and old people make up a larger part of the total population than they used to. If there are more people old enough to be likely to die of heart diseases and cancer than there used to be, that fact by itself will send the death rates from these causes up. If children became really scarce the death rates from diseases like whooping cough and measles would go down, again for purely statistical reasons. This sort of change confuses the issue.

To see as clearly as possible what has been going on it is best

* The six in New England, New York, New Jersey, Indiana, Michigan.

to stick to a single geographic area and make trial samplings to rule out the effect of changes in age distribution. Take for instance the ten states whose vital statistics were good enough in 1900 to justify the Bureau of the Census in setting up the original registration area. Chart II shows their annual death rates, from 1900 to 1938, from four major causes or groups of causes which taken together account for four-fifths of all the deaths attributable to infection. The thing that strikes the eye is that all these rates go down, decisively and in the main steadily (always excepting the extraordinary phenomena of 1918). The sharpest decline is in the communicable infections of the intestinal tract— diarrhea and enteritis, the dysenteries, typhoid fever—which, so far as they are spread by water and milk, are shining targets for public health effort.

It is dangerous, however, to draw comparisons from a chart of this common arithmetic type, where the most spectacular declines are those that involve the biggest numbers and a drop from 100 to 90 looks ten times as big as one from 10 to 9, although each is a ten per cent reduction. It is the rate rather than the volume of change that gives shape to the epidemic wave; it is an upswing in the rate, even at low levels, that warns the health officer of trouble. To show rates of change without distortion one must choose another scale (logarithmic) on which the interval between 100 and 90, or 1,000 and 900, is equivalent to that between 10 and 9. Then as a line goes up or down one ten per cent gain or loss will look just as steep as another, no matter how many deaths are involved.*

The next five charts are plotted on such a scale. Chart III repeats the data of Chart II, but now in a form that makes it fair to compare one curve with another. The drop in deaths from the

---

* It follows that one can conveniently compare, on such a scale, rates falling in the tens, the hundreds, and the thousands. By multiplying or dividing all the items of a given series by ten or any power of ten one can move a curve bodily from one part of the scale to another without altering its shape.

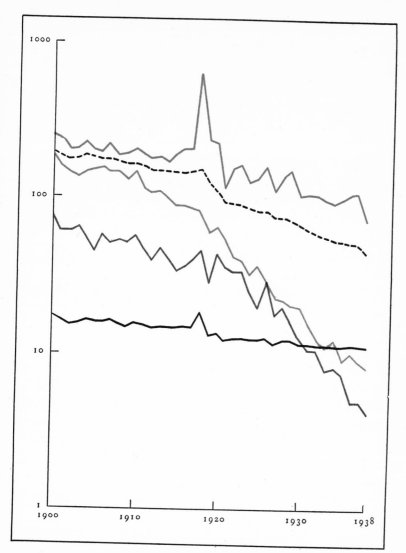

III. *Death rates for acute respiratory infections* ———; *tubercu-losis* – – –; *communicable intestinal infections* ———; *and* "chil-dren's diseases" ——— (all as in Chart II); and the general death rate ———. (Deaths by cause per 100,000, all deaths per 1,000 population, registration states of 1900, on a logarithmic scale)

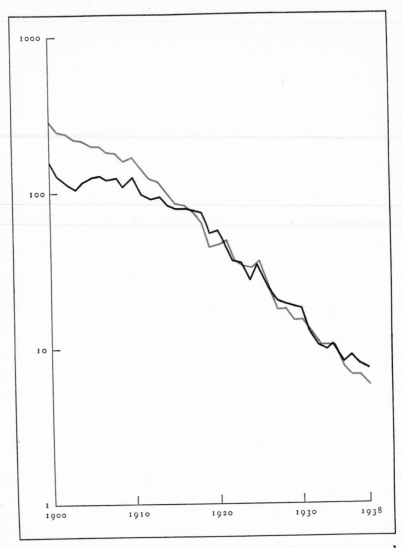

IV. *Death rates for typhoid and paratyphoid fevers* —— *and for dysentery, cholera nostras, diarrhea and enteritis* ——. *(Deaths per 1,000,000 population for the former, 100,000 for the latter, registration states of 1900, on a logarithmic scale)*

typhoid-dysentery-diarrhea group of diseases holds the center of the stage, but it is clear that the deaths from the "children's diseases," too, have been sliding downhill pretty rapidly. Both curves go down faster in recent years than the death rate from tuberculosis, and even the death rate from the acute respiratory infections, influenza, bronchitis, and the pneumonias—so hard to prevent and, until recently, to cure—has resumed the decline that began before the interruption of 1918. All these curves go down more steeply than the general death rate: infection as we know it is losing ground as a cause of death.*

Three of the curves relate to groups of diseases. Do they mask important differences between individual rates? Nothing much can be done about the first group, for the acute respiratory infections are too confusing in diagnosis to be cleanly separated in the records. The intestinal group we shall split into typhoid (with paratyphoid) fever and other diseases;† the four major children's diseases we shall plot separately.

Chart IV shows that since 1900, in these eastern and northern states, there has been no very striking difference in the downward slope of the two curves in the intestinal group. The advantage lies with the typhoid curve during the first half of the period, when, as was said in Chapter 6, major changes in public water supplies were still under way.

Chart V tells an interesting story. Diphtheria death rates go down steadily and conspicuously all through these years, the downgrade getting steeper and steeper; after leading the other diseases for a quarter of a century diphtheria drops below first

---

* A generation ago, in these ten states, two deaths in five were caused by infectious diseases; now, the country over, the ratio is only one in five.

† Diarrhea and enteritis and the several kinds of dysentery still form a mixed group, but they overlap considerably, while typhoid fever is a relatively clear-cut diagnosis. The two groups are by no means similar in size: one must multiply the typhoid death rates by ten to bring them into the range of easy comparison with the diarrhea-dysentery rates, which are fattened by infant deaths.

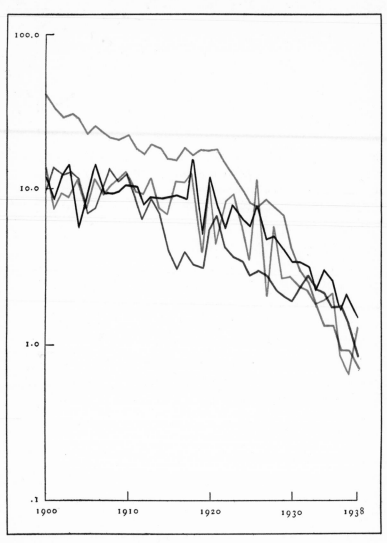

V. *Death rates for diphtheria*——, *measles* ——, *scarlet fever* ——, *and whooping cough* ——. (*Deaths per 100,000 population, registration states of 1900, plotted on a logarithmic scale*)

one and then another. Scarlet fever, though not so consistently, drifts lower too. Measles and whooping cough, when one disentangles the trend from the jerky epidemic fluctuations, change little for the first half of the period, then start definitely downward. In late years all four have run close together. The recent tobogganing of the diphtheria death rate may plausibly be connected with the use of toxin-antitoxin to prevent the disease (this began on a large scale in the twenties), but since the other rates swing downward without comparable pressure from the public health men one looks for a more general underlying cause.

These death rates are based on total population: so many deaths for each 100,000 people of all ages. But few except children die of the children's diseases, and the number of children in proportion to the total population is shrinking.* Have the rates gone down not because children are better off but simply because there are relatively fewer of them to fall sick or die? The way to answer that is to figure the rates not on people of all ages but on children, say on each 100,000 children between birth and five years of age. If these "age-specific" rates stood still while the general rates went down the latter change would manifestly be due to the rearrangement of age-groups within the population, and would represent a statistical accident rather than a real gain: the children would be no better off. Whooping cough should offer an acid test of this possibility since 95 per cent of all the deaths from this cause are at ages under five. But as Chart VI shows, the rate for children under five goes down steeply all by itself, quite as much so as the rate for persons five and older. So the change in the general death rate from whooping cough does reflect a net gain for that part of the population most threatened by it. The curves for measles, scarlet fever, and diphtheria (omitted here for reasons of space) tell essentially the same story.

* In the New England states children under five were 9.9 per cent of the total population in 1900, 8.4 in 1930; in New York 10.4 in 1900, 7.9 in 1930; in the whole country 12.1 in 1900, 9.3 in 1930.

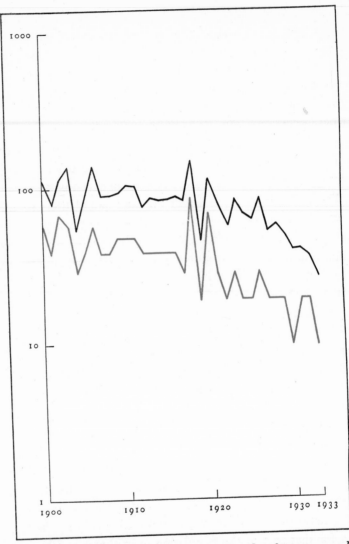

VI. *Death rates for whooping cough under five ——— and at five years and over ———— . (Deaths per 100,000 children under five, per 10,000,000 persons of five and over, registration states of 1900, plotted on a logarithmic scale)*

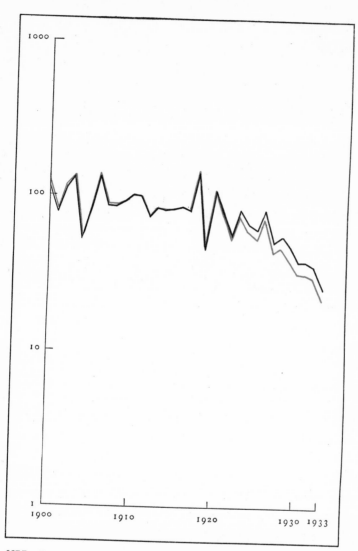

VII. *Death rates for whooping cough under five* —— *and at all ages* ——. (*Deaths per 100,000 children under five, per 1,000,000 persons at all ages, registration states of 1900, plotted on a logarithmic scale*)

In the case of measles and whooping cough, where the concentration of deaths in early childhood is most marked, one further turn of the screw sharpens the focus. If the death rate of children under five is plotted against the death rate of people at large the latter goes downhill just a shade more steeply than the former. This effect, illustrated for whooping cough in Chart VII, cannot be due to any relative advantage among persons of five and over, for this has been ruled out in Chart VI, and must be due to an altered ratio between persons under five and the total population. So changes in age-distribution have played some slight part in the gross decline of mortality from the children's diseases, but not nearly enough to be a primary cause of the trend.

This is no place for an attempt to unravel the effect of changes in age-distribution on the death rates from diseases spread more evenly over the life span. One simple breakdown of the influenza-bronchitis-pneumonia rates does indicate that children under five have gained ground against these causes of death a little faster than people at all other ages.

We are fully justified in saying that in this country since 1900 the major communicable diseases have been perceptibly fading as a threat to human life, that death rates from these diseases show a common tendency to fall, and that the decline seems to have gained momentum in recent years. Trying to explain these phenomena would take us into a fog of speculation. There are plenty of plausible reasons why particular rates should have gone down, but it is hard to believe that they tell the whole story when the decline has been so general. What underlying causes can be found or guessed at?*

---

* One may as well be honest and say "guessed at." The death rates alone will not support a very good syllogism. Nobody has counted sicknesses long enough, or widely enough, or well enough, to get infection rates comparable in scope and accuracy to the death rates, and so we do not know much about the ratio of deaths to infections. Measles is still so nearly universal that we know its incidence cannot have changed significantly, and we have every

In the last two generations we have got a working knowledge of bacteria and viruses and their means of travel that has implemented epidemiology, has revolutionized some phases of medicine, and has sifted down to plain men and women in the form of a blurred but genuine awareness of the nature of infection and some defenses against it. This has changed public habits at many points: we boil the baby's bottles, douse little cuts with iodine, keep children with running noses out of school. All this should have slowed up the spread of infection. Changes in the size of the family may have had a like effect. What better arrangement for passing germs around than a chain of children neatly spaced from the cradle to the grammar-school? Children scattered in one and two-child families are *ipso facto* more sheltered from disease at the dangerous early years than their forebears were.

We have learned something too about what to eat, and particularly about those key substances, the vitamins—not as much as we should like to know, but enough to alter food habits decisively, particularly in infancy. If the vitamins are as closely linked to resistance as some recent work suggests, the mounting consumption of fresh vegetables and citrus fruits may have been even more important than the dietitians think.* It is hard to say just what standard of living means, but it does mean something in relation both to the spread of infection and to resistance, and it is the general impression that standards of living were rising in this country during much of the time covered by the figures cited

reason to believe that scarlet fever is less deadly than it used to be. Generally speaking, however, we cannot say whether the death rates have gone down because infections have become less common (but not less fatal), or less fatal (but not less common), or both less common and less fatal.

* It is reported that car-lot shipments of carrots in the United States increased from 1,630 in 1920 to 12,028 in 1929, spinach acreage from 10,000 in 1919 to 58,000 in 1929. The per capita consumption of fresh oranges in 1930 was almost four times what it was in 1899; of grapefruit, 269 times what it was in 1899.

here.* It is not strange that children should show conspicuous gains against disease, for changes in personal hygiene, food habits, and standards of living affect the very young more directly than the rest of us, who drag our accumulated handicaps along as we climb the ladder. One seldom sees today in a city hospital the kind of child who used to die of measles.

When one remembers how few specific remedies the doctor has, and how new the most promising drugs and serums are, it seems doubtful that changes in the care of the sick can be credited with much effect on the death rates charted in this chapter. Public health services, on the other hand, were definitely stepped up during this period, and these may have affected both the spread of infection and the underpinnings of resistance. No public health maneuver of recent years (except perhaps the improvement of milk supplies) has had the immediate and dramatic effect that the purification of city water supplies had about the beginning of the century. Yet the slow piling up of precept on precept and service on service must have made itself felt even though it is usually impossible to isolate its influence.

Weighing these factors one against another would be a thankless task. Moreover thirty or forty years are an insignificant slice of experience with diseases that rise and fall through the centuries. It would take someone wiser than the author to strike a trial balance of man's account with his parasites and someone wiser than the reader to audit the result. All we can do here is to consider briefly a handful of specific problems which are still, as in-

* Real wages seem to have made an indisputable gain in the decade which followed the first world war. But evidence on the matter is sketchy, and when the President's Research Committee on Social Trends made its report in 1933, Leo Wolman and Gustav Peck reversed the argument, citing health and mortality experience as "indirect or presumptive evidence of advance in the living standards of nearly all grades of American labor."—*Recent Social Trends in the United States,* New York: McGraw-Hill Book Company, Inc., 1933, ii: 827.

dicated by the statistics, of major importance, or have recently taken a surprising turn. If in so doing we can find here and there a landmark for a longer view, so much the better.

INFLUENZA, PNEUMONIA, THE COMMON COLD

Nearly one death in ten, in the United States, is due to an acute infection of the lungs or air passages—influenza, pneumonia, "pleurisy," or bronchitis. One would have to wipe out the whole population of Albany or Chattanooga to duplicate the yearly loss officially debited to these diseases.* Add tuberculosis (now far outdistanced by pneumonia) to the group and one has accounted for two-thirds of all the deaths that can be clearly attributed to infectious causes. Americans, moreover, have some four hundred million colds a year.† Great and small, the respiratory infections are indubitably unfinished business.

These common ailments form a nosological jungle in which bacteria and viruses roam at will, despoiling the human race and defying both classification and control. Symptoms overlap and no one knows how many different diseases lurk behind them.‡ For some of them the doctor can do little. The epidemiologist who hacks his way into this mess courts frustration. The statistician has to content himself with omnibus calculations. The plain citizen talks glibly of grippe or flu, gulps or sniffs his favorite panacea, and, without any clear notion of what is happening to him, hopes for the best.

* Pneumonia plays a part in many deaths attributed primarily to other causes; in New York City in 1937, for instance, there were four deaths with bronchopneumonia as a secondary or associated cause for every three which were counted as due to bronchopneumonia.

† They haven't all been counted, but this is not mere guesswork. Careful studies of sample population groups suggest that the average incidence of colds—coryza, sore throat, bronchitis, and influenza—is more than three per person per year.

‡ This is true even if one disregards as obvious interlopers some of the acute diseases of childhood which begin with respiratory symptoms.

Though pneumonia is not one disease, in the epidemiological sense, for it may have many causes, it is a condition easily discovered by the doctor and so it makes a good starting point for a brief consideration of this very confused field. The epidemiologist, of course, has to think about a whole flock of pneumonias—one for each of the thirty or more kinds of pneumococcus, not to mention all the other bacterial and virus invaders of lung tissue which may have generally similar effect.* What he has found out about the pneumococcus, which causes nearly all lobar pneumonia and is the chief offender in other forms of the disease, is sufficiently curious.

It is an extraordinarily pervasive parasite. Among all the people on a given street on a given winter afternoon almost half the adults and at least a third of the children will be found to have pneumococci in their noses or throats. Perhaps everyone plays host to this parasite at some time in the year. People with colds sometimes have so many pneumococci that the other parasites living peacefully in the nose and throat are killed off. Unlike the tubercle bacillus, the pneumococcus has no need to set up a desperate illness in order to keep on multiplying and traveling; it can support itself beautifully in an atmosphere of snuffles and sneezes. It mastered long ago the technique of penetration without war. Unless ultraviolet radiation of our common air proves to be a practicable means of checking its spread or immunization is more effective than present experience suggests, it is hopeless to try to exterminate it.

There may be fifty million carriers of pneumococcus in the United States at any given time in the pneumonia season, and many more than that in the course of a year, but the average annual yield of cases is probably under three-quarters of a million

---

* In the last season or two a generally benign pneumonia, so contagious in some instances that it may leap from patient to nurse unless glasses as well as masks are worn in the sickroom, has been attributed to an unidentified virus.

*The sneeze: one good reason why infections of the air-passages are un-finished business. Photograph by M. W. Jennison using the Edgerton technique of high-speed illumination, exposure about 1/30,000 second*

and not all of these are due to the pneumococcus.* Evidently pneumonia does not follow pneumococcus as the Constitution follows the flag, or as measles follows the virus of measles. The odds against its doing so vary with different types: judging by the ratio of carriers to cases Type III pneumococci are much less likely to set up active illness in the lungs than Types I and II, which is fortunate because the disease caused by Type III has also been more refractory to treatment.

We do not usually think of pneumonia as a communicable disease nor take any great precautions to prevent its spreading from the sick. Yet it is obvious that the pneumococcus must be communicated and in limited groups of people it is sometimes possible to demonstrate the importance of contact infection. Small epidemics in mental hospitals have been traced to carriers; families in some New York villages exposed to a case of pneumonia seem to have more cases soon afterward than families not so exposed; interns on the medical wards of a large hospital, caring for many pneumonias, have pneumonia themselves more often than young men of their age in other circumstances.

But if exposure to pneumococci is so nearly universal, what makes one man a carrier and the next a case? One must assume that sickness falls on those who, habitually or temporarily, have less than average resistance to the parasite. Like tuberculosis, pneumonia prefers the poor; it is particularly frequent in certain occupations where abrupt changes of temperature are common; everyone knows that it often follows a cold. These are useful clues, but they fall short of explaining the great disparity between infection and illness: not all the poor blast-furnace work-

* Pneumonia is not fully reported and its total incidence must be estimated. Surveys of sample white groups suggest that something like five cases of pneumonia may be expected in each thousand person-years of life—that is, in each thousand persons in a single year, or in any mathematically equivalent aggregate of experience. This checks well enough with the accepted clinical estimate of four cases to each death.

ers with colds get pneumonia; the riddle of resistance is still unsolved.

Can we lessen pneumonia by increasing individual resistance? Nature herself has gone a long way down that road, or we should not succeed so often in holding the parasite at bay in the nose and throat. Some obvious things could be done: we might (if we knew how) better the economic mess that keeps people poor; we might diminish known occupational risks; we might *all* go to bed when we have colds. Only a very optimistic person would expect pneumonia to disappear in the face of this course of action. We may eventually be able to set up specific resistance to the pneumococcus by immunization; the difficulties (outlined in Chapter 6) are considerable.

What can't be prevented must, if God permits, be cured. Until recently the doctor was almost as fogbound as the epidemiologist in dealing with pneumonia. A century ago he was bleeding, purging, and drugging his patients, apparently without increasing the fatality rate, but, we can be sure, without lowering it. Eighty years ago or thereabouts, he began to do nothing as skilfully as possible—that is, to keep the patient at rest and under competent nursing care while nature fought the infection. Fifty years ago it was observed that the serum of animals artificially immunized by injections of pneumococci had curative power, and the doctors began to feel their way toward the use of immune serum on human patients, clumsily at first because the difference between one type of pneumococcus and another was not understood. Twenty-five years ago the doctors had learned how to determine the type of the parasite and to administer the serum of horses immunized against the same type. Ten years ago these serums, at first given inconveniently in bulk, had been effectively concentrated. Serum worked best against Type I; promptly administered, it might cut fatality in this group from one death in four cases to one in ten.

Serum therapy was still spreading slowly from the medical

centers into general practice when, in the spring of 1938, a new drug crashed into the picture. Sulfapyridine, closely related to sulfanilamide, was put forward in Great Britain as a possible chemical cure for pneumococcus infections. Since it could be given without regard to type differences, cost far less than serum, acted promptly, and seemed to be not too poisonous, it quickly came into general use. Its future is not yet clearly indicated: it may prove to be most useful in connection with serum therapy, it may supersede it, or it may fail to live up to its initial promise. Should sulfapyridine or some related drug justify the hopes it has aroused pneumonia may be pushed out of its place as the deadliest of the common infections.*

So far we have been thinking of pneumonia as a clinical entity and pneumococcus pneumonia as a distinct disease. Pneumonia may also be the killing phase of influenza, which is another story. The death rate from pneumonia and influenza follows a dual pattern. It rises and falls with the seasons, rolling smoothly to a crest in the early months of the year, and at irregular intervals it also shoots up in a sharp peak that may dwarf the annual waves (Chart VIII). One such peak in 1920, soon after the pandemic of influenza, added something like a hundred thousand deaths to the normal toll of these diseases in the United States; another in 1928–29, when the pandemic was well in the past, accounted for fifty thousand excess deaths. There were many lesser peaks.

While these exacerbations of mortality from respiratory infections were called epidemics of influenza, no one really knew what they were. Influenza—"an apparently sudden disturbance of the

---

* The death rates for lobar pneumonia dropped very sharply in the United States in 1938, those for bronchopneumonia less sharply. In New York State, where this phenomenon was carefully studied, it seemed unlikely that new forms of therapy could have accounted for more than a part of this decrease, which was accompanied by a decline in morbidity and also by a decrease in the severity of the disease, as measured by the incidence of cases showing infection of the blood-stream.

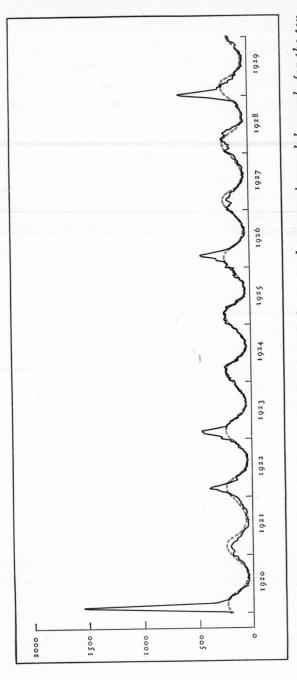

VIII. Expected - - - and actual ——— mortality from influenza and pneumonia, week by week, for the ten years 1920–1929. (Deaths per 100,000 population in 95 American cities.) From Public Health Reports, 50:1671, Nov. 29, 1935, by courtesy of Selwyn D. Collins and the United States Public Health Service public health by the occurrence of a very large number of cases of illness characterized as regards a majority by signs and symptoms affecting the respiratory system" [1]—could be recognized with assurance only in its major appearances. Smaller outbreaks fell into a great grab-bag of etiology, with influenza shading off into the common cold when it was not severe, and into pneumonia when it was. One could sort out the bacterial pneumonias if one could find the bacteria in the sputum and took the trouble to do so, but there was nothing to pin a diagnosis of influenza to except a rather shadowy symptom complex.

In 1933, however, English workers found that washings from a sick man's nose and throat, after the bacteria had been filtered out, would set up an influenza-like disease in ferrets.* The virus thus revealed was found in the following year by American workers in throat-washings from Puerto Rico, and turned up in the next winter or two in New York, Philadelphia, Alaska, Australia, and Russia. This substance has been transmitted to mice by way of ferrets and directly, and has been preserved in the laboratory for long periods on living tissue in flasks and more briefly on the membrane of the chick embryo. Passed back to human beings, it gives them influenza; a ferret conveniently supported this impression by sneezing† on an English investigator who promptly came down with typical aches and pains, and Russian workers produced experimental infections in human volunteers. It can be neutralized by antibodies found in the blood of human convalescents.

---

* Later it was found that the ferret itself obligingly ruled out bacterial contamination in most instances, being able to sterilize in its nasal passages all the common bacteria that infect the human respiratory system. The ferret is so susceptible to other viruses, however, that the experimental colony in London is isolated with extreme care. A moat of lysol three inches deep guards the only entrance to the ferret house, and workers put on rubber coats and boots which are sloshed with lysol before they enter it.

† An exercise at which the ferret is even more gifted than man.

This substance is evidently the virus of an epidemic influenza —but not of all the diseases that behave like epidemic influenza. Some epidemics, with present techniques, yield up the virus and some do not, and thus far it is impossible to tell one "influenza" from another by anything short of a series of laboratory tests. The relation of the newly identified influenza to the disease which ran riot in 1918 can only be surmised; we shall have to wait for a new pandemic for a presumptive answer to the question and may never have a conclusive one. At least, however, an influenza which has occurred in many places and in several successive years has been caught and branded. English and American workers have now agreed to call this disease "influenza A," leaving the rest of the alphabet free for other members of the family.*

So long as influenza was ill defined and people kept having something they and their doctors called influenza over and over again, it was generally thought that the disease paid little or no dividends in the way of immunity. But ferrets infected with "influenza A," after they get well, are strongly resistant to reinfection for some months, and are protected even longer against damage to the lungs. Men too have antibodies in their blood on recovery from this disease. Moreover when blood samples are taken from people at random about half of them have enough antibody content to protect mice fully against the active virus, and another quarter give some protection. Evidently some degree of resistive power—presumably acquired in former infections—is common, but it is hard to gauge its effect in everyday experience. It may be too slight to prevent reinfection under the circumstances of human contact. It may be just strong enough to reduce influenza on

* A different and versatile virus was isolated in 1936 during an influenza-like outbreak in California; it was capable of infecting either the lungs or the brains of laboratory animals according to the route of inoculation. It reappeared in 1940 and is now known as "influenza B" virus. At least two other viruses have been found in the lung tissue of mice.

its later visits to something like the common cold.* Its worth may be greater against some strains of virus than others and the differences between strains are a troublesome factor in evaluating it. One would hardly expect it to give protection against a totally different virus.

By inoculation, mice can be completely protected for a considerable segment of mouse-life against heavy doses of the virus of "influenza A," and ferrets can be given enough resistance to lessen the severity of future attacks. Can human beings be protected too? If the degree of resistance were no greater than that acquired by ferrets it would still be well worth having, for we could manage the aches and pains and fever of influenza if we could avoid pneumonia. Experiments with human inoculation are under way, but—as one has to say so often—they are not yet conclusive. At best, with an immunity of limited duration, one would have to seize the strategic moment for inoculation: as Andrewes says dryly we should immunize "a month or so before the next epidemic"! We may learn enough to limit the killing power of another pandemic, but we had better work fast.†

It is possible now to discuss at least one kind of influenza with one's feet on the ground. There are plenty of questions left, however. What causes the other "influenzas"? Will other viruses be

---

* This might account for some of the confusion between influenza and the common cold. The latter seems to be caused by a distinct virus, which, demonstrated in the chimpanzee (an inconvenient and expensive laboratory animal) has not been so well worked over as that of influenza. See page 109.

† Very curious results have recently been reported from the inoculation of ferrets with virus taken from animals in which an attack of distemper had accidentally coincided with convalescence from experimental influenza. This vaccine, inactivated, gave unusually good protection against several strains of influenza. Giving the viruses separately, or mixing them in the test-tube before inoculation, had no such effect. The possibility of qualitative changes in the antigenic behavior of the influenza virus—changes which might facilitate immunization—is of great interest, and the clue is being followed up in fresh experiments with human inoculation.

found as techniques grow better? Is the common cold one disease or many—a mélange of distinct virus infections (including mild influenzas), bacterial infections, and what not? How do viruses and bacteria work together in colds? In pneumonias? Is there anything more intimate in their relationship than the fact that one breaks a way through tissue for the other? Does the virus always come first? And—here is one of the grand enigmas of medicine—what makes influenza run amok as it did in 1847, 1857, 1874, 1890, and 1918, and as it will doubtless do again?*

A disease without a known cause is like a kite without a tail: it bobs uncertainly in the wind. Influenza undefined has been the sport of every wind of epidemiological theory, and influenza defined is still a wayward problem. One need not go so far as Creighton, who postulated a miasmatic cloud floating from Jamaica to the North Sea to account for an epidemic three centuries before he wrote about it, but one needs a pretty bold imagination to keep up with the astounding facts. It may be true as Crookshank thought a few years ago that we shall not understand pandemic influenza until we can grasp the pattern and interrelationships of a long sequence of curious epidemiological happenings.† It may be true that behind the sudden changes in the spreading and killing power of influenza that startle the world there is

* Influenza in a mild form was pandemic in 1936–37. A Scottish student of its periodicity has predicted a major epidemic for February 1941.

† The chief medical officer of Great Britain was of the opinion in 1920 "that the epidemiological features of the cycle of years within which influenza explodes are different from those of the influenza-free cycles; that preceding epidemic influenza there is often a rise in the general morbidity of the population, an 'epidemic constitution' develops favourable to influenza, there are early though often mild and atypical clinical fore-runners of the disease, and parallel or allied clinical maladies are seen; that there are concurrences, similarities, and inter-relationships between outbreaks of cerebrospinal fever, poliomyelitis, and outbreaks of influenza, bronchitis, and pneumonia."—Great Britain, Ministry of Health, *Report on the pandemic of influenza, 1918–19*, London: H. M. Stationery Office, 1920, p. xvi.

274

some controlling factor which we shall not recognize till we can cope, as Greenwood puts it, with the relativity as well as the simple algebra of disease. Influenza is and will long remain a dark mystery. An Englishman has called it the crux of epidemiology. To think of it in terms of caged mice and sneezing ferrets is a net gain, but huge cloudy symbols still hang about it, and no unfinished business holds greater lure for the speculative epidemiologist.

## TUBERCULOSIS

Killing diseases have been fought with charms and herbs, with prayers and incantations, with royal proclamations and medical manifestoes, with nostrums and guinea-pigs. But tuberculosis is preeminently the disease which has been fought with publicity. It is "tb" and "the great white plague." It has elbowed its way into the Christmas festivities. We "stamp out tuberculosis." The assault on it has set the pace for a dozen health crusades, and has held the spotlight longer than any of them.

And the death rate from tuberculosis goes steadily down.* Long first, tuberculosis now stands seventh among the causes of death in the United States. In New York, Boston, and Philadelphia, where a hundred years ago tuberculosis was killing annually some 400 of each 100,000 people, and sixty years ago was still killing some 300, the tuberculosis death rate today ranges from 50 to 60 (Chart IX). In the registration area the rate was over 200 in 1900, under 50 in 1938. Has publicity pushed it down so far? Hardly. Has organized public health work turned the trick? That would be hard to prove. Has medical science done it? Even that is doubtful. Tuberculosis had already begun to give ground in the United States when Koch discovered the bacillus in 1882. In England the trend began in the fifties. Something started this

---

* This discussion relates to tuberculosis of human origin, chiefly pulmonary. Bovine tuberculosis, thanks to the eradication of diseased stock and the pasteurization of milk, is now relatively unimportant in this country.

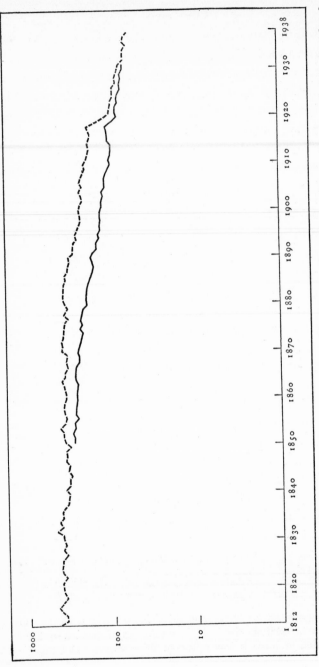

IX. *Death rates for pulmonary tuberculosis in New York, Philadelphia, and Boston* – – – *and in England and Wales* ———. *(Deaths per 100,000 population, plotted on a logarithmic scale. British rates standardized for similarity of age and sex composition.) Adapted from charts prepared by G. J. Drolet, New York Tuberculosis and Health Association*

decline before the doctors knew enough to do so and long before the machinery of health education began to purr.

When we think of epidemics we think ordinarily of ills that strike swiftly, have their day, and subside, like influenza or measles or poliomyelitis. Tuberculosis as we know it best does not fall into this pattern; it moves so slowly that we measure its progress against the span of a man's life. While public health men have begun to talk of family epidemics taking two or three generations to run their course, a longer perspective may be needed to reveal the play of major cycles. Indirect evidence drawn from the clumsy Bills of Mortality in London hints at the possible existence of an epidemic wave with a span of something like two centuries. One can only speculate about it, but perhaps the decline in our own day should be thought of first of all as the downswing of a natural cycle, and only the next upswing will show how far we have managed to establish "control."*

The epidemiologist who tries to work out the pattern of tuberculosis is like a Boy Scout mapping a mountain; he must keep his eye fixed on a few high points and do plenty of filling in. What are the datum-points here? First, that in the white races the tubercle bacillus is practically omnipresent. Repeated samplings (until very recent years) have indicated that more than 90 per cent of white adults become infected.† Second, that though the parasite goes everywhere it flourishes only in a small fraction of the bodies which it invades. Only about one white person in every two hundred, in this country, is at any given time recognizably sick with tuberculosis. Third, that those who do fall sick usually stave off death until a chronic process localized in the lungs has run its course. This is not so true of children as of adults: in very young children the disease spreads more freely

* For further details consult your great-grandchildren.

† The evidence is drawn from positive tuberculin tests and from the discovery at autopsy of small healed lesions where invading bacilli have been walled off.

within the body and may kill speedily. Fourth, that in the white races the parasite establishes itself most readily among the poor, and particularly the urban poor. Men in the professional and generally well-to-do class, in England and Wales in 1930–1932, had only 61 per cent, while unskilled laborers had 125 per cent of the tuberculosis mortality they should have had if all classes, age for age, fared alike. Fifth, that infection is uncommon among primitive peoples beyond the frontiers of white settlement, and that when such peoples are exposed, the disease is widely and quickly fatal. Robert Louis Stevenson is authority for the story that a Marquesan tribe of superb physique was reduced by tuberculosis in a single year from some three hundred souls to a solitary pair of survivors. Even after several generations in a white country Negroes in the United States continue to react in a distinctive way to the bacillus and contribute far more than their share to the death rates.

Are we then to think of the secular accumulation of specific resistance as shaping the pattern of tuberculosis today? The disease is most chronic and least fatal in those races which seem to have been most thoroughly salted with infection and so have had the longest time in which to come to terms with the parasite.* The Jews—urban by habit for uncounted generations—are conspicuously resistant to it. The Negroes—for whom, racially speaking, tuberculosis is still a novelty—are conspicuously susceptible. But this is a little too neat. Tuberculous white men and women tend to die older in the southern states—where Jews and large cities are few—than anywhere else in the world; this does not fit the generalization at all. Moreover, when we shift the focus from racial to individual experience the immunity factor gets cloudier

---

* One general explanation for such adjustments is that the more susceptible strains die out first and the more resistant survive, so that the ratio of resistance constantly rises. Tuberculosis deaths often come so late in life— after progeny has been produced—that the principle hardly seems applicable in this instance.

rather than clearer. There has been much dispute whether an early infection immunizes and so tends to protect, or sensitizes and so tends to weaken the host threatened by reinvasion. It is a long jump from this dubious alteration in the individual to the bold outlines of what appear to be racial differences in response to the disease.

It makes a great difference, of course, whether few or many bacilli attack a given host, but much seems to depend in tuberculosis—more perhaps than in other diseases—on the amount of generalized resistance the host can muster. The lump-sum capacity of a physiologically stable body in a favorable environment to throw off or suppress infection seems to count for more than any specific immunity. Under the same environmental conditions tuberculosis kills more girls and young women than boys and young men, but more men than women over forty. Subtle physiological stresses may account for the first of these phenomena, Adam's curse for the second. Some of the association between poverty and tuberculosis must be due to huddling, some to particular occupational risks, such as those involved in inhaling silica dusts, but much of it seems to go back to everyday physiological status. When people are badly nourished, for instance, they become more vulnerable to tuberculosis than they were when well fed. Even in England the first world war reversed the decline in the tuberculosis death rate, and in Prussia, behind the blockade, the death rate for 1918 was 68 per cent greater than that for 1913.

If race and poverty so strongly influence the distribution and severity of tuberculosis one might expect, in the United States, to find the most tuberculosis in poor states with a high percentage of Negroes. But among the southeastern states (which qualify generally under this heading) Mississippi, which has the largest proportion of Negroes and next to the lowest average property valuation, has also the lowest death rate from tuberculosis.

Tennessee, with the highest rate,* is a middle-of-the-road state, not significantly different from its neighbors. Maryland and Kentucky, ranking first and second in this region in wealth, rank second and third in tuberculosis mortality, and the richest part of Kentucky, when deaths are mapped county by county, has the highest death rate. Evidently no simple formulation fits the facts, or there is something between the lines that we cannot yet read.

One fact, however, stands out bold and clear. Tuberculosis spreads most dangerously in the close contacts of the family. Resistance breaks down before a mass attack, and the steady bombardment of each other by husbands and wives, parents and children, brothers and sisters, is the best of all mechanisms for perpetuating the disease. Taking all ages together, people exposed to tuberculosis in their own homes are roughly ten times as likely to fall sick of it as are people in the population at large.

Here is the place for the public health man to swing into action. He cannot relieve the blacks of their special disability. He cannot cure poverty—though he sees it blocking his efforts to end tuberculosis and many other infections. But he can do something to break the transfer of tuberculosis within the family.

He has, however, come slowly to the realization that this is the most favorable point of attack. For half a century after Koch proved that tuberculosis was communicable people were more interested in treating it than in preventing it. That is what the sanatoria were built for. Men and women were dying tragically of tuberculosis, leaving young children fatherless and motherless; the biggest job in hand seemed to be to save them before they went over the brink. But in spite of all our mutual exhortations to see our doctors early, we never quite caught up with the

---

* Tennessee leads not only the southeastern region but the nation, with the exception of two "resort" states, Arizona and New Mexico, to which the tuberculous flock, and, in quite recent years, Nevada.

new infections. People did not suspect or would not admit that they were touched by infection till the destructive process was well under way. No state has attacked tuberculosis more intelligently or aggressively than Massachusetts, and yet in the past twenty years there has been no material gain in the percentage of cases put to bed in its sanatoria in the earliest stages of disease. Now it begins to be clear that we were not fishing in the likeliest waters; we were throwing the dragnet too wide when we placarded the shops and the trolley cars and x-rayed children by the schoolful; we should have done better to stake our hope of checking tuberculosis on the most intensive study of family contacts that our public health budgets would permit. For if we watch the tuberculous family closely we have the best opportunity there is to break the chain of infection, and to hurry incipient cases to the sanatorium if the precautions fail.

Sanatorium care, however, is costly, few states have more than a fraction of the beds they need, and bed rest alone is not too successful in curing the disease. When doctors learned to rest the infected lung by pneumothorax* or other procedures the effort to control tuberculosis turned an important corner, for that made it possible, in a fair proportion of cases, to put an end more quickly to the ulcerative condition which made the case infectious. Though complete healing still takes time, sanatorium beds can be released earlier, patients restored more quickly to some degree of self-support, and the economic burden of treating tuberculosis lightened. It may thus be possible to speed up the slow-moving processes which have long been wearing the disease down.

These processes are keyed to biological fundamentals. Any parasite, to survive, must find a way of getting out of the first host it colonizes and traveling to another before the first one dies or suppresses it. The tubercle bacillus does not settle down in the

* See page 175.

accessible nose and throat, like the pneumococcus, and when it reaches the lungs it is usually walled off at once so that nothing further happens. Even if it becomes established in the lungs it is shut away from the outside world until the inflammation it sets up has become an open sore—that is, until the infective process is well advanced. Only then can it slip into the air passages and be coughed out. It fails more often than it succeeds. As Frost puts it, this implies that "in order to survive, the tubercle bacillus requires a *surplus*, perhaps a *very great surplus* of chances to establish infection." [2] If tuberculosis cannot spread at all without repeated and heavy attacks on susceptible hosts, many developments of the last half-century—some directly stimulated by health propaganda and some not—may well have had cumulative effect in checking it. If general resistance is increased by better nutrition (and otherwise) fewer foci of infection are established; better housing, the taboo on promiscuous spitting, and the fresh-air cult make it harder for the parasite to move in force from one person to another. Already routine tuberculin tests on students and other groups show a reduction in the inactive infections that used to be nearly universal; it is no longer true that everyone comes to terms sooner or later with the bacillus.*

Complacency would be stupid while tuberculosis is still causing more deaths in this country than any other communicable disease except pneumonia, and while there are less than a hundred thousand sanatorium beds to care for half a million people with recognizable clinical infection. Yet, looking a long way backward and a little way forward, the epidemiologist is encouraged by the

---

* A corollary of this change is that whatever the importance of specific immunity we are losing it and must take the consequences. But there is no reason to suppose that the vague non-specific resistiveness which seems in this instance to be more important, or the public habits which restrict the travel of the parasite, will change for the worse, and we may expect to hold the gains these factors have brought about unless civilization goes completely bad, as it shows quite too many signs of doing.

belief that when he fights tuberculosis biological adaptation is on his side; that every advance in civilization—meaning the spread of education and decent standards of living—is on his side; and that where thoroughgoing study and aggressive medical intervention are available, he can attack the parasite at its weakest point. The less tuberculosis he has to deal with, the better chance he has to hunt it down. Just as typhoid fever has become rare enough to make the search for individual carriers profitable, so there are parts of the country, such as rural Massachusetts, where it seems not impossible to chart all the family foci of this graver infection and gradually clean them up.

Doctors have watched tuberculosis and written about it ever since there were doctors. They are more aware today than ever before of their ignorance of fundamental issues—the interplay of infection and immunity, the impact of the disease on different age-groups, geographical variations. Paradoxically, though the theoretical problem was never more complicated, control of the disease has never seemed so nearly within the reach of human intelligence. Even so conservative a student of disease as Frost was willing to write in 1937: "The evidence indicates that in this country the balance is already against the survival of the tubercle bacillus; and we may reasonably expect that the disease will eventually be eradicated." [3]

## SUNDRY ITEMS

If two out of every three of the recognized deaths from infectious causes in the United States are due to the major infections of the respiratory tract, it is clear at what point Americans are most susceptible to parasitic invasion or where their "control" of communicable disease breaks down—or both. There are, however, other items of unfinished business.

When the deaths from the major respiratory diseases—pneumonia, tuberculosis, influenza, and the like—are subtracted from all the deaths that we have classified as due to infection, something less than a hundred thousand each year are left over. This is naturally a mixed group. Rather more than a quarter of these deaths are due to intestinal infections, another quarter to disorders usually associated with the streptococcus and staphylococcus. The remainder includes a considerably smaller number of deaths from syphilis and its sequelae, those due to the principal "children's diseases" not caused by the streptococcus (whooping cough, measles, and diphtheria), and a motley residue that adds up to less than 20,000 deaths a year. Meningitis, poliomyelitis, other nerve and brain infections, acute rheumatic fever reported as such, gonorrhea, and various other causes find their places here, along with malaria, which must be singled out for fuller discussion.*

Rheumatic fever, parenthetically, is an embarrassing subject for anyone who tries to write a book like this. If it is not infectious, it should be left out; if it is, it deserves more space than many other topics here considered. While it behaves like an infectious disease in a number of ways, no specific causative agent has yet been found for it. Rheumatic fever is now seen as a long-continued process of unknown origin, usually commencing in childhood (with episodes of acute illness and intervals of quiescence), which characteristically damages the heart. It is certainly of the greatest importance: it probably causes four-fifths of the heart disease and most of the deaths attributed to that cause among school children and young adults—say from the fifth to the twenty-fourth year,† as well as a very considerable number of deaths among older persons. If all the deaths in the city of

* Nothing can be said in favor of this grouping except that it is convenient for the purposes of this chapter.

† In spite of our ignorance as to cause and prevention, the rate of deaths from heart disease in this age-group has been going down for a decade or more. In the registration states of 1900 the mean annual death rate for 1930–1936 was 28.5 per cent lower than that for 1922–1929.

New York in 1938 from whooping cough, epidemic meningitis, measles, diphtheria, scarlet fever, and poliomyelitis were added together and multiplied by four they would still fall short of the deaths reported as due to rheumatic heart disease and rheumatic fever. In the same city, it is estimated, one school child in seventeen has rheumatic heart disease. Infectious or not, rheumatic fever runs in families and prefers the poor; it is curiously related to season and climate; and its power to kill or handicap evidently involves some pattern of susceptibility that is still obscure. With this we must leave it for other diseases which are more clearly communicable.

First the intestinal infections. The greatest scourge of the bowels, cholera, has gone back to the tropics and no longer threatens us. Typhoid fever, which like cholera flourished on city water supplies, has been decreasing for half a century or so in some northern states where early attention was given to sanitary problems, and ceased to be of major importance in the United States as the laggard cities one by one cleaned up their water supplies almost a generation ago. It lingers where sanitation is primitive, a rural and southern rather than urban and universal disease, and even there it is losing its grip.* Massachusetts (practically rid of typhoid fever today) had a death rate of over 60 per 100,000 in 1875. In 1938 Arkansas led all the states by virtue of a rate of 6.9, and only half-a-dozen states had a rate as high as 5. Typhoid in the northern states is preserved chiefly by the surviving carriers who link the present with the years of greater prevalence: as they die (or are discovered and isolated) the problem fades away.

Amebic dysentery is a horse of another color. Never as threatening as typhoid fever, it demonstrated thoroughly disagreeable

---

* It would be interesting to look into long-time trends in the South, but sanitation and vital statistics usually make their debut together in a given community and there are no adequate records of the dark past after the War.

potentialities in the Chicago epidemic. The better our techniques for finding the ameba by stool examination the more certain it seems that many carriers and a good deal of latent infection are scattered through the American herd, and control is difficult because the ameba is not killed by the chemicals that rid drinking water of the typhoid bacillus. Fortunately the parasite seldom invades the intestines in sufficient force to cause acute illness or death.

The bulk of the damage done in this group of diseases is due to the diarrheas and dysenteries of bacillary or unknown origin. Like the fluxes of the respiratory tract, these are a hodgepodge; indeed if "intestinal influenza" be anything more than a catchword the two fields may overlap. The bacilli concerned—to say nothing of possible viruses—are vexatiously diverse: different organisms giving rise to similar symptoms may work side by side in the same epidemic. The technical difficulties of hunting them out—the intestines are a regular Garden of Eden for bacteria— are considerable. No explanation can be found at all for some dramatic outbreaks of disease, such as those which kill new-born babies in hospital nurseries so rapidly that there is nothing for it but to close the doors and suspend maternity service till the epidemic dies out. These have occurred repeatedly in recent years, and in the city of New York in the last decade the death rate from diarrhea in babies under one month of age has actually been swinging upward.

Epidemics of dysentery are favored by living at close quarters, as in army camps and institutions—witness "asylum dysentery"—but similar infections kill babies at home. Though diarrhea and enteritis have declined spectacularly they still account for more deaths under two years of age than whooping cough, diphtheria, scarlet fever, and measles at all ages and all together. Since 1910 or thereabouts infant diarrhea has tended to retreat to regions of poor sanitation, and is now at its worst in Arizona and

New Mexico, where the Spanish-speaking "natives" form perhaps the largest island of ignorance in health matters still left in this country. Field studies point to specific infection as its cause, and to healthy carriers as a means of keeping the bacteria in circulation. Making bad privies good seems to check the disease more sharply than making bad milk or water supplies good, which suggests that where infection still lingers in force, flies may be largely responsible for its spread. There is not much experimental evidence that babies suitably fed resist infection better than others, but this sounds like good sense. The gains seem to be traceable to a general betterment of the sanitary environment and a rising standard of living for babies in particular. Remembering the hospital epidemics among the new-born, however, one must admit that the diarrheas are unfinished business at both ends of the scale—where infant care is least and most scientific.

When one passes to the infections caused chiefly by the streptococcus and staphylococcus one finds a welter of unfinished business. These organisms are about us all the time. Some species can, others cannot, cause human disease. Those that do give rise sometimes to frankly epidemic diseases like scarlet fever, sometimes to conditions like "blood-poisoning" which we think of as private rather than crowd disasters, sometimes merely to local suppuration.

The streptococcus in particular is an unpredictable guest. It can break down tissue by invasion, or poison distant cells with toxin. It occurs in many different types but any one of several types can cause any one of several different diseases. The streptococcus at work may reveal itself through septic sore throat, erysipelas (St. Anthony's fire, as the English villager calls it), puerperal fever, or other ills in addition to the scarlet fever and septicemia just mentioned and some of the pneumonias and colds referred to in an earlier part of the chapter. The accoucheur with a sore throat can give his patient childbed fever; the "germ" passed around by a school or family may cause tonsillitis here and scarlet fever there. What happens when the parasite gets a foothold seems to depend on a variety of circumstances, including the host's individual resistance-pattern as well as the characteristics of the invading strain. Its antigenic properties are obscure, the identification of specific types laborious, effective antibacterial serum hard to produce. Antitoxin helps in some infections and not in others. So long as the streptococcus circulates freely (and nothing seems likely to check it unless sterilization of the air proves practicable)* it is sure to cause a steady stream of casualties. Small wonder that in practice sulfanilamide has come as a godsend to the harassed physician.

It is hard to work out the epidemiology of organisms so various in type and so much commoner than the diseases they cause. Clearly, as with the pneumococcus (which biologically is a kind of streptococcus), one must think of frank infection as resulting in part from a deficiency or lapse of individual resistance. This gives a lead for preventive measures: when such lapses are likely to occur, as in childbirth, special precautions to prevent the spread of the parasite from attendants to the susceptible host are called for. Puerperal septicemia no longer sweeps through the lying-in hospitals in great epidemics, as it did before Semmelweis and Holmes, but it still occurs far more often than it should. In the city of New York in recent years it has killed approximately one mother for every thousand live births, twice that many if the deaths caused by septicemia associated with abortion are included.

Though much more needs to be known about type and strain distribution in the streptococcus before one can speak with assur-

* The pasteurization of milk, a necessary but limited resource in discouraging the spread of the streptococcus, helps to prevent epidemics of scarlet fever or septic sore throat.

ance of changes in virulence, the curious way in which scarlet fever becomes now mild, now lethal, now mild again suggests that biological cycles in the parasite may profoundly affect its impact on the human herd. At present, while one person out of every dozen or so in this country may expect to have scarlet fever some time in his life—so that it can hardly be called uncommon —only a small fraction of cases (perhaps less than two in a hundred) end fatally. It would be rash to suppose that we shall soon be finished with this particular infection even though in our own day it has been gentled: we do not understand and cannot control the forces which have altered it, and they may deceive us. Immunization against the toxins which cause scarlet fever is still undependable, immunization against the organism itself beyond our reach till several knotty technical problems have been solved. Yet a British bacteriologist comes to a reassuring conclusion:

Anyone who has traced the history of the streptococcal diseases from the first adequate records of the eighteenth century to the present day must needs be struck by the gradual decline in severity of epidemics which seems to have begun in the days of Lister and the pioneers of bacteriology and still goes on. In the war of attrition between streptococci and the human race civilised man seems to be gradually emerging as the victor. This is not, I think, because the human race has become less susceptible, nor because any dramatic methods of dealing specifically with streptococcal disease have been forthcoming, but rather because the small obstacles set in the way of epidemic spread have slowly but surely had the hoped-for effect, possibly by placing some control on the passage and exaltation of the infecting agent.[4]

Not much need be said here about syphilis, now the subject of a widespread campaign of public education. With half a million new cases turning up every year in clinics and doctors' offices and no one knows how many more at large, with four out of five of the patients treated for early syphilis wandering off while they

289

are still infectious, with sixty thousand babies born every year under the taint, there can be no argument about the job to be done. It bristles with difficulties: a powerful instinct favors the spread of infection and powerful taboos work to conceal it; immunization is impossible and treatment slow, uncomfortable, and costly. But for two facts the task would be impossible: the mechanisms of infection are such that large epidemics are unlikely in civilized societies, and given time the doctor can definitely cure the disease. In Sweden syphilis has become as uncommon as typhoid fever in New York City. The United States still has a long way to go to bring this plague under control.

⌒

We are not allowed today to forget the importance of syphilis, but few people not at the moment parents of very young children can bring themselves to take measles or whooping cough very seriously. In retrospect they may even seem faintly humorous, like mumps. It is true that the "children's diseases" kill relatively few of the millions who have them, but just because millions do have them they account for a considerable number of deaths. Only the common cold is more universal than measles, which attacks nine out of ten of us before we are old enough to vote. Three out of four of us have whooping cough; two out of three, mumps. Half of us escape chicken pox. Only one out of ten actually has diphtheria, but a majority pick up enough immunity against it to produce a negative Schick test. Diphtheria is the only one of these diseases which is traditionally feared, but whooping cough causes the most deaths—almost a third more than diphtheria, half again as many as measles, twice as many as scarlet fever, nearly five times as many as poliomyelitis.*

When it kills, whooping cough strikes earlier in life than any

* These comparisons are based on the deaths reported in the United States for the five years 1933–1937.

other of these diseases. Sixty per cent of the deaths are of babies under a year old. Prevention should therefore be swift and sure, and vaccination with killed bacteria has been attempted, but unfortunately the bacillus which causes the disease goes lackadaisical in the laboratory and there has been much trial and error in the production and administration of the vaccine. Though recent work is promising, prophylaxis is not yet as dependable as pediatricians and parents would like to have it. Prevention by isolating the sick is difficult because the disease spreads most readily before the characteristic whoops begin.* Public health men are more helpless in dealing with whooping cough than with either measles or diphtheria.

Measles like whooping cough is most dangerous to infants (the peak of mortality is in the second year of life) and thumbs its nose at quarantine, spreading easily and quickly before the rash appears. As common as dirt, measles is still an obscure disease: its periodicity—epidemics are spaced two or three years apart—is a riddle; its virus is hard to cultivate. Yet one can at least lessen mortality by modifying or deferring it,† so that the odds in favor of deliberate control are better than in the case of whooping cough.

The story of diphtheria is more dramatic. The diphtheria death rate in Boston in 1881 was more than four hundred times what it is today. Fifty years ago the disease was killing nine out of ten of those who suffered from its croupous form; today more than eight out of ten are saved. The use of antitoxin for treatment, be-

---

* Even in the early stages when whooping cough behaves like a cold in the head, however, it is often possible to make a bacteriological diagnosis by the neat and simple method of holding a prepared plate in front of the child and letting him cough on it. After a due interval the bacilli may show themselves in typical colonies on the plate.

† See page 195. Very recent reports suggest that it may become possible to bring about modified measles at will by inoculation with virus attenuated by many transfers from one chick embryo to another.

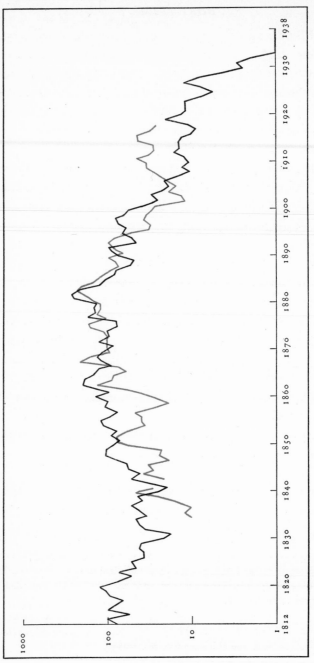

X. *Death rates for diphtheria and croup in Baltimore —— and in Berlin ——. (Deaths per 100,000 population, plotted on a logarithmic scale.) Adapted from a chart in An outline of the epidemiology of diphtheria, by James A. Doull, M.D., The Nation's Health, 9:45–55, November 1927*

ginning in the nineties, and of toxin-antitoxin or toxoid for prevention, beginning on a large scale in the twenties, has lifted a great burden of fear.

Proud as one may be of this achievement, there are some facts worth remembering when one is tempted to think of diphtheria as virtually finished business. The first is that diphtheria, like tuberculosis, began to decline as a cause of death before public health procedures could have affected it, and it is hard to say how much of the decrease has been due to natural momentum and how much to deliberate effort. We have been measuring our gains against the background of a devastating pandemic which swept the world about the middle of the last century, in which diphtheria was so much more malignant than it had previously been that doctors called it a new disease. While preventive medicine may have carried the downward trend farther than it would have gone without help, it is only reasonable to suppose that biological rather than artificial forces have chiefly shaped curves such as those shown in Chart X. This seems the more likely when one reads that sample studies of immunity, carrier infection, and disease suggest a progressive decline in the last two decades in the ratio of cases to carriers even among children who were not protected by artificial immunization. It is already clear that as the disease becomes less common public health effort must make allowances for the decline in natural immunization, which is thought to have played an important part in maintaining herd resistance.

The second point to remember is that the diphtheria bacillus is protean and unpredictable. For some years odd differences in its behavior in the north and in the south have been observed. Contrary to the usual assumption, natural immunity is found much more widely in rural Alabama than in the city of Cleveland. Moreover, diphtheria is beginning to show itself in several parts of the world in a severe form which may strike so rapidly

293

that the child is doomed before antitoxin is given. Opinions differ as to whether these malignant diphtherias can be traced to a distinct type of the bacillus, but in view of past alterations in the disease their presence is sobering.

~

Some of the plagues mentioned in this chapter have shown striking vicissitudes, but most of them seem to be growing less deadly if not less common. Certain virus infections of nerve tissue, on the other hand, seem not to be declining significantly and may even, in some instances, be on the make.

Few diseases have so thoroughly frightened people in recent years as anterior poliomyelitis, familiarly but not very accurately called infantile paralysis, which attacks nerve cells controlling muscles. However old this malady may be—and there is no good reason for supposing that it is new*—one began to hear of epidemics only in the last century and the outburst that stamped the disease on public consciousness all over the world came early in the present century. In this country it reached its high point in a sharp epidemic in 1916, in which 27,000 cases and 7,000 deaths were counted.

Poliomyelitis is terrifying because of its dual threat of crippling and death, but the numbers involved are after all not very large. According to a rough estimate made by a leading authority on the disease, based on American experience since the epidemic of 1916 and smoothing out age and geographical differences, only one

* A new disease capable of infecting both infant and adult tissue (as this is) should attack people of all ages indiscriminately. Poliomyelitis, on the contrary, was already a "children's disease" when it first came to notice, indicating that it had had time to establish itself so thoroughly that most adults were immune. Curiously enough, poliomyelitis now seems to be working its way into older age-groups than those predominantly affected twenty years ago. This apparent change may be due in part to changes in diagnostic habits, or to actual changes in age distribution of the population, but it remains essentially unexplained.

person out of 3,000 is likely ever to die of poliomyelitis, one out of a thousand to be paralyzed, and one out of five hundred to have the disease in a clinically recognizable form. The scatter of recognized cases, in fact, is so striking as to be a cornerstone of epidemiological thinking about the disease. As Frost put it with characteristic elegance as early as 1913:

> The rapid spread of epidemics over wide areas, their spontaneous decline after only a small proportion of the inhabitants have been attacked, and, above all, the preponderating incidence in young children, have not been satisfactorily explained by any hypothesis other than that the infective agent, during epidemics, is widespread, reaching a large proportion of the population, but only occasionally finding a susceptible individual, usually a young person, in whom it produces characteristic morbid effects.[5]

Poliomyelitis then poses two questions that sound simple and are really very difficult: why do some people have it, and why do most people—so far as one can see—escape it?* Take the second question first. The generally accepted answer is a paradox: poliomyelitis, a paralyzing infection, does not usually paralyze. It is the paralysis, and the deaths that may go with it, that advertise the presence of the disease, but there is reason to think that the infection travels farther incognito than in its familiar trappings.

The evidence for this assumption is simple and plausible. Blood taken at random from sample adults—particularly those living in cities—often neutralizes the virus (in monkeys) just as blood from human convalescents does. This might mean that adults *as adults* have protective substances in their blood, but experience with other diseases makes it seem much likelier that the presence of protective substances is the result of past infection.

---

* It poses many other questions too and most of them are at present too hard to answer. Recent work has thrown doubt even on the orthodox belief that the virus normally invades the body by way of the nerves of smell in the nose. In this discussion it seems better to outline a single coherent theory and leave it at that than to fish farther in very murky waters.

Moreover the doctors, who first thought of poliomyelitis only in terms of paralysis, have now learned to recognize by clinical observation and laboratory tests a fringe of mild cases around the fatal and paralytic ones, and it is reasonable to suppose that this fringe in turn shades off into a still broader penumbra of cases that quite escape attention.*

Indeed it seems possible that the virus of poliomyelitis has salted the human herd almost as thoroughly as that of measles—which in an average year kills more than three times as many people as poliomyelitis does—and therefore may actually be less deadly to most people than measles. This seems absurd. Yet if the rash which marks the presence of the measles virus were invisible, and doctors were able to recognize the disease only by the sore ears that sometimes accompany it, would the situation be so very different from that of poliomyelitis? How few cases of measles would be identified, how hard it would be to trace the connection between them, and how mysterious measles would seem! Poliomyelitis without paralysis *may* be as common as measles without middle-ear complications.

When we say that epidemics of poliomyelitis come in the late summer we are saying in effect that recognized and severe cases cluster in late summer. What happens the rest of the time we cannot say, but it is conceivable that a given wave of infection may produce a summer epidemic at one point, travel inconspicuously through the winter, and reappear as a visible epidemic at the point which it happens to reach in the next summer.

One answer to the question why so many people escape poliomyelitis is then that they do not—but have it so lightly that it passes unnoticed and leaves no ill effects. This leaves still unanswered the harder question: why does the virus kill or cripple

* In a small institutional outbreak in 1939 the virus of poliomyelitis was found in the stools of several healthy children and children with transient undiagnosed fever.

one or two children in a thousand while the rest seem to throw it off easily and acquire some sort of immunity to boot? Is it merely chance that makes these few children suffer, or are they earmarked somehow for sickness if the virus comes their way? And is this earmarking, if it exists, associated with variations in nutrition, or bodily structure, or physiological behavior—inherited or otherwise? It seems to cluster in families, and some observations suggest that the endocrine glands are seriously concerned in it. Susceptibility seems to alter with the temperature, unless some other unsuspected factor accounts for the summer incidence. These are meager clues on which to base a successful search for the mechanisms of destiny, but it is clear that the stubborn riddle of individual resistance and susceptibility to infection may have to be solved before practicable steps can be taken to prevent the damage poliomyelitis can do.

Poliomyelitis may leave withered muscles behind it but other infections of the nervous system may do worse, damaging the brain and sometimes warping the personality. Since the last war a bewildering lot of infections of brain tissue or the sheath around the brain and cord, attacking men or beasts or both, have been described and named, though the names are of the sort with which the epidemiologist modestly advertises his own finely subdivided ignorance. One reads of type A or von Economo's encephalitis; type B or Japanese encephalitis; St. Louis encephalitis; equine encephalomyelitis in five different types (Borna disease, named after a district in Saxony, an eastern and a western type in the United States, a Russian and a Venezuelan); louping-ill, which makes sheep in Scotland "loup" or leap oddly and is capable of infecting men; and—frankest of all—X-disease in Australia.\*

\* One bizarre malady upsets the nervous system, usually for a brief time only; it can apparently be mistaken for the common cold, is harbored by the household mouse, and according to some authorities may already have infected one in ten of us! This has been carefully christened lymphocytic

Some of these diseases have turned up under the very noses of established research workers and have been carefully studied in the laboratory; they must be watched longer in the field, however, before their epidemic patterns become clear. Some older workers, matching recent experience with what they could infer from medical history, thought that such ailments as a group came with special frequency at or about the time when influenza was pandemic. Most investigators today are too busy trying to tell one virus from another to indulge in such generalizations.

One broad line has been drawn between the winter and summer diseases—type A encephalitis coming with the respiratory infections in the cold months and most of the others in the warm season. The winter disease is what most of us have heard of as sleeping sickness—the kind that may show itself in drowsiness or jerky restlessness, make one irritable or wakeful for months or years, and leave one with a mask-like paralysis of the face, or unwonted sluggishness of mind, or (especially in children) with strange and tragic changes in temperament. Its virus is unknown; it strikes at any age; it is wholly unpreventable.

Some of the brain infections that spread in the summer, St. Louis encephalitis,* for instance, are generally kinder to their victims, but the newest and most startling, equine encephalomyelitis, may also leave its stigmata on those whom it does not kill. This disease of horses, first defined in California in 1931, seems to have spread very widely. It was epidemic among horses in eastern Massachusetts in the summer of 1938; when several children in this region died with the symptoms of brain inflam-

choriomeningitis; in Switzerland and alpine France a somewhat similar ailment goes by the bucolic name of the "disease of young swineherds."

* First recognized in 1933, when it attacked about one person in every thousand in the St. Louis area, bearing most heavily on the old, killing one patient in five, and leaving most of the others without serious after-effects. The same virus caused a second epidemic in St. Louis in 1937 and has been found elsewhere in the United States.

mation someone guessed that they had caught the horse disease, and the guess was verified by identification of the virus in the laboratory. Few of the sick had been close to horses, but since several kinds of mosquitoes (including the common pest of the salt marshes) transmitted the virus in the laboratory, and the disease spread in a hot wet summer, it seemed probable that mosquitoes had bridged the gap. It would be odd to begin to fear horses in this all-but-horseless age, but the story has a still more curious twist. The virus may not belong in the horse any more than in the human being; it has been passed experimentally from chick to chick; some strains will infect the English sparrow, the vulture, the stork, the duck, the goose; in Connecticut and Massachusetts it has been found in nature in the pheasant and pigeon. If the virus is at home in wild birds and travels in them, some epidemiological puzzles—such as the simultaneous sickening of horses on both shores of Chesapeake Bay—clear up, but the problem of control becomes fantastic. Fortunately killed virus seems to have some power to immunize horses, and since the disease is highly fatal it pays the owner to protect his stable; it is estimated that about a fifth of all the horses and mules in the country have already been inoculated. Whether a barrier among horses will be enough to protect human beings remains to be seen; certainly the grave potentialities of the disease, which killed twenty-five out of less than forty recognized human cases in Massachusetts, should stiffen the effort to suppress mosquitoes.

None of these diseases is yet of great statistical importance. Few of them, probably, are as new as they sound. But there is something undeniably sinister about the cumulative effect of so many unfamiliar threats to what we like to think of as the seat of reason. Greenwood goes so far as to suggest that if civilization goes to pot again the infections of the nervous system, together with influenza, may be destined for an important role in human affairs.

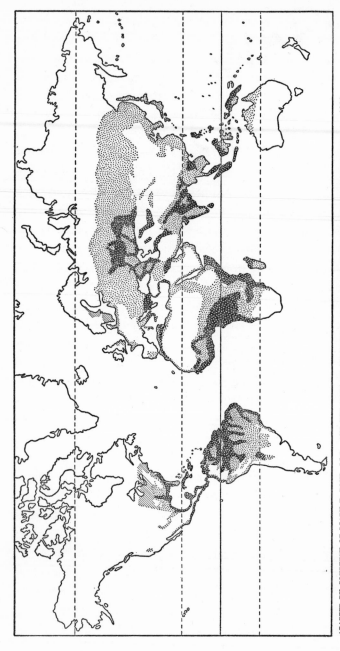

ADAPTED BY COURTESY OF MARK F. BOYD, M.D., AND THE HARVARD UNIVERSITY PRESS FROM AN INTRODUCTION TO MALARIOLOGY, 1930

*Malaria in the contemporary world. Malaria is endemic in the areas marked ▨▨▨ and ▮▮▮, the darker shading indicating greater prevalence. From the areas marked ⩨⩨⩨ malaria is said to have receded*

## MALARIA

We turn now from sudden obscure maladies to one which is leisurely and familiar. Nothing about malaria makes much sense. It seems so simple, and is really so baffling. When yellow fever and plague strike, they kill, and tragic stories cluster around them. Malaria mostly makes people wretched or merely tired without killing them, and who ever wrote a *Journal of the Ague Year*, or made a play about the malaria mosquito? It is as commonplace as poverty and just about as persistent. It bulks larger than any other communicable disease on earth today.

If we knew as much about poliomyelitis as we know about the cause and mechanics of malaria we should think we were very lucky and might even pin the Nobel Prize on the person who found it out. But though the classic defenses—drainage and quinine—have been used against malaria for centuries, and the role of the mosquito has been known for nearly half a century, we still do not know how to get rid of the principal disabling infection of humankind.

The tropics seethe with malaria, and a glance at the map shows how far it spreads beyond the tropics. It has haunted the Mediterranean since before Hippocrates. Some people think it has cut the industrial output of our own South by a third.* No one knows how much of it there is in the world, but the available scraps of information point to astronomical totals. Nearly eighteen million people were reported to the League of Nations to be under treatment in 1931, and the untreated far outnumbered them. Something like two million people are infected in the United States in an ordinary year—about one out of every eight persons in the states with the highest death rates.† Though malaria seldom kills

* One Georgia county was stirred to action against malaria when its languid pecan-pickers failed to harvest a bumper crop in time to catch a favorable market.

† This is an estimate based on the reported malaria deaths for 1936 in South Carolina, Arkansas, Florida, and Georgia.

(about once in six hundred cases in this country, it is estimated) infection is so general that global mortality may reach appalling proportions. More than 1,500,000 deaths were attributed to malaria in India alone in 1936; this may be an exaggerated figure, but one could pare it down liberally and still leave more than three times as many deaths as those from plague, cholera, and smallpox together.

Malaria is distinctly a place-disease, found only where warmth and wet permit the right sort of mosquitoes to breed and there is a reservoir of infection in human blood. So the figures for the United States as a whole mean little. In 1936, for instance, when the malaria death rate for the nation was only 3.1 per 100,000, the rate for the fourteen southern states was more than three times as large, and for some states in that group six, seven, or eight times as large. For some counties in those states, in 1933–1936, the rates ran over 100 per 100,000. Where malaria is common official reports tend to understate the number of cases, for nobody bothers to count them all, but may overstate the number of deaths, for it is sometimes easier to say that a man died of the malaria he undoubtedly had than to find out what he did die of. Such errors, however, would hardly change much the relation of one rate to another within a short span of years. Malaria here swings in a cycle of seven years, more or less, and it is significant that the death rates for the last upswing in 1933–1935 were not very different from those for the preceding one in 1927–1929 and the later wave affected a wider area. Malignant infections are found in new territory. While the regional death rate for 1938 was the lowest of record, one cannot say that malaria is now giving ground as a cause of death in the South.

While the southern climate is kind to the mosquito, malaria in the United States has not always been a distinctively southern problem. It appeared in Massachusetts before Harvard did, dogged the footsteps of the men who pushed westward, hung about the Mohawk, the Ohio, the Mississippi in turn, and lingered here and there—in the Hudson valley for instance—till late in the nineteenth century. Early British travelers warned their countrymen who went west to settle on high land, or declared roundly that "no part of the western country is healthy." Dickens wrote savagely of fever in the settlements in *Martin Chuzzlewit*. People who were children in southern Michigan as late as the Civil War, when farms still ran down into the marshes, remember how every family suffered from malaria as summer came on, quinine was a household necessity, and those of sterner stuff took whisky and wormwood for relief.*

Why has malaria—once so common—left the northern states? One must guess a little, but the answers are plausible. Malaria haunts the pioneer who pushes into the wilderness, and begins to take its leave when he tidies it up. People knew this before they could explain it in terms of mosquitoes. In 1816, for instance, an army surgeon wrote that "the northern and western frontiers of New-York, like all new countries emerging from a wilderness state, are more unhealthy than the old settled towns in the same latitudes in the New-England states," and assured his readers that the "intermittent fevers and other autumnal diseases" then common would "vanish as the forests are subdued, and the

* This notoriously unhealthy region was described with great elegance by a Michigan physician in 1859: "Scarcely a stream exists in the southern portion of the State, which does not in every few miles of its course widen into a lakelet of several hundred acres, skirted on one or more sides by savannas which might diversify and adorn the landscape without noxious influence, if properly cleared and drained; but which too frequently have been inundated by a mill-dam at the *dabouche*, converting the semi-aquatic trees and grasses into vast rotten quagmires, to be left uncovered and seethe in the summer's sun, germinating diseases like Python of Egyptian fable, to encircle its sallow victims in folds of endemics and epidemics; the humble votaries of quinine and arsenic, at the hands of *quacks or quality*, until fermentation is checked by autumnal frosts."—Beech, J. H. Report on the topography and epidemic diseases of Michigan. *Transactions of the American Medical Association*, 12:185–207.

marshes and swamps drained."[6] He was right, too, but in retrospect one realizes that the change from pioneering to settled living involved more than clearing and draining: it meant also the gradual spread of the settlements from the waterways and bottomlands to the drier uplands, the building and later screening of substantial houses, and perhaps the diversion of mosquitoes from men to the cattle and horses with which they surrounded themselves.*

Early industries, on the other hand, may have helped to prolong the stay of malaria. The damming of little streams for village millponds† brought mosquitoes into the heart of bustling settlements. People often noticed that sickness followed such developments; sometimes the association was close enough to rouse public wrath. The citizens of New Milford, Connecticut, smashed a dam in 1809. It was not till steam and the railroads killed off the little mills (which, the regional planners say, was a pity) that this factor was canceled out.

The South too went through its pioneering and its settling-down stage, but in parts of it the sequence came much later than in the North and generally speaking rural standards of living never rose quite as high, so that the happy ending of the malaria story is still a long way off. Read what a good reporter has to say of early malaria in the river counties of northwestern Mississippi, first settled about 1825:

In the spring and summer and often until late in the autumn nearly every man, woman, and child in the community was ill with malaria. They burned with fever. They froze with chills. Their teeth chattered and their temples flamed. In the intervals between the attacks which came every third or fourth day they were listless and exhausted; too dull to think and too tired to work. Traveler after traveler noted the physi-

---

* See page 136.
† We forget how numerous these used to be. A traveler in New York State in 1802 counted four grist mills, two oil mills, one iron forge, and three saw mills on a single creek within the borders of a single town.

cal debility of the people. The more charitable ascribed it to unknown causes. The less charitable said that they were lazy. But the disease went on and its cause was unknown. Each year the bodies of the victims were drained of vitality and their minds of vigor. Each year many died and found premature graves where they had hoped to find happy homes.

There is no way to estimate accurately the social and economic damage caused by malaria in the Delta. Its destruction in terms of human pain and suffering is immeasurable, but it was undoubtedly a factor of grave importance in impeding the progress of this section. Men are not active in the white shadows of anaemia. They do not create in exhaustion. They cannot function in fever. Life, to be fruitful, must be more than a rhythm swinging from chill to chill.[7]

Such memories are vivid, but if one wants statistical information there is little to be had until the very recent years of public health expansion. When the curtain began to lift, about 1920, malaria was certainly causing more deaths in the South than it is today. A good beginning had been made in suppressing mosquitoes in the cities, which had suffered severely, but some of the early rural rates were astounding: Dunklin County in Missouri, for instance, reported 296.7 deaths per 100,000 in 1911–1914. Apparently parts of the South were just emerging from a skyrocketing epidemic due to late pioneering and heavy migration (southeastern Missouri, of which Dunklin County is the horrible example, was not extensively settled and drained till after the turn of the century). Outside the cities, the change for the better in the past twenty years seems to be due mostly to the stabilization of population, agricultural drainage, and natural immunization—in other words, to factors independent of public health effort. Pioneer standards of living are still pretty common, however, and if malaria has sagged from epidemic to endemic levels it is still, in all conscience, high enough.

In one respect the South has had the advantage of the North: people did not get around to damming streams extensively for power production until after the relation of mosquitoes to malaria was known. Most of the southern states now have regulations to safeguard impounded waters. The Tennessee Valley Authority has gone to great lengths to prevent its tremendous pools from broadcasting malaria. In turning six hundred miles of running water into standing water the Authority has already created enough shoreline to stretch from New York to Denver and has still larger works in prospect. Where the current is slow and the water warm and shallow—say along a third of this shoreline—there is danger of raising bumper crops of anophelines. To forestall this, the Authority takes pains to clear the bottom of each lake, before the water backs up, of the vegetation which would eventually turn to flotage;* designs its dams in such a way that the public health men have leeway to raise and lower the water level slightly;† and patrols parts of the shoreline during the mosquito season to keep the larvae in check.

Such teamwork between engineers and epidemiologists is not too common. Left to himself, the engineer can make malaria faster than the farmer and the epidemiologist together can get rid of it. There is fresh danger from anophelines wherever railway and highway embankments cut across natural lines of drainage, or where construction gangs leave borrow pits to fill up with water and wigglers, or where good roads and cheap cars take people into the wilderness to play at pioneering and recapitulate malaria history. Nor is the danger confined to the South. Flood control and navigation pools on the Mississippi between Iowa and Minnesota have brought a new malaria problem to five

* Trees and bushes are cut; timber too heavy to burn or move is wired down; even the black willow is extirpated, and the natives say that if you cut down a black willow and chop up the wood and smoke the chips in your pipe and knock out the ashes a new willow will grow where the ashes fall.

† It takes diplomacy and patience to reconcile the conflicting requirements of flood-control, power-production, navigation, and mosquito-control. The established compromise keeps the water rising and falling all summer within a total range of some three feet, on so accurate a schedule that most of the shoreline is kept clean. See page 188.

states after half a century of freedom from the disease. Williams goes so far as to say that "malaria in the United States is almost wholly man made."

The real chore to be done in the South, however, is not merely to prevent new malaria but to root out the endemic infection transmitted by mosquitoes bred in standing water and shuttling between ill-nourished people living in badly built houses. Can it be done? This is hard to say. Theoretically, it can. Practically, it can if people live close enough together to justify the expense. It is still an open question, however, whether by methods now available and at a cost which the public is willing to pay malaria can be wiped out of thinly settled communities living at a pioneer level.*

The only fully satisfactory way to control malaria is to make the breeding of the mosquitoes that carry it impossible within flight range of the population to be protected. Under American conditions this usually means drainage and often means major drainage, not merely local ditching.† Now major drainage, if it is well done, is a serious matter, involving the careful consideration of local and regional land uses, large-scale planning, and enduring construction. It costs so much that some public health men, despairing of getting the job done right, and doubting the value of makeshifts, throw up their hands. Some suggest that it would be cheaper to move people away from pest-holes than to clean them up. The health authorities of Georgia, making a vigorous fight against the disease, say frankly that in their state malaria control "is of the same magnitude as highway construction and maintenance, that its execution must be as carefully planned, and that its cost will be proportionately great."[8]

* For a brilliant picture of the economic and social background against which this and other southern problems must be viewed, see Gerald W. Johnson's *The Wasted Land*, University of North Carolina Press, 1937.

† Since 1933, mostly in close proximity to towns and villages, some 38,000 miles of drainage ditches have been dug with relief labor.

It may be that nothing much will happen to malaria in the South until something drastic is done, something comparable to the wholesale cleaning-up of water supplies that virtually put an end to urban typhoid fever early in the century. Yet in Georgia and elsewhere public health men have not hesitated to take half a loaf when they could not get a whole one. Oiling and poisoning the breeding-places, screening houses, and even medication (if its limitations are kept clearly in mind) have their obvious uses. The odds are by no means all in favor of the parasite. As Hackett puts it, "the mechanism of malaria transmission is so complicated and delicate that it never has been able to resist any long-continued sabotage."[9] The outlook is much better today than it was a quarter-century ago. The South has begun to study its malaria problem county by county and neighborhood by neighborhood, and until a hard-headed estimate has been made of what can be accomplished with the money that can be spent, it is too soon to throw up the sponge.

What has been done so far in the rural South is hardly enough to hasten the natural processes which have brought malaria down from its fantastic early levels. In states where malaria kills twice as many people as typhoid fever—and disables far more—one finds well-meaning county health departments hammering away at typhoid and virtually ignoring the more serious disease. This is understandable, for there are cheap and easy ways of fighting typhoid that seem to bring results, while to do anything effective against malaria usually takes more money than health departments are accustomed to ask for. But it is none the less anomalous. Granted that the job is hard, it still seems as if we should be getting on faster with this unfinished business.

## YELLOW FEVER

The roster of the ills that still harass the United States is as remarkable for what it omits as for what it includes. Yellow fever has no place in it, but Americans have been so close on the heels of this retreating scourge, and so intimately concerned in its surprising history, that some account of it belongs in this chapter.

A quarter of a century after Walter Reed demonstrated in Havana that mosquitoes carried yellow fever the strategy of controlling the disease seemed well established and the hope of actually putting an end to it was bright. In 1918 Noguchi had found what he believed to be the causative organism, a spirochete. The epidemiology seemed clear: the disease belonged to the cities and particularly to the seaports; outside the tropics it was a summer visitor; in the tropics it festered the year round in urban "seed-beds" of infection. If these were cleaned up, it disappeared from their environs and from the ports of call with which they communicated. No *Aedes aegypti:* no yellow fever. From this sequence, so brilliantly illustrated in city after city, it was easy to pass to the corollary: no yellow fever without *Aedes aegypti.* The accepted formula had led to great victories, won mostly in sight of salt water—Havana, Panama, Rio. When Guayaquil also fell, the end of yellow fever in the Americas seemed to be in sight.

In 1925, as was said at an earlier page, the cases of yellow fever reported from the whole continent could be counted on the fingers of one hand. Man had never before come so close to a triumph over pestilence. But the annual report of the Rockefeller Foundation, jubilantly recording the figures for 1925, was not printed till June 1926, and then it was necessary to add a footnote calling attention to a new outbreak in northern Brazil. This might have been taken, but was not, as an augury of vast disillusionment.

The next year brought hopeful news from Africa. Rockefeller workers there, visiting sick blacks at their mosquito-infested mud huts, were patiently searching blood samples for Noguchi's spirochete, or failing that, for some other clue to the cause of the disease. They needed urgently to find some way of studying the infection in the laboratory, and tried to plant it in a great variety of animals—African monkeys, guinea-pigs, rabbits, white rats, white mice, pouched rats, puppies, kittens, and even goats. Nothing happened until bloods from a fresh epidemic on the Gold Coast were injected into a couple of crown or hooded monkeys (an Asiatic variety) just received from Hamburg; these, to the delight of the investigators, fell ill and died with lesions that looked much like those of yellow fever. Indian *Rhesus* monkeys —common in both zoo and laboratory—took the fever even more readily. Noguchi's spirochete had no part in this demonstration: a virus in the blood did the work. Moreover when viruses from Africa and South America were brought together in a neutral laboratory in New York, immune serum from one continent gave protection against virus from the other and vice versa. The cause of yellow fever, wherever it occurred, was known.*

It takes time for the fruits of such discoveries to ripen, as one needs to remember when reading the science news in the daily paper. Meanwhile yellow fever continued to postpone its departure from South America. In 1928 livers damaged by yellow fever were found at autopsy in parts of Brazil supposed to be free of the disease, and the fever broke out, after twenty years' absence, in Rio de Janeiro. The next year there were puzzling epidemics in Venezuela and in the Colombian mountains.

Where was all this infection coming from? Where did it lurk between outbreaks? The condition of liver tissue is a good index

* Noguchi's spirochete was the organism causing infectious jaundice, which, by clinical observation alone, is almost indistinguishable from yellow fever. Noguchi himself died of yellow fever in Africa, after he had become convinced that yellow fever was caused by a virus, but before the two diseases had been completely untangled. It is curious that the discovery of the virus lagged so far behind Reed's solution of the puzzle of transmission. Reed and his men had indeed tried to infect a monkey in Havana, but they had not guarded against the fact that the animal might already be immune. So their experiments came to nothing and a quarter of a century was lost.

of yellow fever infection. If the doctors could see more livers they would know better what was going on and where to concentrate preventive measures. Wholesale autopsies were of course impracticable, but staff workers in Brazil devised an instrument that cut out a small piece of liver tissue quickly and cleanly. This was put in the hands of school teachers and other locally important personages who, with the leverage of new burial regulations and the incentive of fees and rewards, began to send the government laboratories great numbers of specimens from the bodies of persons who had died within ten days of falling sick and so might conceivably have had yellow fever. The first systematic use of this device showed that people were dying of yellow fever in thinly settled rural areas where no one thought the disease could possibly persist in the absence of urban infection. To rid the cities of *Aedes aegypti* was evidently not enough.

While livers were being studied in Brazil the virus was being studied in New York and Boston. In 1930 Theiler at Harvard injected the virus into the brains of white mice and found that they developed not the usual visceral lesions but a characteristic brain inflammation or encephalitis. This happened consistently unless serum from an animal which had recovered from yellow fever was injected along with the virus; then it did not happen. The encephalitis was a form of yellow fever, and the epidemiologist had another animal, small, cheap, and convenient for use in the field, with which to study the disease.

This made it possible to do on a grand scale something already done in a small way with monkeys. If virus kills an animal but virus plus a given serum does not, then that particular serum must contain something which checks the virus—in a word, antibody. But antibody is formed in response to invasion; the man or monkey from whom the serum came must have met and conquered the yellow fever virus. The fruits of such a victory last a long time: bloods from six persons who had yellow fever in

Norfolk in 1855 were tested in monkeys seventy-five years later, and five of the six still had power to neutralize the virus. To find out whether any given individual X has ever had yellow fever, therefore, one injects a sample of his blood along with virus into a monkey or mouse. If the animal lives, the blood has protective power and X has presumably had yellow fever (though he may never have been sick enough to know it). If the animal dies, the blood has no protective power and X has never had yellow fever.* When many such tests are made in suspected areas one can map systematically the regions where yellow fever has occurred within the lifetime of living persons.

Yellow fever in the mouse had other uses. Soon after the virus was found in monkey blood, various efforts were made to weaken it sufficiently to permit its use as a vaccine, but without much success. Now it appeared that the passage of the virus through many mice in sequence lessened its virulence for monkeys and presumably for men. Feeling their way cautiously, with preliminary tests on monkeys, Rockefeller Foundation workers began to vaccinate a few people who were in particular danger of infection, using a mixture of this mouse-virus with immune human serum obtained at first from convalescents. The method was clumsy, because large quantities of serum were needed, but it did put an end to a distressing series of deaths among investigators.

With the mouse-protection test to demonstrate past infection in the living and the examination of the liver to reveal it in the

* This is the principle of the protection test. The details are more elaborate. Not one mouse but several are inoculated, with suitable controls, according to a standardized technique worked out by Sawyer and his associates. Young mice destined for use in this test are brought up rather more carefully than the Dionnes: as soon as they are weaned they are segregated in colonies of ten shut off from all contact with the mouse world, are fed from sterilized tin cups, and are handled only with forceps washed in lysol. Though the inferences drawn from the test are soundly supported by the statistics, a few odd variants have been recorded—instances in which blood protected mice though it seemed impossible that the donor could have had yellow fever.

dead, the epidemiologists took a fresh start. In Muzo, in Colombia, where local authorities had persisted in suspecting yellow fever for many years in the face of repeated head-waggings by more eminent persons, the tests suggested strongly that yellow fever must occur without any help from *Aedes aegypti*. A curious spotty little epidemic in a thoroughly rural setting in eastern Brazil confirmed this revolutionary finding. It began to be clear that for at least twenty silent years unsuspected yellow fever had been at work in the Amazon valley. Out of these and other evidences of a great inland pool of infection a new concept of the disease began to emerge.

In 1934 this concept crystallized. Deep in the interior of Brazil, where a few small farmers cut their farms out of the jungle, planted crops for two or three years, and then moved on to new clearings, there was a creeping epidemic. The only city from which infection might be spreading was not only free of the disease but had been free so long that children had no immunity. The cases were occurring in scattered stay-at-home families. Typical was an old mulatto who died with textbook symptoms in a palm-thatched hut nearly four miles from any neighbor. Infection seemed to have reached him from the jungle itself. There were no *Aedes aegypti*, but other mosquitoes were numerous. Jungle monkeys were found with evidence of past infection in their blood.

Gradually it became clear that wide areas in Brazil, Colombia, and Bolivia were affected in the same way, and jungle yellow fever began to take its place beside the classic yellow fever of the seaports. Clinically the two are identical; though jungle fever is often mild, it may duplicate the horrid course which was once so familiar in Memphis and New Orleans. Epidemiologically the differences are striking. Urban yellow fever spreads rapidly through a huddled population, passing from man to man in the *Aedes aegypti* which breed and bite about the house, striking at all ages and both sexes indiscriminately until most of the human material has been used up, and then picking off the newcomers—children and immigrants—or dying out entirely. It can be suppressed by suppressing the mosquito which carries it. Jungle yellow fever does not so much spread through a human herd as stray into it here and there; it attacks men of working age and particularly those who frequent the woods and clearings, often sparing their families, and seems to be carried by various kinds of outdoor mosquitoes biting in the daytime. The gaps between one case and another are so great that the virus must be perpetuated elsewhere, perhaps in monkeys or opossums or some other prolific jungle family. In a recent epidemic in Brazil howling monkeys were found dead in the jungle just as rats have often been found dead in a town visited by the plague. Certain mosquitoes caught in the jungle, moreover, proved to be carrying the virus and some, allowed to bite monkeys in the laboratory, transmitted the fever to them by this natural process.*

Since it is found where people are few, jungle yellow fever does not flare up in tremendous epidemics, but—and here is the crux of the matter—there is nothing to prevent a man who has been bitten in the forest from carrying his virus into a town where *Aedes aegypti* and human tinder are both ready for a typical urban conflagration. This has been seen to happen on a small scale, and it may happen any day on a larger one unless constant watchfulness prevents it.

The cities can suppress their *Aedes,* but what can be done about the fever in the jungle? It is impossible to kill the mosquitoes there, or to exterminate the animals they feed on. The only resource left is to immunize the people.

For this ambitious task the original mouse-virus vaccine buff-

* Studies of yellow fever in Africa have not yet reached the point where one can say whether a similar epidemiological picture is to be found in that continent.

314

ered by immune human serum would have been quite impracticable. An American and a Frenchman had weakened the mouse-virus to the point where they thought it safe for injection by itself, and had tried it out on thousands of African natives with apparent success, but in a few cases sickness followed the vaccination. The Rockefeller Foundation workers tried to eliminate even this slight hazard by transplanting the mouse-virus to a medium in which it lived only on minced chick embryos during a long series of transfers, and then—fantastic refinement—by feeding it on minced chick embryos from which the embryonic brain and spinal cord had been removed, so that it should lose still more of its taste for nerve-cell protoplasm! This virus was considered wholly safe, and when a series of preliminary experiments proved successful, it was adopted for general use.*

Vaccination against yellow fever is now a practicable public health measure: more than 1,500,000 persons have been vaccinated in Brazil. The present strategy is to protect persons actually exposed to jungle infection and to create a belt of immune villages around infected areas to keep the virus away from the cities.

Far from being on the point of extinction, yellow fever now seems likely to last as long as the jungle does. The most to be hoped for at present is that the frontiers can be guarded by immunization, and that the barriers between these outposts and the great mass of susceptible humankind shall be kept intact. Protection tests supplemented in some places by post-mortem studies on liver tissue and by records of overt cases show that the present domain of the disease is a broad belt straddling the equator on both sides of the Atlantic Ocean from the Andes to the Nile, or beyond.

What is the danger that yellow fever will push beyond its present barriers and ravage susceptible populations in new terri-

---

* Quantity production is secured by inoculating the tissue-culture virus into chick embryos.

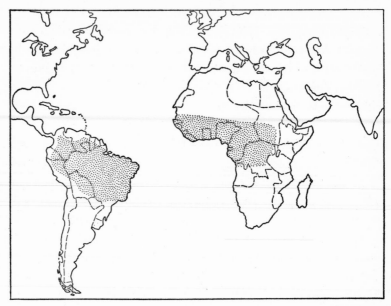

*Yellow fever is probably endemic throughout the shaded area and is occasionally reported from a number of points within it. In South America the shading follows chiefly the distribution of immunity among children, indicating the presence of the disease within the past ten or fifteen years. On the Brazilian coast yellow fever is now prevented by control measures. In Africa the shading shows where yellow fever has been present within the lifetime of living persons*

tories? Until travel by air began, western Africa was far removed from India and the Indies; now Juba, in the Sudan, within the borders of the yellow fever belt, is only five days by air from Karachi in India. Yellow fever takes six days to develop. In India the jungle and the villages swarm with infectible hosts, both beasts and men, and there are *Aedes* in plenty. Our own peril from air traffic from the south is less extreme, for our winters and piped water limit the insect vectors, but the history of yellow fever in the United States is grim enough to justify a sharp watch.

316

The nations have united to keep yellow fever within bounds by controlling air transport. The International Sanitary Convention for Aerial Navigation, which came into effect in 1935, holds public authorities at the point of embarkation responsible for barring the virus from the air. Aeroplanes are inspected and, if necessary, fumigated to kill mosquitoes. Passengers must report where they have been just prior to embarkation, so that their opportunities to pick up infection may be recognized; they are examined by a physician who may detain those showing disquieting symptoms till the period of incubation is over. On both American and African air routes crews have been vaccinated so that they cannot transmit infection themselves and can fly the mails without interruption even if passengers must be delayed. Such regulations, coupled with the usual control of incoming passengers at ports of entry,* have thus far seemed to be effective; at least no epidemic has yet been traced to air travel.

As for the towns and cities within easy reach by land or sea of the great reservoirs of infection, they must face the prospect of permanent control of *Aedes aegypti*. So long as the virus lingers out of reach in the jungle, and universal immunization has not been secured, there is no other way of safety.

## PLAGUE

Finished or unfinished, yellow fever belongs in the American tradition along with San Juan Hill and the Panama Canal. By any similar test plague seems pretty far afield. One thinks of Defoe, or of sing-song funeral processions in the East. It doesn't seem to concern us. Yet plague has spread farther in our own day

---

* At Miami, for instance—now close to possible centers of infection in South America—residents arriving by air who have come from such centers within six days must report in person to the city health officer. Transients landing at Miami and going on to other destinations are reported to local health authorities by the United States Public Health Service, so that they may be watched during the danger period.

than ever before, and plague infection of a sort is at this moment creeping slowly eastward across the United States.

Plague is primarily a disease of wild rodents in the hinterlands of Asia, as yellow fever is a disease of jungle creatures in the hinterlands of South America. Plague in our day has come from some shadowy Asiatic lair by way of one of those borderlands which are at once the front yard of the wilderness and the back yard of civilization—specifically the province of Yunnan, in the southwest corner of China.* Here it lingered unobtrusively, perhaps for several decades, toward the end of the nineteenth century. Occasionally spilling over along the nearby trade routes, it reached Canton and then Hongkong in 1894, and so came in force to the seaways.

Plague in 1894 was an uncontrollable disease. Its relation to rats, though long familiar, had never been explained.† The epidemic at Hongkong brought Koch's pupil Kitasato and Pasteur's pupil Yersin to study it. Working independently, both found and described the *Bacillus pestis* before the year was out. But to control plague more was needed than Yersin's talk of flies and soil pollution, or the vague measures of general sanitation that Kitasato advised. It took several years to work out and more than a decade to establish beyond dispute the cycle by which the bacillus passed from rats to fleas to man. Meanwhile, presumably by sea, the plague had slipped into Bombay.

This was in 1896. The disease appeared in August or September in one of the most crowded native wards, said to house more

* Yunnan, usually forgotten by the western world, came into the news again in 1938 when the defenders of China, cut off from their own seaports, built a mountain road through it—the Burma Road—to reach the sea at Rangoon.

† In 1897 the surgeon-general of the United States Marine-Hospital Service said, in a paper on plague, "The fact that mortality among rats precedes an outbreak of plague among human beings is explained by Lowson by the fact that rats have their snouts about one inch above the floors of houses and are more liable to inspire plague-infected dust than are human beings."

people to the acre than any other spot on the globe. By the new year—the year of Victoria's jubilee—it was raging furiously in Bombay and was beginning to spread farther. By 1903 there were more than a million cases per year, by 1904 more than a million deaths. By the end of 1936 forty years of plague in India had killed more than twelve million people.

The story bristles with ironic and grisly details. The English municipal authorities were reluctant to admit the existence of a disease so inconvenient for merchants and hotel-keepers.* Early efforts at control followed, for want of a better lead, the outworn pattern of the sanitarians. A thousand tons of silt were taken out of the drains. Whitewash was applied freely. Red circles and crosses marked the plague houses. Half-heartedly, the authorities tried to segregate the sick, but this ran afoul of cherished privacies among both Hindus and Moslems. A fantastic complication increased the terror: some malcontent defaced the statue of Victoria, and rumors flew through the native city that the queen had demanded in revenge the livers of 30,000 of her subjects. Elsewhere the story ran that the aged queen required Hindu hearts to nourish her. Naturally the natives shunned the doctors, mobbed the hospitals, and fled. Julian Hawthorne, sent to report the disaster for American readers, told how a search-party in a dark room found a dead man propped up in a line of his comrades to deceive the English inspectors. Under such conditions, Hawthorne wrote, "the effort to check the plague is like fighting in deep water to save a man resolved to drown himself." [10]

Once aroused, the British attacked the scientific problems presented by the plague with great thoroughness. The British Plague Commission demonstrated conclusively in 1906 how the disease was transmitted, and its reports became a classic of plague epi-

* They were soon overruled by the governor. Some Californians acted much the same way a little later.

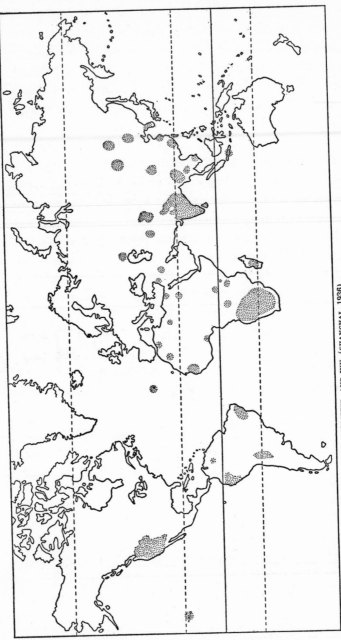

ADAPTED FREELY FROM PLAGUE, BY WU, CHUN, POLLITZER, AND WU (SHANGHAI, 1936)

*Plague in the contemporary world. The shading shows, very roughly and without differentiation, areas now infected and old centers of infection likely to become active at any time. In our own West, southern South America, South Africa, Russia, and Manchuria scattered infection is found in wild rodents* demiology.* It came to the sound conclusion that "insanitary conditions have no relation to the occurrence of plague, except insofar as they favour infestation by rats."[11] Yet the plain fact was that conditions all but universally did "favour infestation by rats," and the practical problems of control remained terribly difficult.

Houses were rat-paradises. Even in cities of considerable size, they characteristically sheltered both animals and people; floors were of dried cow-dung, walls of brick; lofts filled with grain and rubbish were often found between the sleeping quarters and the tiled roofs. In the small city of Belgaum one house of three rooms and a verandah sheltered twelve adults, three children, four buffaloes, six bullocks, one goat, one dog, and three fowls. In a three-room grocery shop and house occupied by six Moslems and two ineffectual cats, 197 rats were caught.

All this is picturesque and shocking. Standards and ways of living in India were obviously such as to encourage the ravages of plague. But one cannot say that they caused the ravages of plague, for the ways of living persist and plague has gradually and steadily declined for a number of years. In 1935, when plague deaths in British India were but 32,000, the public health commissioner reported that "the decrease cannot be attributed, at least in rural areas, to permanent improvement in sanitary conditions. Housing and other conditions inherently favourable to the rat populations are to a large extent essentially the same as when plague first made its appearance in Bombay forty years ago."[12] The same difficulty arises when one tries to explain the abrupt

* Surely no scientists ever reported their findings more decorously. One series of experiments was thus described: "In which a monkey was safely exposed in a plague-infected place where the free access of fleas to his person was prevented, whereas his companion not so protected succumbed." In explaining the fact that well-to-do natives, like the Europeans, generally escaped, it was solemnly asserted that "as the people rise in the social scale" they "show much aversion to live in association with rats."

departure of plague from many parts of Europe in the seventeenth century.

So much for India. Though no other country was to suffer so long and so heavily in this pandemic, plague spread within six years to every continent. To the east, it struck at China, Japan, the Philippines, Australia, Hawaii, and in 1900, for the first time in history, crossed the ocean to North America. To the west, it passed by way of the Levant to north Africa and to the European seaports, even as far as London. By way of Madagascar, perhaps, it reached the African littoral and spread along both coasts. South America was invaded from both the Atlantic and the Pacific; Rio was afflicted for years.

Plague still lingers in many parts of the world, but there has been no Black Death. Outside the Orient, plague this time has been a Flying Dutchman of disease, sailing the seven seas but finding no home. It has not quite made its threats good. Times have changed. Civilized men have learned to keep their vermin at a distance. Perhaps the disease itself has changed. The circumstances governing its spread have been studied with elaborate care; differences between one species of flea and another seem to be important; some factors are still elusive.* Sometimes infection just peters out. It did so, for instance, in England between 1906

* Some findings in those aspects of the subject which the French elegantly call *rodentologie* and *pulicologie* (pulex = flea) are curious. In Kenya, for example, there are rats in plenty and, in good seasons, abundant grain for them to feed on. The rats live in the thatched roofs of the native huts (arranged in groups of ten or less to accommodate one villager and all his wives, one wife per hut) and slip down the overhanging thatch at night to forage in the grain stores outside the huts instead of keeping company with their human hosts. Moreover roof rats here have different fleas from ground rats, and the roof-rat flea is relatively inefficient in transmitting the disease. The women smear themselves with red earth and castor oil; it is suggested that the fleas may prefer to bite the unoiled males. Anyway the men have more plague than the women. One is tempted to contrast this generally cheerful picture with the habits of itinerant mule-drivers in the Peruvian Andes. These gentlemen sleep, often on the floor, in wayside huts where guinea-pigs

and 1918, when it had a foothold among the rats in a stretch of Suffolk farmland (hard by some small North Sea ports to which grain cargoes came from the East), but caused something less than a score of human deaths. "In plague, as in other sicknesses," Greenwood comments, "something more is needed to generate an epidemic than even widespread and quite uncontrolled means of infection." [13]

American experience, on the whole, justifies a like conclusion. But there has been plenty of excitement along the way. When the body of a Chinese man with signs of plague on him was picked up in the basement of a Chinatown hotel in San Francisco in March 1900, the local board of health promptly stretched a rope around the twelve blocks where the Chinese lived and put policemen along it to keep them inside. As other cases followed, the federal health authorities tried to limit the infection to San Francisco by regulating the travel of Orientals out of the city, or at least to hold it within California by inspecting railroad passengers at the state line.

These measures raised a tempest. It was blasphemy to suggest that there might be plague in California. It was bad for business. The Republican governor, his state board of health (when he was able to get control of it), all but one of the local newspapers, and the Chinese themselves lined up in stubborn opposition to the Democratic mayor, the city board of health, and the federal health men. The Chinese barred their doors, hid the sick in their incredible rookeries, went to court and succeeded in breaking down one after another the restrictions laid upon them. The disease spread slowly, with interludes that gave aid and comfort to the do-nothing party. The newspapers ignored the proved cases and lampooned the health workers. The governor went to such

run loose and at night, according to Dr. John D. Long of the Pan-American Sanitary Bureau, the guinea-pigs "snuggle up against them for warmth . . . , thus affording ample opportunity for mutual exchange of fleas."

lengths in the effort to discredit the investigation that the federal Treasury Department sent an impartial commission—three men of unimpeachable authority\*—to establish the facts. The commissioners reached San Francisco late in January 1901 and found six cases of plague before the middle of February. The governor, still intransigent when these findings were reported to him, stalled for time and finally made a grudging promise of cooperation.†

A joint campaign to scrub, spray, fumigate, air, whitewash, and generally purify Chinatown followed. Hundreds of tons of garbage were cleared away. While these maneuvers must have

---

\* Drs. Simon Flexner of the University of Pennsylvania, F. G. Novy of the University of Michigan, and L. F. Barker of the University of Chicago.

† His capitulation (addressed to the Secretary of the Treasury, and published in the Report of the Marine-Hospital Service for 1901, p. 520) is not without charm as a specimen of political writing: "In reply to your dispatch of date February 21, you are aware that a dispute originally arose between the Federal authorities and the State authorities in reference to health conditions of California, and whereas, since then the Federal authorities have made investigations in which the State authorities were not allowed to participate, and whereas the commissioners who prosecuted the investigations for the United States under such circumstances have concluded that the health conditions at San Francisco need certain attention, and whereas heretofore I expressed my views in regard thereto by message to the legislature of California, still, in view of all the circumstances and conditions, believing that it will be for the best interest of all concerned, first having been assured by your office that your Department would take the steps hereinafter referred to, if requested and in the performance thereof would, among other things, be particular to avoid publicity and that the management would be pursued with the least possible detriment to our commercial interest; and believing that, if the Federal authorities be given control in the premises all other States of the Union may be better satisfied, and that all general quarantine of this State and of its cities will thereby be avoided, and that all quarantine of other States against this State may be avoided, and so forth; I therefore respectfully request the United States authorities to take charge of the matter within this State and deal with the situation from the standpoint of the report of its commissioners, but without cost or charge to this State, at the same time assuring you of my hearty cooperation, I thank you for your courtesy and await your reply."

disturbed the rats, there was no systematic effort to kill them till some months later. Meanwhile cases of plague began to turn up again, and kept doing so until early in 1904, when this first American epidemic ended with a total of 121 cases and 113 deaths. Control had been handicapped by lack of knowledge and official obstruction,* and yet, though sickness had fallen heavily on Chinatown, the city as a whole escaped serious consequences.

By 1907, when plague came back to San Francisco, the British in India had found out what to do about it, and a half-million dollars were spent to good advantage in and about the port in killing rats. Yet seventy-seven persons, mostly whites, died in the city and a dozen elsewhere in the state before the infection ran out.

Just as plague disappeared from the rat population it showed itself in a new quarter. "A man would go hunting ground squirrels on Saturday or Sunday. The following Tuesday or Wednesday he would develop headache and fever, and perhaps backache and chill. The next day there would be a bubo, and the case from that time forward would run the usual course of plague." [14] Such incidents made the federal health men prophesy that plague would be found in these wild rodents, and presently it was. The first case in which the chain of evidence was completely worked out was that of a thirteen-year-old boy who had never seen a trolley car till he was brought into the city for treatment. Plague had gone rural.

The ground squirrel (a brownish animal much like a good-sized tree squirrel in appearance) was often found in the markets, a familiar pest in the uplands, and fair game for a boy with a gun. Farmers disliked its thievery in the fields, and had an innocent custom in some counties of trying to exterminate it by carry-

---

* A new state administration in 1903 reversed the head-in-the-sand policy and since that time California has kept step with the best current thinking and practice in plague control.

ing a forkful of corpses from a ranch where the squirrels seemed to be dying fast to another where they were still bothersome. Plague may have passed to the ground squirrels from the rats of San Francisco as early as 1903. For some time after its existence was proved in the laboratory, ground squirrel infection seemed to be limited to a small part of California and in 1914 some workers thought it had been eradicated. But twenty years later it was found in the foothills of the Sierra Nevadas and in Oregon; it has since been discovered in Washington, Montana, Idaho, Wyoming, Nevada, Utah, New Mexico, and Arizona. Chipmunks and prairie dogs as well as ground squirrels can carry the bacillus, which has already crossed the continental divide and may travel east as far as the colonizing rodents are common— say to the longitude of central Texas.*

What does this mean for human beings? At the least, it means that those who hunt and dress ground squirrels court infection, and that now and then someone gets plague by a curious mischance: a boy is bitten by a squirrel, or a woman buries a dead chipmunk, or a university professor is troubled by fleas at his mountain camp. Two small epidemics in California cities have been traced to wild rodents: twelve persons died in Oakland in 1919, thirty in Los Angeles in 1924. In Los Angeles squirrels seem to have passed the infection to town rats; if this happened where rats were common enough a slum epidemic might result.†
In both these epidemics the disease took the pneumonic form.

* Meyer, studying the habits of the ground squirrel, finds little support for the current assumption that imported infection has been carried twelve hundred miles inland from the ports of entry, and suggests that plague may be indigenous in the western wild rodents as it is in their Asiatic cousins, long antedating the rat-borne epidemics on the coast. He considers B. pestis as one of the "crash factors" which operate to reduce cyclical overpopulation in the ground squirrel colonies.

† The kind of rat flea, Xenopsylla cheopis, that has been associated in the tropics with plague at its worst is common on rats in the South and has even been found in a church at Rochester, New York.

326

When pneumonic plague occurs under the right conditions of climate and human association grave consequences can follow; California seems not to have provided these conditions, but it is conceivable (if not very likely) that some other part of the country might do so if an unsuspecting traveler brought infection to it.

So we are no longer dependent on Asia for plague; we have our own reservoir, a vast and probably permanent one. We cannot wipe out the ground squirrels and their susceptible relatives in the great open spaces. It is possible, in "scorched earth" fashion, to keep the squirrels away from the immediate vicinity of a city, and to exercise some control over the squirrel population in and about recreation areas by periodic poisoning. The public health men try to keep an eye on the wandering bacillus so that they will know where to be on guard against human infection. Several teams of workers, state and federal, are continuously hunting squirrels and other wild rodents and examining them for evidences of plague. Sometimes these workers find infection in apparently healthy herds by making a sort of soup of their fleas and injecting this into guinea-pigs. The conditions which make an American squirrel-flea infective as well as infected are being studied with great care.

Since the pandemic began, not only San Francisco, but Seattle, New Orleans, Beaumont, Port Arthur, Galveston, and Pensacola have suffered from sea-borne plague. Many years have passed, however, since the last of these port infections, and New York, the largest American port, has still to experience its first case. The inspection of ships to control rats is regular and precise; there are manuals which tell one how to draw statistical inferences from rat droppings. Only about one ship in ten now puts in at an American port with enough rats to be called infested. It is not by sea but by land that plague now threatens us; its fury has gone, but a whisper runs over the prairie to remind us that it is still unfinished business.

REFERENCES

1. Greenwood, Major. *Epidemics and crowd-diseases.* London: Williams and Norgate, Ltd.; New York: The Macmillan Company, 1935, p. 320.
2. Frost, Wade Hampton. *The outlook for the eradication of tuberculosis.* American Review of Tuberculosis, 32:644–650, December 1935.
3. Frost, Wade Hampton. *How much control of tuberculosis?* American Journal of Public Health, 27:759–766, August 1937.
4. Okell, C. C. *Clinical and epidemiological interrelationships in streptococcal disease.* Milroy Lecture. Lancet, 1:867–873, April 23, 1932.
5. Frost, Wade Hampton. *Epidemiologic studies of acute anterior poliomyelitis.* Hygienic Laboratory Bulletin No. 90, October 1913. Washington: Government Printing Office, p. 250.
6. Mann, James. *Medical sketches of the campaigns of 1812, 13, 14.* Dedham, Massachusetts: H. Mann and Company, 1816, p. 108, 109, 110.
7. Cohn, David L. *God shakes creation.* New York: Harper and Brothers, 1935, p. 37–38.
8. Georgia Department of Public Health. *A standard plan for county-wide malaria control in Georgia.* Mimeographed, May 1938.
9. Hackett, L. W. *Malaria in Europe: an ecological study.* London: Oxford University Press, 1937, p. 320.
10. Hawthorne, Julian. *The horrors of the plague in India.* Cosmopolitan, 23:231–246, July 1897.
11. Government of India. *The etiology and epidemiology of plague: a summary of the work of the Plague Commission.* Calcutta: Superintendent of Government Printing, 1908, p. 93.
12. Government of India. *Annual report of the Public Health Commissioner with the Government of India for 1935.* Delhi: Government of India Press, 1937, p. 24–25.
13. Greenwood, *op. cit.,* p. 294.
14. McCoy, G. W. Unpublished manuscript.

A NOTE ON SOURCES

Dr. Halbert L. Dunn of the United States Bureau of the Census kindly made available special tabulations on which some of the statistical material which opens this chapter was based. Thomas W. Duffield of the New York City Department of Health, Dr. Herbert L. Lombard of the Massachusetts Department of Health, G. J. Drolet of the New York Tuberculosis and Health Committee, and Dr. Louis I. Dublin of the Metropolitan Life Insurance Company also generously provided data. Dr. Lowell J. Reed and Dr. Ross L. Gauld of Johns Hopkins and Dr. Haven Emerson of Columbia were helpful in the interpretation of this material.

For the incidence of influenza I draw on papers by Collins, for causation and immunization on papers of Andrewes, Laidlaw, and Stuart-Harris in England and Francis here, and on the Harvard virus symposium previously mentioned. Smillie's little book on *The common cold* (New York: Funk and Wagnalls, 1937) is worth knowing.

For a broad view of tuberculosis one could find nothing more illuminating than Dr. Frost's papers, cited above. Among other sources I have drawn on Drolet's epidemiological article in volume I of Goldberg: *Clinical tuberculosis* (Philadelphia: F. A. Davis, 1935); on interesting papers by Wolff in Human Biology for February and May 1938 (10:106–123, 251–284); and on the curious geographical findings of Dauer and Lumsden (see Public Health Bulletin No. 225, March 1936, and American Review of Tuberculosis, 35:43–61, January 1937). Dr. Alton S. Pope of the Massachusetts Department of Health was very helpful.

The health departments of Connecticut, Massachusetts, and Rhode Island kindly made special tabulations of typhoid fever rates, and Dr. A. V. Hardy of the United States Public Health Service was helpful on infant diarrheas. Okell's interesting lecture on the streptococcus is cited above. Collins' *Age incidence of common communicable diseases of children* (Reprint No. 1275 from Public Health Reports of April 25, 1929) is full of interesting data. Dr. Kenneth F. Maxcy of Johns Hopkins, Dr. E. S. Godfrey, Jr., of the New York State Department of Health, Dr. James A. Doull of Western Reserve, and Dr. Charles F. McKhann, now of the University of Michigan, were helpful in correspondence. A supplement to the American Journal of Public Health for March 1940 gives important current information on diphtheria. On the epidemiology of poliomyelitis I follow Dr. W. Lloyd Aycock of Harvard, who took pains to answer special questions. Dr. Leroy D. Fothergill of Harvard told me about equine encephalomyelitis and I draw on his paper in the Harvard virus symposium; the Massachusetts outbreak was reported by Feemster in the American Journal of Public Health for December 1938 (28:1403–1410).

There is nothing on malaria in this country covering quite the ground that Hackett covers for Europe. Boyd's *Introduction to malariology* (Cambridge: Harvard University Press, 1930) is useful as of that date, but recent history must be pieced together from such sources as the annual symposia on this subject in the Southern Medical Journal. Thanks are due to Dr. L. L. Williams, Jr., of the United States Public Health Service, Dr. Mark F. Boyd of the Rockefeller Foundation, Dr. W. S. Smillie of Cornell, Dr. E. C. Faust of Tulane, Dr. M. P. Ravenel of the University of Missouri, and Dr. Justin Andrews of the Georgia Department of Health, all of whom helped me to get a general picture of malaria, and to Dr. E. L. Bishop and Dr. R. B. Watson of the Tennessee Valley Authority, who were good enough to show me malaria control on a grand scale.

For yellow fever one turns to the Rockefeller Foundation, whose annual reports summarize recent history in this field and whose workers, particularly Sawyer and Soper, tell the story in detail in the journals. A brochure published as nos. 7–9 of the Epidemiological Report of the Health Section of the League of Nations for 1935 reviews the world situation as of that date. Dr. W. A. Sawyer of the Rockefeller Foundation was generous with his help.

I found interesting eye-witness comments on the plague in Bombay in The Nation for April 8, 1897 (64:259–261) and The Forum for August 1897 (23:737–749), both by E. W. Wilson, a Yale professor. The California episode is reported in great detail in the annual reports of the Marine-Hospital Service (now the United States Public Health Service); the controversy in San Francisco is reviewed by Kellogg in the American Journal of Public Health for November 1920 (10:835–844). The annual reports of the Sylvatic Plague Committee, published in the same journal, tell the current American story, which is summed up in Public Health Reports for June 28, 1940. Dr. C. L. Williams of the United States Public Health Service, Dr. G. W. McCoy, formerly of the same service, Dr. W. O. Shepard of the Metropolitan Life Insurance Company, and Dr. Karl F. Meyer of the University of California helped me with perspective and details.

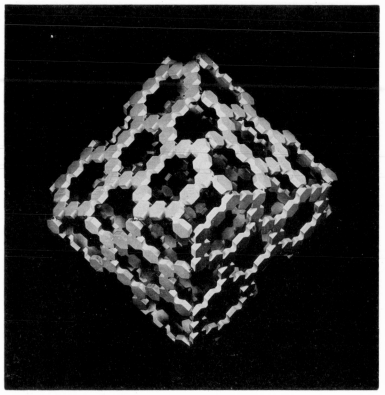

*Diagrammatic model of a protein molecule according to the cyclol cage hypothesis. This particular model accommodates 288 amino-acid units. Only major geometric relationships can be suggested by this static abstraction, which would be more life-like with a fuzz of side-chains and a continual flutter of change. The structure of the proteins must be of crucial significance for infection and resistance*

# 9

## EPILOGUE

PESTILENCE has become an old-fashioned word. Most of the great plagues have shrunk into the background of time. We are sitting at the moment on an epidemiological powder-keg, and things may change abruptly, but at present the foreground is occupied by what our forefathers would have thought very small plagues indeed, hardly worth putting into the Book of Common Prayer.

Is this our doing? Only in part. Leprosy, plague, typhus, and tuberculosis began to recede because of cloudy biological trends or broad social changes, not because of deliberate control. Syphilis, still uncontrolled, seems to have lost some of its severity. Malaria, along its geographic frontiers, has yielded to the farmer rather than the epidemiologist. Cholera had probably shot its bolt before we learned how to hold it at bay. We have been harrying a retreating enemy, and building defenses against his return. The human race has had a generous allowance of what looks like blind luck in dealing with its parasites.

At some points where human intervention has been decisive, moreover, knowledge of "germs" has played a relatively small part in shaping the strategy of control. Smallpox was done for by an immunological procedure stumbled on long before immunology began. Yellow fever was driven back to the jungle by men who did not know the agent that caused it. We owe to

331

Pasteur and his successors a concept of infection and a technique of investigation that have revolutionized the diagnosis of communicable disease and rationalized our efforts to prevent and cure it. Yet the net effect of the measures bacteriology has proposed for the control of disease has been, to some bacteriologists, disappointing.

The diseases stopped in their tracks by the use of vaccines or antisera are few, and those still unpreventable by such means are many. One can get first-rate protection against smallpox and diphtheria, and possibly yellow fever and typhus; second-rate protection against plague, cholera, typhoid fever, and tetanus. We are not sure about whooping cough, even less so about pneumonia. Against influenza, malaria, syphilis, tuberculosis, and dysentery, against infections with the streptococcus, staphylococcus, meningococcus, and "influenza bacillus," immunology has as yet nothing decisive to offer in the way of prevention, and not too much in the way of cure. Antitoxin normally cures diphtheria. Serum therapy has been notably successful against pneumococcus lobar pneumonia and has been put to good use in a number of less common infections, such as meningitis, but even in its own territory chemotherapy begins to outdistance it.

One cannot say yet whether vaccines have been disappointing because of extravagant hopes or inadequate technique. The methods used in their production are often crude. With more "exact knowledge of the anatomy of the microbial cell—anatomy at the biochemical level," as Dubos puts it, we might be able to handle antigens more skilfully and so get more efficient antibodies. The bacteriologists are digging for such knowledge, and while they dig the doctors and public health men turn hopefully to the chemists—now so active—for weapons more decisive than those now at hand. Perhaps we must look to drugs to take up the lag in the control of disease by curing what the bacteriologist cannot prevent.

Pasteur, identifying the cause of disease with an extraneous living agent, turned the eyes of a couple of generations of investigators toward the parasite and away from the host. Some of his contemporaries protested, not too intelligently, but not without reason. "It is not the disease, an abstract being, which we have to treat," said one Piorry, "but the patient, whom we must study with the greatest care by all the physical, chemical, and clinical means which Science affords."[1] Yet the sick man had been studied for centuries without revealing the cause of disease, and it is not surprising that where Pasteur led the young men eagerly followed. While the bacteriologists were busy at their world-shaking discoveries, physiology languished. What Henderson calls the "biological and philosophical" outlook of Claude Bernard, who was defining experimental medicine and the "inner environment" about the time Pasteur was busy with his silkworms, had to wait a long time for fruition.

Even today we know little of the physiology of infection and resistance. Except in a superficial way, it is still impossible to draw a base-line and say this is health; that is disease. The sick man can be recognized by gross indications, often tardily perceived; the sick organ can be distinguished in some instances from one functioning according to expectation (but standards of normal function are not too good); the sick cell is virtually unknown except for the meager morphological evidence the pathologist can get, usually after the event, with his dissecting knife and microscope.

In fact what is known of the cell under any circumstances is known spottily, and the spots seldom join. We know the cell is made of a complicated elastic jelly with a persistent pattern, and most of the things that matter to it happen at its surface or at the interfaces between two different kinds of stuff within it. We know the cell wall lets some things through and holds other things back and spends energy in doing so. We know the production of energy in the cell keeps a great troop of chemical entities (enzymes and the like) shuttling through a catalytic dance that would dazzle the Rockettes; they rush atoms of hydrogen from one to another like a fire-brigade passing a bucket. In trying to understand these processes, "not only do we have to deal with extremely complicated molecules, we have also to deal with them in extremely complicated situations."[2]

At some points the physiologist must mark time till the physicist or the chemist gives him new methods; at others he is painfully conscious of the anomalous position that borrowed methods put him in. What he knows of the chemical content of tissue, for instance, has been learned largely from the wreckage of cells that have been sliced, mashed, ground, pulverized, boiled, frozen, acidified, alkalinized, or otherwise manhandled. Yet if the cell is patterned rather than amorphous its structure must be inseparable from its function,* and how can the physiologist be satisfied with chemical facts gained by the sacrifice of structure?

It is easier to manipulate bacteria in a controlled environment than to coax a living cell out of an animal body, and the bacteriologist himself has thrown light on the behavior of intact protoplasm by his meticulous study of bacterial food requirements, metabolic activities, and response to poisonous drugs. The physiologist has learned something by experimentation on the large cells of certain sea-plants; something from single cells dissected, injected, and manipulated under the microscope by the use of incredibly fine needles controlled by finely adjusted screws; something from fragments of tissue kept alive in drops of fluid hanging from the underside of a microscopic slide. These are exacting techniques, and they yield information slowly. Meanwhile the people who study the structure of the cell have

---

* Even so simple a pattern as inside-outside has been shown to be of great importance; certain stuffs applied to the outside of an ameba, for instance, poison it, while the same stuffs injected inside it leave it quite unharmed, and vice versa.

little to do with those who study chemical phenomena within the cell, and no one is yet able to describe the cell as a functioning whole or to relate it comprehensively and clearly to its environment.

So while one can guess that changes in the permeability of the cell wall or interference with an enzyme-system may be characteristic of disease; or that a fifth column within the body may join the parasite in damaging tissues; or that a stream of physiological events, once diverted from its normal course by an invader, may go on to become a ruinous flood, one can do no more than guess until the physiologist, the cytologist, the biophysicist, and the biochemist learn more and pool what they know. With no clear picture of health or disease, how can we hope now to understand the balance between them—the nature of susceptibility and resistance?

There is still a deeper level, moreover, at which answers to these questions must be sought. Beyond the cell lies the molecule. This too has structure, and details of that structure hold great significance for biological processes. Take for instance the polysaccharides* of the capsule of the pneumococcus, so important in the antigen-antibody reactions on which serum therapy of pneumonia is based. By breaking down natural antigens of this sort to see what is in them, and building up almost but not quite identical compounds in the laboratory, and then comparing the behavior of the natural and artificial substances in the test-tube or living animal, much has been learned about the relation between chemical and antigenic differences. It has been proved that the capacity of a given antigen to elicit, and react with, a particular antibody is destroyed if a single one of its many constituent groups of atoms is replaced by another, or if the link-

* Multiple sugars, formed like trains of cars out of simple sugars.

335

age between two major units is altered, or even if a single carbon atom holds a split molecule of water bottomside up instead of topside up. In general the character of the last molecule in the chain—the one that is freest to react with other substances—has a good deal to do with the antigenic behavior of the whole compound. An agile cluster of atoms sticking out into molecular space may lead the whole molecule into immunological activity.*

It took years of imaginative and patient work to reach the conclusions here paraphrased so flippantly—eight years, in one instance, to find out how a particular synthesis could be brought about. By hooking a synthetic sugar of his own choosing to a natural protein Goebel was eventually able to form an artificial antigen which could be used to counteract experimental infection: injected into rabbits, it made them produce antibodies, and their serum then protected mice against heavy doses of Type II pneumococci. This in itself may or may not be of practical importance. The significant finding is that the capacity to elicit the formation of specific antibodies is closely linked with both the identity and the spatial pattern of atoms within the molecule.

There is every reason to suppose that the principle thus demonstrated in a limited situation runs throughout life. "The plans of living systems," Needham remarks, "are written in chemical molecular structure, a language with a great wealth of expression." Certainly we shall not fully understand the primary phenomena of infection and resistance until we can relate them to

* If one hasn't looked into a chemistry book for a long time the confidence now shown by chemists in their capacity to divine the architecture of the invisible molecules may take one's breath away. This is one of many instances in which scientific theory circulates briskly (like paper money based on a few bars of gold in the vault) with a rather modest reserve of sensory observation to back it up. The evidence comes chiefly from experiments with polarized light and from the cryptic patterns made by x-rays refracted from the inwards of crystals. But the formulas click and interlock and one step leads to another and if the chemists are satisfied that they know what they are talking about the layman need not worry.

the architecture of the more active molecules in the parasite and its products, the cell and its environment. This is not likely to happen soon, for living matter is preeminently protein, and protein is as baffling as the contemporary world.

Protein is made of familiar elements: carbon, hydrogen, oxygen, nitrogen, often sulfur. Analysis and synthesis have revealed the composition and suggested the structure of many of the amino acids—the individual units of which protein is composed. But one's notion of a molecule is badly strained by stuff with molecular weights that vary according to circumstances and that run up into the millions;* one's thinking about structure is discomfited by stuff which now seems to be long and fibrous and now acts as though it were spherical; one's categories of chemical behavior are upset by stuff that is "denatured" as easily as one boils an egg. Like the contemporary world, protein is too big to be fitted into old concepts, too complex to be covered by any convenient formula, too changeable to be dealt with confidently. It lies, as Wyckoff says, in a no-man's land between the biologist working his way down to smaller and smaller living things and the chemist working his way up to larger and larger chemical entities.

Protein has thus far stood off a frontal attack by the methods of organic chemistry. No protein has been completely analyzed,† nor has synthesis gone beyond the linking of something like a score of amino acids—only a handful compared with the hundreds to be found in a natural protein. There is a feeling in the

---

* The molecular weight of water is 18, of cane sugar 342. The average weight of the individual amino acid in the form in which it occurs in protein is thought to be somewhere around 125. The least of the proteins so far identified has a weight of approximately 10,000, and molecular weights of 17,000,000 and 40,000,000 have been estimated for the nucleoprotein of tobacco mosaic virus.

† The roster of amino acids in zein, the protein of corn, is all but complete.

337

air, however, that even if the synthesis of proteins along classic lines is a task for the millennium, the people who keep on exposing amino acids to enzymes borrowed from living tissues—enzymes that are known to break proteins down and may very probably play a part as catalysts in building them up too—may get surprising results.

Meanwhile the physical chemists are circling around the protein molecule (while the mathematicians blow the ram's horn) with a variety of ingenious devices and nimble inferences. They can estimate the molecular weights of proteins by computations based on the rate at which the molecules are thrown down in the ultracentrifuge.* These weights group themselves roughly in multiples of a unit of approximately 18,000 (or perhaps 9,000), which strongly suggests the presence of geometrical order in protein formation, especially in connection with the chemists' discovery that the distribution of amino acids in given molecules also seems to follow a periodic law. On the other hand the findings as to the shape of the molecule discourage generalization: some proteins would seem to be nearly spherical, some rod-shaped, many of intermediate forms.†

While the chemist is accustomed to base a structural formula on a careful round-up of chemical properties and to check it by synthesizing the material he is describing, theories of protein structure have already been put forward with enthusiasm and debated with vigor. The classic theory is that the amino acids,

* See page 80.

† One of the several methods used to determine the general shape of molecules is based on an argument like this: if twigs and acorns float in a swiftly running stream the twigs will adjust themselves more quickly to the direction of flow, and, when the flow stops, will more slowly return to a random arrangement, or, in the charming scientific phrase, will have a greater "relaxation time." By suspending molecules in liquid held between two cylinders which can be spun or stopped at will, and watching the patterns they make by polarized light, one can set up this sort of situation and draw appropriate inferences.

338

which are fundamentally similar, are linked in a serpentine chain, with the radicals that make them differ from each other branching off in side-chains. This serves the purpose well enough when one thinks of fibers like wool or silk, in which stretching and shrinking can be nicely correlated with the straightening or kinking of the chain of atoms. It does not work so well for the proteins which physical tests show to be more nearly round. Is the chain then rolled up like a ball of string, or folded over and over like a strip of postage-stamps in the purse, or does it become a three-dimensional structure by the random tangling of its loose ends? None of these suggestions sounds as though the resulting molecule would be well fitted to maintain its identity. Wrinch, starting from geometrical premises, has suggested that the basic pattern may be not a chain but a fabric, normally taking the form of a regular polyhedral cage, but capable of unfolding and separating into plane or linear fragments. One might then have what she calls extrovert or introvert proteins, with the potentially active side-chains thrust outward or inward from the surface of the cage.

Whether a cage opens and shuts or a chain folds and unfolds, it is clear that the protein molecule, with its hundreds or thousands of separable components, its thousands or hundreds of thousands of atoms, is immensely variable. There may be a continuous stir of activity in its labile linkages, endless rearrangements of its supercargo. Within the prevailing pattern the ways in which one molecule may differ from another are past counting. Can one imagine a more precise and more sensitive instrument for the chemical virtuosity to which we give the name of life?

The proteins have often been called the building blocks of protoplasm; they appear now in more masterful roles: some are antibodies, some enzymes, some hormones, some perhaps even genes. It is a very small part of the truth to say that they do much to shape the continuum in which disease occurs.

339

To understand disease, which is a disturbance in a going system,* one must understand the system it disturbs. Disease is the interaction of exogenous and endogenous factors—factors from without and from within. In some diseases one sort of influence is dominant, in others the opposite. Infectious diseases group themselves about the pole where an exogenous factor—the parasite—plays so conspicuous a role that we call it *the* cause of the disorder. But there are degrees even in this dominance: everybody gets measles, but not everybody exposed to poliomyelitis gets the disease in any overt form. One might stake out a middle zone between communicable and non-communicable diseases—a zone in which communication is the prerequisite but not the determinant of disease, in which the fact of invasion seems no more decisive in shaping the course of events than the physiological climate of the invaded body.† Rheumatic fever, perhaps because we know so little of its causation, seems at the moment an excellent example of a disease on the borderline where exogenous and endogenous factors are closely balanced. Perhaps we shall get better perspective on the frankly infectious diseases by exploring this borderline: where there is no obvious hypothesis, no short cut to etiology, one has to beat the bounds of the total situation. The chronic non-infectious diseases, in fact, point the way most directly to physiological fundamentals: cancer has drawn its students deep into problems of cell-growth, heart and kidney disease into a maze of obscure regulatory mechanisms.

We cannot be sure that the endogenous factors which seem to

---

* It is worth remembering that it is the tendency of all going systems—from the spinning top to the human body—to persist in an established course and to return to that course after being temporarily disturbed, unless the disturbance is strong enough to destroy the system altogether. The phenomena of resistance must be studied against this background.

† A climate, one may add, which seems often to be shared by blood relatives, so that families may pass particular disease hazards from generation to generation.

dominate these diseases are altogether different from those affecting the response of the body to parasitic invasion. There are indications in recent work that some pathological changes thought to be characteristic of specific infection can be brought about experimentally by wholly non-infectious agencies. Resistance may be general as well as specific. Immunological functions may be more closely tied into other physiological patterns than we have supposed; some of the fantastically numerous chemical tools postulated by the physiologist and the immunologist may do double duty. We may come to think of infection not as a special kind but merely as a special case of disturbance in a chemical system. We may find the way to reinforce the body at vulnerable points against threats from any quarter—infectious or otherwise—and without waiting for the threat to declare itself. At the very least, we cannot hope to learn what we need to know about communicable disease without knowing more about the body that has it— and the body that throws it off.

When pestilence falls on the people there is a story to tell. The story of the people who do not fall sick has never been told. Perhaps it is the most important part of epidemiology.

### REFERENCES

1. Vallery-Radot, René. *The life of Pasteur.* Translated by R. L. Devonshire. New York: Doubleday, Page and Company, 1923, p. 264.
2. Needham, Joseph. *Order and life.* New Haven: Yale University Press, 1936, p. 110.

### A NOTE ON SOURCES

This chapter represents the precipitation of a good deal of talk with a good many people, among them (in addition to persons gratefully mentioned elsewhere) Dr. Lawrence J. Henderson (whose introduction to Claude Bernard's *Experimental medicine,* New York: Macmillan, 1927, helps to light up historical perspectives), Dr. Edwin J. Cohn, and Dr. J. T. Edsall of Harvard; Dr. W. J. V. Osterhout and Dr. Walther F. Goebel of the Rockefeller Institute; Dr. Robert Chambers, Dr. Homer W. Smith, and Dr. J. Haskell Milstone of New York University; Dr. George H. Smith of Yale; Dr. Dorothy M. Wrinch of Oxford and Johns Hopkins; and my colleague Dr. Lester J. Evans. I thank them all.

I have no systematic suggestions for reading in the broad fields here touched on. I would like to call attention to the little book by Osterhout on *The nature of life* (New York: Holt, 1924) and to the Terry Lectures by Needham, mentioned above. I have not happened to find any comparable brief aids to orientation in biochemistry. *Protoplasm*, by Seifriz (New York: McGraw-Hill, 1936), has interesting chapters both on the structure of protoplasm and on the proteins: he quotes a comment by Pauli which I found especially suggestive. There is good browsing in *Perspectives in biochemistry*, a collection of papers by pupils of Sir Frederick Hopkins of Cambridge (Cambridge: The University Press, 1939); one of the contributors, the Hungarian Szent-Györgyi, writes with exceptional charm, both here and in a Harvey Lecture (Bulletin of the New York Academy of Medicine, 15:456–468, July 1939), on the complicated subject of cellular metabolism. Langmuir sums up current thinking and argues for the cyclol cage in *The structure of proteins*, reprinted from the Proceedings of the Physical Society (51:592–612, 1939). Volume 6 of the *Cold Spring Harbor Symposia on Quantitative Biology*, 1938, is a mine of technical information about proteins: it staggers the layman to see how many facts have to be heaped up before a concept crystallizes; how much the men of science know about things they still do not understand.

# INDEX

347